PEARSON

ALWAYS

Compiled by Marcella Mandracchia

Science, Technology, and Society
A Microcosm of Technological Trends

Fourth Custom Edition

Pearson Learning Solutions, 330 Hudson Street, New York, New York 10013
A Pearson Education Company
www.pearsoned.com

Printed in the United States of America

1 2 3 4 5 6 7 8 9 10 V092 17 16 15

000200010272012519

ML/KS

ISBN 10: 1-323-29307-8
ISBN 13: 978-1-323-29307-2

CONTENTS

■■■

PREFACE

■ ■ ■

HOW TO USE THIS BOOK

This textbook was developed for undergraduate and graduate STS (Science, Technology, and Society) courses. STS was developed in the early 1970s as a program of teaching and research devoted to the study of science and technology in society, in both historical and contemporary perspectives. STS is constituted as a multi- and inter-disciplinary program. Similar programs exist around the country and abroad. STS courses are developed on the belief that science and technology are two of the most undeniable forces for individual, societal, and global change in the contemporary era. Every major issue going forward will be affected by how it intersects with tech innovation. I think those who hold onto the conviction to learn will stay more relevant and be better able to lead. The changes driven by technology's evolution are happening faster than most of us can fathom. Let's work together to broaden our understanding. I aim to practice what I preach. I intend to make our discussions democratic and multidisciplinary, and to take advantage of the tools of technology to expand and empower our audience. The broader and more diverse the community is engaged in the dialogue, the better. Technology's integration into every part of the economy creates more opportunity for rapid progress, and can mean a better future for business, society, and the planet.

This textbook explores the impact of technology and engineering design on society: past, present and future. It stresses to find simple, yet powerful principles that govern the relationship between the latest technology and society. The main themes are technology and industry, the economy, the environment, the social, educational and psychological implications, energy and society, war, and emerging technologies of the 21st century.

This anthology of articles were collected to provide students a domain for dialogue among students of engineering, humanities, natural sciences and social sciences—a common ground where important cross-disciplinary studies transcending the gaps between the technical and non-technical fields are not merely envisioned, but practiced.

Articles in this edition were written by prominent scholars and leaders that have focused on the most current issues and debates. They were drawn from a variety of contemporary social issues, and touch on numerous disciplines, from philosophy and sociology to engineering and computer science. Chapter summaries are provided as a study guide for exams in Appendix A. The tearaway sections of the book can be used to conduct attendance in Appendix C.

As this textbook is being developed, technology grows to affect the society in which we live. Assignments, lecture slides, and other additional course-related content can be found online.

ABOUT THE AUTHOR

EDWIN TJOE, ED.D. is the Assistant Dean of E-Learning for St. John's University: School of Education, NY. In addition to his administrative duties he teaches doctoral and graduate classes on educational administration, statistics, instructional leadership and technology. He also is a faculty member at Stony Brook University, NY where he teaches graduate and undergraduate courses in the sociology of technological trends. Edwin is an innovator at building communities and capacities for teaching and learning in a global context. Through online projects and collaboration tools, he empowers others to expand the walls of the classroom to the virtual community. Edwin works with K–12 communities to improve the use of technology in the Diocese of Brooklyn and Diocese of Rockville Centre, Archdiocese of New York. He also is working with ePortfolios in both higher education and K–12 in an effort to build digital citizenship.

MARCELLA MANDRACCHIA, ED.D is currently an Adjunct Professor and Post Doctoral Fellow at St. John's University. She completed her doctorate in Instructional Leadership at St. John's University in Queens, NY. She worked as a Doctoral Fellow in the Division of Administration and Instructional Leadership on numerous grants. Marcella completed both her Master and Bachelor degrees at St. John's University, majoring in Adolescent Education with a concentration in History. At the age of eighteen, Marcella completed her Associate degree in Liberal Arts from Bard High School Early College.

More about the Chapter Authors (in no particular order)

JESSE BRASCO is currently pursuing his doctorate in Instructional Leadership at the St. John's University School of Education. He holds an MBA from the Tobin College of Business at St. John's University with a concentration in executive management. He is a member of multiple honor societies, such as Beta Gamma Sigma (business honor society) and Sigma Iota Gamma (professional management fraternity). Jesse has his BA from Stony Brook University, with a major in economics. One of his current research interests is financial literacy and its application to the educational system. In his spare time, Jesse enjoys playing video games with his friends. Some of his favorite games include Super Smash Bros.: Melee, League of Legends, and Guild Wars. When he's taking a break from video games, he plays sports casually, and roots for his beloved New York Mets and New York Giants.

JENNY YANG is a graduate of St. John's University in New York. Dr. Yang completed her B.S. in biochemistry and M.A. in education at Stony Brook University. Her research interests include topics on gifted education and ELL students.

ALLAN ORNSTEIN is the author of 65 books and 400 articles. He received his doctorate from New York University, and he served as an inner-city teacher and subsequently as a consultant for more than 60 different government and education agencies. Dr. Ornstein is a former Fullbright Hayes Scholar and screening committee member, ETS test designer, and guest editor for ten professional journals including *Phi Delta Kappan, NASSP Bulletin,* and *Educational Forum.* One of Dr. Ornstein's books, *Foundations of Education,* is in the 32nd year of print and tenth edition. His books *Educational Administration* and *Curriculum* are in their fifth edition and are leading books in their respective fields.

NANCY WOZNIAK has worked as an instructional designer, educational technologist and online learning coordinator for 12 years, and has been dubbed the Wizard of Woz at her previous academic positions. She has taught online and traditional courses in computer applications, multimedia and web design, communication, and business. Her experience with community education and continuing education includes the development of a Web 2.0 series for promoting a business and multimedia design in advertising. Previously, Nancy worked in broadcast news as a graphic artist and a producer and program manager in public/government access television. Currently, she is documenting future technology trends and challenges in Distance Learning and the pedagogy of Web 2.0 and 3.0 technologies in the distance and tradition classroom. Nancy is currently the Learning Architect of Stony Brook University in New York.

MARY L. GRAY is an associate professor at Indiana University. Her teaching and research interests include: intersections of new media, social movements, and cultural identity; social theory and ethnography of gender and sexuality; sociology of youth and public culture; qualitative methodologies, particularly ethnography online and in non-urban settings; and pedagogy of research ethics and its relationship to the construction of scientific knowledge and practice.

JESSIE DANIELS is associate professor of Urban Public Health at Hunter College (Ph.D., Sociology, University of Texas-Austin). She is the author of two books *White Lies* (Routledge, 1997) and *Cyber Racism* (Rowman & Littlefield, 2009), and numerous articles about race, gender/sexuality and various forms of media. She is currently at work on research with LGBTQ homeless youth and their use of mobile technology. In addition to her work as an academic, Daniels also worked in the Internet industry. She maintains an academic blog (RacismReview) with Joe Feagin and was recently named one of "20 Inspiring Women to Follow on Twitter," by *Forbes* magazine.

LORRAINE BEAUDIN is the assistant dean at the University of Lethbridge in Canada.

GAIL BAILEY is a registered provisional psychologist at the University of Lethbridge in Canada.

REBECCA LAVE is an assistant professor at the Department of Geography at Indiana University. She received her Ph.D. in 2008 from UC Berkeley. Her research focuses in political ecology, stream restoration and fluvial geomorphology, political economy and social theory, nature/society studies, and science and technology studies. Lave has also published four books.

PHILIP MURKOWSKI is a historian and philosopher of economic thought at the University of Notre Dame. He received a Ph.D. in Economics from the University of Notre Dame in 1979.

VIVI NASTASE is a postdoctoral fellow at Heidelberg Institute for Theoretical Studies (HITS) in Germany.

MICHAEL STRUBE leads the Natural Language Processing (NLP) Group at HITS gGmbH. There, he is involved in NLP related projects, works with the computational linguists at HITS, and supervises Ph.D. students. In addition, he is an Honorarprofessor in the Computational Linguistics Department at the University of Heidelberg.

SAMUEL RANDALL has been a lecturer in Human Geography at UCL from 2007–present. From 2002–2006 he received his Ph.D. at the University of Birmingham. Also his BA was received from Birmingham in 1998–2011 in Geography.

LEO MARX was a professor at the Massachusetts Institute of Technology. He is also an author known for his works in the field of American studies. Marx's work in American studies, the relationship between technology and culture from the 19th to the 20th century. He graduated from Harvard University with a B.A. in History and Literature, and with his Ph.D. in the History of American Civilization in 1950.

WILLIAM JAMES EARLE is Professor of Philosophy at Baruch College and the Graduate Center, The City University of New York. He received his Ph.D. from Columbia University, where he studied with Justus Buchler and Arthur Danto, and wrote a dissertation on William James. He has taught at Baruch College since 1983. Professor Earle is also the editor-in-chief of the international quarterly, *The Philosophical Forum.*

CATHERINE HILL is the director of research at AAUW, where she focuses on higher education and women's economic security. Prior to her work at AAUW, she was a researcher at the Institute for Women's Policy Research and an assistant professor at the University of Virginia. She has bachelor's and master's degrees from Cornell University and a doctorate in public policy from Rutgers University.

CHRISTIANNE CORBETT is a research associate at AAUW and co-author of *Where the Girls Are: the Facts about Gender Equity in Education* (2008). Before coming to AAUW, she worked as a legislative fellow in the office of Rep. Carolyn Maloney and as a mechanical design engineer in the aerospace industry. She holds a master's degree in cultural anthropology from the University of Colorado, Boulder, and bachelor's degrees in aerospace engineering and government from the University of Notre Dame. As a Peace Corps volunteer in Ghana from 1992 to 1994, she taught math and science to secondary school students.

ANDRESSE ST. ROSE is a research associate at AAUW, where she focuses on gender equity in education and the workplace. Before joining the AAUW staff, she worked as an academic counselor at Northeastern University in Boston and taught high school math and biology at the International School of Port-of-Spain, Trinidad. She is a co-author of *Where the Girls Are: the Facts about Gender Equity in Education* (2008). She has a doctoral degree in education policy from George Washington University, a master's degree in higher education administration from Boston College, and a bachelor's degree in biology from Hamilton College.

THOMAS CAVANAGH has been in the e-learning world for 15 years and has worked as an instructional designer, program manager, faculty member, and administrator. Currently, Tom is UCF's Assistant Vice President of Distributed Learning. He has developed award-winning e-learning programs for Fortune 500 companies, government agencies, and the military. Prior to that, he spent several years in film and television entertainment where he wrote a number of award-winning children's television programs for producers such as Nickelodeon, the Disney Channel, and Anheuser Busch Entertainment. In addition to courses at UCF, he has taught Technical Report Writing at Embry-Riddle Aeronautical University, Digital Storytelling at Valencia Community College, and Screenwriting at Full Sail University.

JOHN HARMEN MARBURGER, III was an American physicist who directed the Office of Science and Technology Policy in the administration of President George W. Bush, thus serving as the Science Advisor to the President. He also served as the President of Stony Brook University from 1980 until 1994, and director of Brookhaven National Laborator from 1998 until 2001.

RAYMOND "RAY" KURZWEIL is an American author, inventor and futurist. Aside from futurology, he is involved in fields such as optical character recognition (OCR), text-to-speech synthesis, speech recognition technology, and electronic keyboard instruments. He has attracted significant criticism from scientists and thinkers. Kurzweil has received many awards and honors, including: First place in the 1965 International Science Fair for inventing the classical music synthesizing computer. In 1990 he received "Engineer of the Year" award from *Design News*. In 2011, Kurzweil was named a Senior Fellow of the Design Futures Council.

ANDERSON HUNTER DUPREE is a distinguished American historian and one of the pioneer historians of the history in the United States. He was the son of a lawyer and attended Oberlin College. He graduated summa cum laude in 1942 with a Bachelor of Arts degree. Upon completion of his undergraduate work, he joined the United States Navy in 1942, and became a Lieutenant in the U.S. Naval Reserve.

PAUL E. CERUZZI was born in 1949. He is keeper of Aerospace Electronics and Computing at the Smithsonian's National Air and Space Museum in Washington, D.C. Ceruzzi received a BA from Yale University in 1970, and a Ph.D. from the University of Kansas in 1981, both in studies. Before joining the National Air and Space Museum, he was a Fulbright scholar in Hamburg, Germany, and taught History of Technology at Clemson University in Clemson, South Carolina.

SANDEEP DALAL is an Assistant Professor at DCSA, M.D. University in Rohtak, from 2009 to present. He was a Lecturer at A.I.J.H.M. College Rohtak from 2005–2006 then 2008–2009. In 2008 he received an M.Phil from V.M. University Tamil Nadu.

RAJEN DER SINGH CHHILLAR is Professor & Former Head of Dept. of Computer Science & Applications M.D. University, Rohtak-124001, Haryana, India. In 1997 he received his Ph.D. from M.D. University, Rohtak. He has been a professor at MDU in Rohtak from 2008 till present. He was Head, Department of Engineering & Technology at M.D. University in Rohtak from 2006 to 2007.

JULIAN DIBBELL is an American author and technology journalist with a particular interest in social systems within online communities. Dibbell was born in New York City and grew up in Claremont. Dibbell is currently attending the University of Chicago Law School, where he is a member of the University of Chicago Law Review.

UNIT 1

■ ■ ■

The Answer Is in the Question, or Is It the Other Way Around?

CHAPTER 1

■ ■ ■

Introduction: STS and Neoliberal Science

Rebecca Lave
Indiana University, USA

Philip Mirowski
University of Notre Dame, USA

Samuel Randalls
University College London, UK

ABSTRACT

In this special issue, we focus on the particular impacts of neoliberalism as a regime of scientific management. Drawing on a wide range of studies from other fields, as well as the four cases in this issue, we argue that while there are important differences in how neoliberalism has been implemented across nations and disciplines, there are a set of key principles and common outcomes that can serve a heuristic function for STS scholars attempting a more careful examination of neoliberalism. These common outcomes include: the rollback of public funding for universities; the separation of research and teaching missions, leading to rising numbers of temporary faculty; the dissolution of the scientific author; the narrowing of research agendas to focus on the needs of commercial actors; an increasing reliance on market take-up to adjudicate intellectual disputes; and the intense fortification of intellectual property in an attempt to commercialize knowledge, impeding the production and dissemination of science. Taken together, these shifts suggest that the impact of neoliberal science policy and management extends far beyond the patent system into the methods, organization, and content of science. We thus urge STS scholars to undertake a detailed exploration of exactly how the external political–economic forces of neoliberalism are transforming technoscience.

Keywords

commercialization, neoliberalism, political economy, privatization

While the idea that the 20th century was a golden age of science free from outside influence is clearly mythic (Kleinman, 2003; Mirowski and Sent, 2002; Rasmussen, 2002, 2004), it is also clear that the relations between public science and private profit have shifted dramatically over the past 30 years with the broad global movement towards neoliberalism.[1] Neoliberal policies, while varying across national contexts, have shifted methods, organization, and content in similar ways throughout the university. Given both the powerful impacts on the university and the growing attention to neoliberalism across the social sciences, it is surprising that STS scholars have not given more concerted attention to neoliberalism. The existing literature in STS has been notably vague about neoliberalism's definition and temporal and geographical specificities, as well as the extent to which neoliberal political–economic relations beyond academia shape what happens within it. The tendency instead has been to attribute many of the great transformations to actors internal to the university, ranging from the 'performativity' literature on economics (MacKenzie et al., 2007) to the rise of strong intellectual property (IP) (Berman, 2008), and to the accommodation to corporate protocols (Shapin, 2008). Curiously enough, this may have been one legacy of the modern STS field's repudiation of the Mertonian division between internal and external influences on science. While rejecting this division has been enormously productive for building the STS field, we believe it is time to reconsider what it portends for science studies in an age of neoliberal policies.

Thus, for this special issue, we have brought together four case studies that explore the broader territory of relations between private profit and public science. In each case, the authors identify neoliberal-influenced policies and philosophies at work in reshaping the production and consumption of a particular scientific discipline, focusing on the contextually specific ways in which neoliberal practices have been adopted. It thus falls to this introduction to briefly gather together the threads from the individual papers in order to speak to broader themes about commercialization and privatization in science.

In this introduction, we first provide an outlandishly brief history of neoliberalism and introduce its key concepts and the debates that surround it. We then describe the limited treatment of neoliberalism in STS to date, and make the case that such political–economic analysis should become a more prominent part of the STS toolkit. We conclude by introducing the papers in the special issue with particular attention to the lessons that can be drawn from comparison of these four case studies on issues such as the role of the state and the impacts of neoliberalism on the practice, content, and management of science.

NEOLIBERALISM

Neoliberalism can best be understood as the product of an ('inFleckted') historical 'thought collective' (see Plehwe, 2009) constituted through the Mont Pelerin Society, which was founded in 1947. The Society was formed to create a transnational network of neoliberals (academics and professionals) to promote their image of the market as the central agent in human society, and thus shift government focus from public welfare to market creation and protection. Its first President (1948–60) was the Austrian economist Friedrich von Hayek. Consequently, neoliberalism has been associated with Austrian economics, although there are good reasons to incorporate far more than this (see the essays in Mirowski and Plehwe (2009)). Other early members more recognizable to the STS community were Karl Popper and Michael Polanyi. Through decades of vigorous debate, Society members developed neoliberalism's core principles on issues ranging from public universities to legal frameworks, and their thinking eventually came to dominate a set of influential institutions, from Chicago School Economics to think tanks such as the Heritage Foundation and the Manhattan and George Marshall Institutes (Mirowski, 2008), to international financial institutions such as the World Bank and International Monetary Fund (IMF).

While neoliberalism has varied in its manifestations in different countries and regulatory arenas, the common core has been the promotion of market-based solutions to a broad range of issues. Neoliberalism brings together the classical liberal economic faith in the ability of properly functioning markets to improve social welfare with a new political commitment to expand market relations into traditionally public arenas such as healthcare, education, and environmental management (Harvey, 2005; McCarthy and Prudham, 2004; Mirowski and Plehwe, 2009; Peck and Tickell, 2002). As it developed after World War II, neoliberalism diverged from classical political liberalism by renouncing the passive notion of a laissez-faire economy in favor of an activist approach to the spread and promotion of 'free markets'.[2] Contrary to classical liberalism, neoliberals have consistently argued that their political program will only triumph if it becomes reconciled to the fact that the conditions for its success must be *constructed*, and will not come about 'naturally' in the absence of concerted effort. This had direct implications for the neoliberal attitude towards the state, as well as towards political parties and other corporate entities that were the result of deliberate organization, and not simply unexplained 'organic' growths. 'The Market' could not be depended upon to naturally conjure up the conditions for its own continued flourishing. It needed a strong state (divested of its unnecessary social welfare encumbrances) and the backing of international institutions such as the World Bank and the IMF to take its proper place in the neoliberal order.

Chile became the infamous first test case for neoliberal policies in the 1970s under General Pinochet, as national policy was substantially shaped by Chicago School economists, including students of Milton Friedman (President of the Mont Pelerin Society, 1970–2). Neoliberal policies were subsequently rolled out at the state level in a number of countries, including the UK and the U.S. through the rise of Milton Friedman-inspired politicians under Margaret Thatcher and Ronald Reagan. Neoliberalism became the dominant philosophy of the World Bank and IMF, leading to the era of structural adjustment and the global dominance of neoliberal principles. As Margaret Thatcher infamously declared, 'There is no alternative', a quote so frequently repeated to assert the dominance of neoliberalism that it is now referred to simply as TINA. While the ongoing global financial crisis has created doubt in some quarters about the rationality of neoliberal policies, neoliberalism remains the dominant organizing rationale for the global economy.

The key to understanding the relevance of neoliberalism for science studies is to appreciate that it is based upon some foundational precepts concerning *knowledge and how it is best organized*. On the organizational front, as part of the shift towards market-based solutions, national science policies have been (and continue to be) molded to encourage private investment in science and university–industry partnerships, through avenues such as strengthening intellectual property and decreasing public funding. At an even more fundamental level, neoliberalism reifies the primary function of an ideal economy as a 'marketplace of ideas'. The fundamental role of the market is not, according to neoliberalism, the mere exchange of things, but rather the processing and conveyance of knowledge or information. No human being (and no state) can ever measure up to the ability of the abstract marketplace to convey existing ideas and to summon forth further innovation.[3] Hence the novelty of neoliberalism is to alter the ontology of the market, and consequently, to revise the very conception of society. By its very definition, the market processes information in ways that no human mind can encompass or predict. Both of these characteristics of neoliberalism have profound implications for the organization and practice of science.

In the interests of summarizing our immediate concerns with what eventually became the core principles of neoliberalism—the commercialization of science and the university—we here risk oversimplifying its tenets into eight grossly telegraphed propositions:

1 *The Market is an artifact, but it is an ideal processor of information. Every successful economy is a knowledge economy.*

It knows more than any individual, and therefore cannot be surpassed as a mechanism of coordination. This is the core neoliberal argument for why socialism must fail.

2 *Neoliberalism starts with a critique of state reason.* The limits of government are related to intrinsic limitations on a state's power to know, and hence to supervise. These limits are not fixed for all time. Nevertheless, the Market always surpasses the state's ability to process information.

3 *Politics operates as if it were a market, and thus dictates an economic theory of 'democracy'.* This explains why the neoliberal movement must seek and consolidate political power by operating from within the state. The 'night-watchman' version of the state ends up repudiated. This tenet justifies alliances with the powerful in order to push the neoliberal agenda, and reinforces right-wing suspicions of what they consider 'radical democracy', that is, political action outside a market framework. This is combined with an advocacy of the 'wisdom of crowds', as long as that wisdom is expressed through market-like frameworks.

4 *Governmental institutions should be predicated on the government of the self.* Freedom is not the realization of any *telos*, but rather the positing of autonomous self-governed individuals, all naturally equipped with a neoclassical version of 'rationality' and motives of self-interest. Foucault (2004, 2008) is strongest on the role of these 'technologies of the self', which involve an elaborate reassessment in concepts of human freedom and morality.

5 *Corporations can do no wrong, or should not be blamed if they do. Competition always prevails.* This is one of the most pronounced areas of divergence from Classical Liberalism, with its ingrained suspicion of joint stock companies and monopoly. It underwrites a 'degovernmentalization of the state' through privatization of education, health, science, and even portions of the military.

6 *The nation-state should be subject to discipline and limitation through international initiatives.* This was initially implemented through neoliberal takeover of the IMF, the World Trade Organization, the World Bank, and other previously classical liberal transnational institutions. It began as advocacy of 'free trade' and floating exchange rates, but rapidly became subordinate to the wider agendas of transnational corporations, to whom it became attached. Neoliberal 'reforms' can therefore be imposed outside of standard political channels by supra-national organizations.

7 *The Market (suitably re-engineered and promoted) can always provide solutions to problems seemingly caused by The Market in the first place.* Monopoly is eventually undone by 'competition'; pollution is abated by the trading of 'emissions permits'; McCarthyism is mitigated by competition between employers (Friedman, 1962: 20). There is no such thing as a 'public good' or 'market failure', but only a series of problems handled by different governance structures, themselves determined by relative transactions costs (Coase, 1960, 1974).

8 *Redefinition of property rights is one of the most effective ways the state exerts neoliberal domination, since once such rights become established, they are treated from then on as 'sacred'.* Neoliberal economics often presents property rights as though their specific formats were relatively unimportant for the operation of 'The Market', but simultaneously they admit that, once created, they are very difficult to reverse. Hence the best way to initiate the privatization program in any area that previously had been subject to communal or other forms of allocation is simply to get the state to institute a new class of property rights.

The last 30 years demonstrate clearly that these principles manifest in contextually specific ways. They are useful, however, as heuristic devices for STS scholars interested in more careful examination of neoliberalism. These principles point towards commonalities across technoscientific contexts, and also to key arenas for analysis of changing patterns in the organization of science and technology under neoliberal regimes, as states enact policies (often with the aid of international institutions) to develop and protect property rights, self-government, privatization, and the prioritization of the market in delivering services.

NEOLIBERALISM AND STS: WHY WE SHOULD PAY MORE ATTENTION[4]

STS scholars have primarily addressed the impacts of neoliberalism through studies of the commercialization of biomedicine and biotechnology, addressing topics such as the impacts of patenting, the power balance between states and corporations, and the effects of private funding on public science. The authors of these studies tend to polarize into what Mirowski and Van Horn (2005) refer to as Economic Whigs (for example, Baltimore, 2003; Owen-Smith and Powell, 2003; Thursby and Thursby, 2003)—promoting technology transfer and public/private partnerships—and their opponents the Mertonian Tories—sounding the alarm to protect the norms of science, while preaching deliverance through a return to the supposed Mertonian Golden Age (for example, Brown, 2000; Croissant and Restivo, 2001; Krimsky, 2004).

This debate does not address many critical issues raised by the increasing privatization and commercialization of science. The ongoing integration of public science and private profit has not been limited to the biomedical sphere, but has spread out across the natural sciences and into the social sciences as well. Further, the impact on universities and the sciences is more profound than the biomedical debate would suggest, as demonstrated by a small but growing body of literature (Fallis, 2007; Fisher, 2009; Michaels, 2008; Nedeva & Boden, 2006; Foucault, 2008;[5] Giroux, 2008; Goldman, 2005; Pestre, 2003, 2005; Tyfield, 2010). The surge in university patents is indeed important, but as a manifestation of much deeper changes in scientific practice, management, and content as neoliberal concepts have been used to justify major innovations in the structure and organization of science.

The Shifting Relationship between Markets and Universities during the 20th Century

Some STS scholars argue that because science has always been beholden to its patrons, the character of those patrons is not particularly important; science has 'always been commercial', so the rise of neoliberalism is simply a difference in intensity, not in kind. For example, Steven Shapin writes that:

> Throughout history, all sorts of universities have 'served society' in all sorts of ways, and, while market opportunities are relatively novel, they do not compromise academic freedom in a way that is qualitatively distinct from the religious and political obligations that the ivory tower universities of the past owed to the powers in their societies. (Shapin, 2003: 19)

By contrast, we argue that particular regimes of science management and funding have specific and profound impacts on the character of scientific production.[6] Science may always have had economic and political dependencies, but the character of those dependencies matters deeply. As Dominque Pestre pointed out, 'the fact that Galileo successively worked in a university, then for the Republic of Venice, and finally at the court of the Grand Duke of Tuscany is of direct relevance to the kind of knowledge he produced' (Pestre, 2005: 30; also Biagioli, 2006a).

The U.S., for example, experienced three quite different regimes of scientific organization during the 20th century. The post-World War II shift to military organization and funding of science was a marked change from the decentralized organization, pedagogical focus, and rejection of public funding that had characterized academic science during the first half of the century. As we will describe in the next section, the shift away from military organization and funding with the rise of neoliberalism created a similarly stark contrast.

Why Neoliberalism Is Different

In the name of national security and nation building, the Cold War science management regime provided a sustained subsidy of academic research via the innovation of overhead payments on research grants. The state also supported the democratization of education via the GI Bill, provided generous fellowships integrated into grant structures, and insisted on the open distribution of research results (Asner, 2004; Mirowski, 2010). The rise of neoliberal science management regimes since 1980, particularly the insistence on the commercialization and privatization of knowledge, has created substantive shifts in the organization and practice of science. Perhaps the most obvious shift is the rollback of government funding for, and organization of, public research universities. During the Cold War, excelling at science was considered a key element of national security, and thus the military served as the primary manager and patron of public research. But by 1980, private spending on scientific research in the U.S. surpassed Federal funding for the first time in decades. This private funding is not being spent on in-house research and development, however: American corporations have been steadily jettisoning in-house research and development functions over the past three decades, and are investing in targeted research by contract research organizations and by university-based scientists newly starved for funding (Mirowski and Van Horn, 2005; Varma, 2000). Similar trends can be found in other advanced nations.

In the U.S., public universities also are losing direct subsidies at the state level. As universities have been increasingly re-envisioned as providers of human capital, rather than educational institutions that prepare students for citizenship (Lambert et al., 2007), it has become increasingly difficult to maintain public support for state-subsidized higher education (Apple, 2003, 2006). Individual universities are thus encouraged to solicit more private funds to offset cuts in state subsidy. But the more the university becomes embroiled in market activities, the more it loses any political justification for state support, resulting in a downward spiral of appropriations and the de facto privatization of the American public university system. Before the current global financial crisis, state contributions to budgets of flagship public research universities hovered at about 20 percent, but with the economic contraction, even that paltry contribution has fallen. As a number of analysts have pointed out, this neoliberal re-envisioning of the role of higher education is part of an effort to turn universities into competitive global service industries. Universities are being exhorted to become more like corporations—whose products are 'information' and 'human capital', and whose customers are students—as a prelude for the state to withdraw from all responsibility for the provision of education.[7]

Another impact of the emphasis on commercialization is the reversal of the Cold War trend of viewing teaching and research as mutually reinforcing activities. If the goal is to produce knowledge that leads to profits, teaching becomes a secondary function. Thus many universities have started replacing tenured faculty with adjunct, often temporary, faculty (as well as with legions of postdocs). As of 2005, more than 48 percent of faculty positions at American colleges that award federal financial aid were part-time and non-tenured, according to the National Center for Education Statistics (Lederman, 2007).

As Sismondo (2009) reveals, commodification of research has also led to the dissolution of the scientific author through the growth of industries devoted to ghost-writing of papers and ghost-management of the research process. Companies hire specialists not only to control data as intellectual property, but also to shape the interpretation of those data by writing papers and then approaching academics to append their names to the finished product. It is a consequence of neoliberal conceptions of knowledge to buy the 'person' to whom the research will be attributed, as well as buying the research itself.

A last widely noted impact of the neoliberal science management regime is the aggressive promotion and protection of intellectual property in hopes of gaining commercial value from knowledge. There is an intimate connection between the neoliberal recasting of the market as an information processor, and the growth of the conviction that knowledge should be commodified. This connection seems all the stronger when one considers that, as several recent studies have pointed out, for the vast majority of universities patenting has been a losing financial proposition (Geiger & Sa, 2008; Greenberg, 2007; Newfield, 2008: ch. 12; Powell et al., 2007). Insisting upon the commercialization of knowledge has, so far at least, proven more ideologically effective than economically practical.

While STS scholars tend to focus on patents and point to the 1980 Bayh-Dole Act as the watershed moment, it is important to note that neoliberal intellectual property protection is more complicated. Bayh-Dole was only one bill in a sequence of legislation throughout the 1980s that expanded the reach of intellectual property in the U.S. and internationally (Berman, 2008; Slaughter & Rhoades, 2002: 86). Vastly expanding the scope of this American legislation, representatives of corporations in high-tech industries formed the International Intellectual Property Alliance in 1984 to insert issues of intellectual property into larger trade negotiations (Drahos and Braithwaite, 2002; Sell, 2003). They were wildly successful in doing so, using the Uruguay Round of negotiations over the General Agreement on Tariffs and Trade to impose U.S. standards and levels of intellectual property protection on developed and developing countries alike, and to enforce them with trade sanctions through the World Trade Organization. Over the same period, corporations sought and won numerous amendments to strengthen both patent and copyright, and in 1982 they managed to have a special Court of Appeals in the Federal Circuit dedicated to patent cases.[8] The scope of what is deemed susceptible to patenting in America has been progressively broadened, and challenges to the legitimacy of patents have become less successful. It is now possible to patent anything from living beings, to computer code, to business practices; the patent system has come dangerously close to allowing the patenting of ideas themselves, *particularly when those ideas arise in scientific research*.[9] The very notion of a public sphere of codified knowledge has been rolled back at every point along its perimeter.

Patents are not the only, or even the most important component, of the rapidly expanding protection of intellectual property. Even with loosened patenting standards, it would still be far too unwieldy and time-consuming to patent every single research tool. Material transfer agreements (MTAs) have thus become the instrument of choice to control the commercial implications of cutting-edge research. MTAs affect scientific practice through confidentiality clauses and various permutations of prior restraint upon publication or other disclosure of findings, which retards their presentation and publication, as Evans (2010) demonstrates in his paper in this special issue. But the deeper effects of MTAs come from the so-called 'reach-through clauses' that lay claims upon any IP that might arise in future research by the recipient of the research tool. These clauses lately have come to include options for licenses on future research materials, grant-backs for newly discovered uses for the existing material, splitting of future royalties (or costs), royalty-free access to the organization's patent portfolio, broad claims over 'derivative' materials (such as off-spring of organisms, related cell lines, collateral secretions), patent prosecution controls, indemnification against any liabilities that might arise from use of the research material, and time limits on the use of the material (Mirowski, 2010).

Unwillingness to sign such overreaching clauses has slowed, and sometimes blocked, both individual research projects and knowledge transfer among scientists. Surveys of scientists published both in mainstream science journals and in specialist biomedical journals argue that MTAs are an increasingly common roadblock in the practice of science.[10] Henry et al. (2003: 446) report in a survey of 46 research organizations that all of their respondents used MTAs to protect unpatented information and material, and that almost 75 percent of them reported having at least one MTA negotiation breakdown within the past year. In one survey in Belgium, 60 percent of researchers reported abandoning projects because of problems with intellectual property restrictions on research tools (Rodriguez et al., 2007). As the university becomes more commercialized, the circle of research tools encumbered by MTAs has continued to widen, and so have the impacts on scientific practice.

We have argued here that neoliberal science policy is creating a regime of science organization quite distinct from the Cold War science management regime. While there are important differences in how neoliberal ideology has been implemented across nations and disciplines, there are some telling similarities: the roll-back of public funding for universities; the separation of research and teaching missions, leading to rising numbers of temporary faculty; the dissolution of the scientific author; and the intense fortification of intellectual property in an attempt to commercialize knowledge, impeding the production and dissemination of science. We turn now to the ways in which these broad trends manifest in the particular cases in this issue.

THE CASE STUDIES IN THIS SPECIAL ISSUE

Neoliberalism has had a broad range of impacts on scientific practice and organization, and the papers in this issue thus examine a variety of phenomena, investigating the impacts of public/private partnerships on scientific publication practices (Evans, 2010), the privatization of an existing science to enable a new market in ecosystem services in the U.S. (Lave et al., 2010), the commercialization and privatization of legal science in Britain (Lawless and Williams, 2010), and the contextual specificity of the embrace of neoliberal ideas by private sector science in the U.S. and Britain (Randalls, 2010). Despite this diversity, there are notable patterns across the papers.

First, the breadth of the scientific fields covered in these cases clearly demonstrates that neoliberalism's effects are being felt beyond biomedicine. Environmental sciences ranging from stream restoration (Lave et al., 2010), to plant biology (Evans, 2010), to meteorology (Randalls, 2010), and to the field of forensics (Lawless and Williams, 2010), are covered in this issue. It is worth noting that in response to the call for papers for this issue we received dozens of abstracts dealing with neoliberal impacts on everything from fisheries science, to materials science, and to sociology.

Second, while there is no singular storyline here, either on how neoliberal policies have been implemented or the extent to which particular fields have acquiesced to (or embraced) them, the papers in this issue demonstrate some common impacts. In each case, science is increasingly produced in direct response to corporate requirements, as scientists attempt to create forms of research that will enable new environmental and legal markets to function. Unsurprisingly, this increasing commercialization creates a tension featured in all the papers, but most especially in the case Lawless and Williams examine: the need to meet market imperatives while still allowing the products of science to be seen as value-free. The attempt to preserve the external sanctity of 'Science' whilst encouraging the internal proliferation of commercialization ties scientists and administrators in rhetorical and practical knots.[11]

It is also noteworthy that in all the disciplines addressed in these papers, what is accepted as good data has become highly contested, leading to shifts not only in the applications, but also in the basic core of these scientific fields. In three of the case studies in this issue (Lave et al., 2010; Lawless and Williams, 2010; Randalls, 2010) these contests are adjudicated not through the traditional mechanisms of science, but simply by what is taken up (or not) by the market. One notable consequence of this appears to be a narrowing of focus. For example, in stream mitigation banking, which Lave et al. (2010) discuss, broader concerns about stream ecology and water chemistry are sidelined in restoration projects in favor of a more pointed focus on variables far easier to both engineer and measure.

Third, there are some common actors promoting shifts in practice characteristic of neoliberal science regimes. Most notably, the state has been the major protagonist in promoting market-based solutions.[12] Evans' paper demonstrates some of the impacts of long-standing state attempts to neoliberalize universities and research laboratories by encouraging private funding for public researchers. Lave et al.'s paper highlights the ways in which government regulation enables a market in stream restoration, whilst both Lawless and Williams, and Randalls, show the UK government not simply enabling, but actively promoting the commercialization of forensic science and the privatization of meteorological science and service provision. Clearly, commercialization is not an independent trend to which government regulation merely reacts. Instead, states are key players in the expansion of neoliberal policies into scientific practice and management. Once commercialized, science becomes more easily privatized through expanded property rights, corporate (and university) secrecy and ownership of ideas, and the development of a competitive rather than collaborative enterprise of science.

Finally, as best demonstrated by Evans, the direct effects of commercial imperatives on scientific research are not necessarily obvious. It is only by looking beyond what appear as rational, neutral claims about the proper role of science and its increasingly commercialized organization that we can understand the influence of neoliberal philosophies. STS scholarship is ideally suited for revealing the continuous, diverse, and sometimes subtle ways in which neoliberal stances are being promulgated and cultivated in diverse fields of study.

CONCLUSION

Based on existing studies of neoliberalism and its effects, and the cases in this special issue, we have argued that the impacts of neoliberal policies on the conduct, products, and organization of science have not been trivial. First, the character of the university is changing as new privatized regimes of science management shift the sources and quantities of funding, the organization of research and teaching, and the intellectual and commercial status of knowledge claims.

Second, the strengthening of intellectual property protections and the linked insistence on the commercialization of knowledge are transforming the production and dissemination of knowledge. Evans, in this issue, points to a drop in publications by researchers engaged in public/private partnerships, and surveys cited above report that research projects have been frustrated and even stopped entirely by disputes over MTAs. The focus upon patents only serves to divert attention from where the real obstacles have been erected. The cases also demonstrate that science is increasingly being produced for particular markets, with a resulting contraction in the focus of research. This narrowing is only compounded when market uptake becomes a tool for adjudicating scientific disputes, as is reported in three of the papers in this issue. Further, contestations of what constitutes good evidence in power struggles over the creation of new markets call into question the validity not just of the scientific applications under dispute, but also of the basic core of fields. Thus it seems possible that instead of producing widely touted innovations for clients, neoliberal science regimes may leave us with the production of ignorance.

Finally, the impacts of neoliberal science policies include disturbingly elitist patterns that STS scholars are uniquely positioned to expose. For example, Leigh Johnson's work on the privatization of hurricane forecasting highlights the growing split in access to the products of privatized science. Through a spin-off business, university-based researchers have developed forecasts for a major energy company that predict the path of hurricanes 7 days in advance, with an accuracy of 100 miles (160 km); by contrast, the U.S. National Hurricane Center's forecasts can achieve the same track accuracy only 48 hours in advance (Johnson, 2009). Consider what the Federal Emergency Management Agency (FEMA) and the State of Louisiana might have been able to do had they been able to access accurate forecasts of the path of Hurricanes Katrina and Rita a week in advance; at present, the only entity with access to such knowledge is a major energy company. Equally, consider the potential social justice issues that could arise if geoengineering became dependable enough for major insurers and other corporations to deflect hurricanes into less economically damaging pathways (Block, 2006). Jill Fisher's (2009) work shows a similarly disturbing trend in access to medical treatment, as clinical trials increasingly use the bodies of the poor and uninsured to test drugs they will not have access to if approved.

Neoliberalism continues to have profound impacts on the organization, practice, and social implications of science. We thus suggest that STS scholars undertake a detailed exploration of exactly how neoliberal theories of society are transforming technoscience. Such an exploration will require not just the more familiar elements of the STS toolkit, but also analysis of external political–economic forces: to understand the neoliberal regime of science organization and management, we must understand where it's coming from.

Acknowledgments

This special issue started life as a session at the 2007 Society for Social Studies of Science meetings in Montreal, and we would like to acknowledge our fellow participants in that session—Arthur Daemmrich, Kerry Holden, and Arthur Mason—for their help in crystallizing our thoughts on this topic. We would also like to thank Mike Lynch and the anonymous SSS reviewers who helped us bring each of these papers, and the issue as a whole, into sharper focus.

Notes

1. For various approaches to this phenomenon, see Mirowski and Van Horn (2005), Ciafone (2005), Davies et al. (2006), Robertson (2006), Canaan and Shumar (2008), Fisher (2009), and Sismondo (2009).
2. The history of neoliberalism is a burgeoning topic in its own right, and would require a separate survey. The interested reader might consult Hartwell (1995), Foucault (2008), Mirowski & Plehwe (2009), Harvey (2005), and Plehwe and Walpen (2005).
3. This doctrine is itself relatively recent, dating at its earliest from the 1930s. It is eminently a *political* and not simply a cultural phenomenon, because it was developed as part of a concerted effort to counteract the rise of planning and other market-skeptical movements that grew out of the Great Depression and the experience of World War II.
4. This section draws heavily from Mirowski (2010).
5. Although Foucault's lectures date from the late 1970s, they have only recently been translated into English, which has magnified their impact on the literature on neoliberalism.
6. We draw the concept of 'regimes' of science organization, funding, and thought styles literature from authors including Coriat and Orsi (2002), Coriat and Dosi (1998), Coriat (2002), Coriat et al., (2003), Asner (2006), Tyfield (2006), Nedeva and Boden (2006), Johnson (2004), and Pestre (2003, 2004, 2005, 2007).
7. Some of the best studies have been Slaughter and Rhoades (2004), Apple (2005), Kirp (2003), Marginson (2007), Frank and Gabler (2006), and Douglass (2008).
8. A number of STS scholars have explored the history of the patent system (Biagioli, 2006b; Biagioli and Galison, 2002; Cooper, 2008; McSherry, 2001; Metlay, 2006; Sherman, 1996).

9. In June 2006 the Supreme Court rendered a decision in the case *Laboratory Corporation of America Holdings v. Metabolite Laboratories, Inc.* (126 S. Ct. 2921, 2926 (2006) (Breyer, J., dissenting)) 'which allowed this patent on a biological fact to remain in effect' (Andrews et al., 2006: 1395). In this case, researchers at Columbia University had found that a high level of homocysteine (an amino acid) is correlated with a vitamin deficiency. The investigators formed a startup firm, Metabolite Labs, and filed for a patent to capitalize on their discovery and a test for homocysteine. With startling hubris, the patent application asserted that the petitioners should be allowed to patent the basic physiological fact, so that they could claim a royalty whenever *any* test for homocysteine was sold (despite the fact that tests for homocysteine were already available, and used to diagnose several medical disorders). When a private corporation, the Laboratory Corporation of America (LabCorp), which had licensed the right to the test from Metabolite, published a scientific paper suggesting that high homocysteine levels might indicate a deficiency to be treated by a vitamin regimen, Metabolite sued for breach of contract and patent infringement. The U.S. Court of Appeals for the Federal Circuit astoundingly ruled that publishing the fact infringed the patent, and further ruled that doctors would infringe the patent merely by contemplating the physiological relationship. The Supreme Court originally allowed a review of the case, but then dismissed it on essentially technical grounds, so the lower court ruling still stands.

10. See for example mainstream science articles such as Cohen (1995), Abbott (2000), Marshall (1997), and Cyranoski (2002), and discipline-specific papers such as Cuiker (2006), Rounsley (2003), Streitz and Bennett (2003), Campbell et al. (2002), and Vogeli et al. (2007).

11. There are interesting parallels here with debates over military science. See Mukerji (1989) and Eyal (2010).

12. This is consistent with Harvey's observation that under neoliberalism, the state becomes the primary agent of neoliberal reform (2005: 162).

References

Abbott, Alison (2000). 'Mouse Geneticists Call for Unified Rules of Exchange', *Nature* 403: 236.

Andrews, Lori, Jordan Paradise, Timothy Holbrook & Danielle Bochneak (2006). 'When Patents Threaten Science', *Science* 314: 1395–96.

Apple, Michael (ed.) (2003). *The State and the Politics of Knowledge* (New York: Routledge).

Apple, Michael (2005). 'Education, Markets and an Audit Culture', *Critical Quarterly* 47: 11–29.

Apple, Michael (2006). *Educating the Right Way,* 2nd edition (London: Routledge).

Asner, Glen (2004). 'The Linear Model, the U.S. Department of Defense, and Golden Age of Industrial Research', in K. Grandin, N. Wormbs & S. Widmalm (eds.), *The Science–Industry Nexus* (Sagamore Beach, MA: Science History Publications): 3–30.

Asner, Glen (2006). *The Cold War and American Industrial Research.* Unpublished PhD Dissertation, Carnegie Mellon University.

Baltimore, David (2003). 'On Over-weighting the Bottom Line', *Science* 301: 1050–51.

Berman, Elizabeth Popp (2008). 'Why Did Universities Start Patenting? Institution Building and the Road to the Bayh-Dole Act', *Social Studies of Science* 38: 835–72.

Biagioli, Mario (2006a). *Galileo's Instruments of Credit: Telescopes, Images, Secrecy* (Chicago, IL: University of Chicago Press).

Biagioli, Mario (2006b). 'Patent Republic: Specifying Inventions, Constructing Authors and Rights', *Social Research* 73: 1129–72.

Biagioli, Mario & Peter Galison (eds.) (2002). *Scientific Authorship: Credit and Intellectual Property in Science* (London: Routledge).

Block, Walter (2006). 'Katrina: Private Enterprise, the Dead Hand of the Past, and Weather Socialism: An Analysis in Economic Geography', *Ethics, Place and Environment* 9(2): 231–41.

Brown, James R. (2000). 'Privatizing the University', *Science* 290: 1701.

Campbell, Eric, Brian Clarridge, Manjusha Gokhale, Lauren Birenbaum, Stephen Hilgartner, Neil Holtzman et al. (2002). 'Data Withholding in Academic Genetics: Evidence from a National Survey', *Journal of the American Medical Association* 287(4): 473–80.

Canaan, Joyce & Wesley Shumar (2008). *Structure and Agency in the Neoliberal University* (London: Taylor and Francis).

Ciafone, Amanda (2005). 'Endowing the Neoliberal University', *Work and Culture* 2005: 7.

Coase, Ronald (1960). 'The Problem of Social Cost', *Journal of Law and Economics* 3: 1–44.

Coase, Ronald (1974). 'The Lighthouse in Economics', *Journal of Law and Economics* 17: 356–76.

Cohen, Jon (1995). 'Share and Share Alike Isn't Always the Rule in Science', *Science* 268: 1715–18.

Cooper, Melinda (2008). *Life as Surplus* (Seattle: University of Washington Press).

Coriat, Benjamin (2002). 'The New Global Intellectual Property Rights Regime and Its Imperial Dimension', paper delivered to BNDS seminar, Rio de Janeiro.

Coriat, Benjamin & Giovanni Dosi (1998). 'Institutional Embeddedness of Economic Change', in K. Nielsen & B. Johnson (eds.), *Institutions and Economic Change* (Cheltenham: Edward Elgar): 3–33.

Coriat, Benjamin & Fabienne Orsi (2002). 'Establishing a New Intellectual Property Rights Regime in the United States', *Research Policy* 31: 1491–1507.

Coriat, Benjamin, Fabienne Orsi & Oliver Weinstein (2003). 'Does Biotech Reflect a New Science-based Innovation Regime?', *Industry and Innovation* 10: 231–53.

Croissant, Jennifer & Sal Restivo (eds) (2001). *Degrees of Compromise: Industrial Interests and Academic Values* (Albany, NY: SUNY Press).

Cuiker, Kenneth (2006). 'Navigating the Futures of Biotech Intellectual Property', *Nature Biotechnology* 24: 249–51.

Cyranoski, David (2002). 'Share and Share Alike?', *Nature* 420: 602–04.

Davies, Bronwyn, Michael Gottsche & Peter Bansel (2006). 'The Rise and Fall of the Neo-liberal University', *European Journal of Education* 41(2): 305–19.

Douglass, John (2008). 'Universities, the U.S. High Tech Advantage, and the Process of Globalization', CSHE Research Paper 8, Center for Studies of Higher Education, University of California, Berkeley.

Drahos, Peter & John Braithwaite (2002). *Information Feudalism: Who Owns the Knowledge Economy?* (New York: New Press).

Evans, James (2010). 'Industry Collaboration, Scientific Sharing and the Dissemination of Knowledge', *Social Studies of Science* 40(5): 757–91.

Eyal, Gil (2010). 'Spaces Between Fields', in P. Gorski (ed.), *Pierre Bourdieu and Historical Analysis* (Durham, NC: Duke University Press).

Fallis, George (2007). *Multiversities, Ideas and Democracy* (Toronto: University of Toronto Press).

Fisher, Jill (2009). *Medical Research for Hire: The Political Economy of Pharmaceutical Clinical Trials* (New Brunswick: Rutgers University Press).

Foucault, Michel (2004). *Naissance de la Biopolitique* (Paris: Galimand).

Foucault, Michel (2008). *The Birth of Biopolitics* (Basingstoke: Palgrave).

Frank, David & Jay Gabler (2006). *Reconstructing the University* (Stanford: Stanford University Press).

Friedman, Milton (1962). *Capitalism and Freedom* (Chicago, IL: University of Chicago Press).

Geiger, Roger & Creso Sa (2008). *Tapping the Riches of Science: Universities and the Promise of Economic Growth* (Cambridge, MA: Harvard University Press).

Giroux, Henry (2008). 'The Militarization of U.S. Higher Education after 9/11', *Theory, Culture and Society* 25(5): 56–82.

Goldman, Michael (2005). *Imperial Nature* (New Haven: Yale University Press).

Greenberg, Daniel (2007). *Science for Sale* (Chicago, IL: University of Chicago Press).

Hartwell, R. Max (1995). *A History of the Mont Pèlerin Society* (Indianapolis: Liberty Fund).

Harvey, David (2005). *A Brief History of Neoliberalism* (Oxford: Oxford University Press).

Henry, Michelle, Mildred Cho, Meredith Weaver & Jon Merz (2003). 'A Pilot Survey of the Licensing of DNA Inventions', *Journal of Law, Medicine and Ethics* 31: 442.

Johnson, Ann (2004). 'The End of Pure Science: Science Policy from Bayh-Dole to the NNI', in D. Baird, A. Nordmann & J. Schummer (eds.), *Discovering the Nanoscale* (Amsterdam: IOS Press): 217–30.

Johnson, Leigh (2009). 'Scientific Diligence, Climatic Urgency, and the Public/Private Expert: Hurricane Forecasts Go to Market', paper read at Society for Social Studies of Science annual meeting, Crystal City, VA (28–31 October).

Kirp, David (2003). *Shakespeare, Einstein and the Bottom Line* (Cambridge, MA: Harvard University Press).

Kleinman, Daniel (2003). *Impure Cultures: University Biology and the World of Commerce* (Madison, WI: University of Wisconsin Press).

Krimsky, Sheldon (2004). *Science in the Private Interest* (Lanham: Rowman and Littlefield).

Lambert, Cath, Andrew Parker & Michael Neary (2007). 'Entrepreneurialism and Critical Pedagogy: Reinventing the Higher Education Curriculum', *Teaching in Higher Education* 12(4): 525–37.

Lave, Rebecca, Martin Doyle & Morgan Robertson (2010). 'Privatizing Stream Restoration in the U.S.', *Social Studies of Science* 40(5): 677–703.

Lawless, Christopher & Robin Williams (2010). 'Helping With Inquiries, or Helping with Profits? The Trials and Tribulations of a Technology of Forensic Reasoning', *Social Studies of Science* 40(5): 731–55.

Lederman, Doug (2007). 'Inexorable March to a Part-Time Faculty', *Inside Higher Education* (28 March). Available at www.insidehighered.com/news/2007/03/28/faculty (accessed 28 February 2010).

MacKenzie, Donald, Fabien Muniesa & Lucia Siu (eds.) (2007). *Do Economists Make Markets?* (Princeton: Princeton University Press).

Marginson, Simon (2007). 'The Public/Private Divide in Higher Education: A Global Synthesis', *Higher Education* 53: 307–33.

Marshall, Elliott (1997). 'Materials Transfer: Need a Reagent? Just Sign Here', *Science* 278: 212–13.

McCarthy, James & W. Scott Prudham (2004). 'Neoliberal Nature and the Nature of Neoliberalism', *Geoforum* 35(3): 275–83.

McSherry, Corynne (2001). *Who Owns Academic Work?* (Cambridge, MA: Harvard University Press).

Metlay, Grischa (2006). 'Reconsidering Renormalization', *Social Studies of Science* 36: 565–97.

Michaels, David (2008). *Doubt is their Product* (New York: Oxford University Press).

Mirowski, Philip (2008). 'The Rise of the Dedicated Natural Science Think Tank', discussion paper, Social Science Research Council. Available at: www.ssrc.org/workspace/images/crm/new_

publication_3/%7Beee91c8f-ac35-de11-afac-001cc477ec70%7D .pdf (accessed 28 February 2010).

Mirowski, Philip (2010). *ScienceMart*™ (Cambridge, MA: Harvard University Press).

Mirowski, Philip & Dieter Plehwe (eds.) (2009). *The Road from Mont Pelerin: The Making of the Neoliberal Thought Collective* (Cambridge, MA: Harvard University Press).

Mirowski, Philip & Esther-Mirjam Sent (eds.) (2002). *Science Bought and Sold: Essays in the Economics of Science* (Chicago: University of Chicago Press).

Mirowski, Philip & Robert Van Horn (2005). 'The Contract Research Organization and the Commercialization of Science', *Social Studies of Science* 35: 503–48.

Mukerji, Chandra (1989). *A Fragile Power: Scientists and the State* (Princeton: Princeton University Press).

Nedeva, Maria & Rebecca Boden (2006). 'Changing Science: The Advent of Neoliberalism', *Prometheus* 24(3): 269–81.

Newfield, Christopher (2008). *Unmaking the Public University* (Cambridge, MA: Harvard University Press).

Owen-Smith, Jason & Walter Powell (2003). 'The Expanding Role of Patenting in the Life Sciences', *Research Policy* 32(9): 1695–1711.

Peck, Jamie & Adam Tickell (2002). 'Neoliberalizing Space', *Antipode* 34(3): 380–404.

Pestre, Dominique (2003). 'Regimes of Knowledge Production in Society: Towards a More Political and Social Reading', *Minerva* 41: 245–61.

Pestre, Dominique (2004). 'Thirty Years of Science Studies', *History and Technology* 20: 351–69.

Pestre, Dominique (2005). 'The Technosciences between Markets, Social Worries and the Political: How to Imagine a Better Future', in H. Nowotny, D. Pestre, E. Schmidt-Assmann, H. Schultze-Fielitz & H. Trute (eds.), *The Public Nature of Science under Assault* (Berlin: Springer): 29–52.

Pestre, Dominique (2007). 'The Historical Heritage of the 19th and 20th Centuries: Techno-Science, Markets and Regulations in a Long-term Perspective', *History and Technology* 23: 407–20.

Plehwe, Dieter (2009). 'Introduction', in P. Mirowski & D. Plehwe (eds.), *The Road from Mont Pelerin: The Making of the Neoliberal Thought Collective* (Cambridge, MA: Harvard University Press): 1–42.

Plehwe, Dieter & Bernard Walpen (2005). 'Between Network and Complex Organization: The Making of Neoliberal Knowledge and Hegemony', in D. Plehwe, B. Walpen & G. Nuenhoffer (eds.), *Neoliberal Hegemony: A Global Critique* (London: Routledge).

Powell, Walter, Jason Owen-Smith & Jeanette Colyvas (2007). 'Innovation and Emulation: Lessons from American Universities in Selling Private Rights to Public Knowledge', *Minerva* 45: 121–42.

Randalls, Samuel (2010). 'Weather Profits: Weather Derivatives and the Commercialization of Meteorology', *Social Studies of Science* 40(5): 705–30.

Rasmussen, Nicolas (2002). 'Of Small Men, Big Science, and Bigger Business: The Second World War and Biomedical Research in the U.S.', *Minerva* 40: 115–46.

Rasmussen, Nicolas (2004). 'The Moral Economy of the Drug Company–Medical Scientist Collaboration in Interwar America', *Social Studies of Science* 34(2): 161–86.

Robertson, Morgan (2006). 'The Nature That Capital Can See: Science, State, and Market in the Commodification of Ecosystem Services', *Environment and Planning: D* 24(3): 367–87.

Rodriguez, Victor, Frizo Janssens, Koenraad Debackere & Bart De Moor (2007). 'Do Material Transfer Agreements Affect the Choice of Research Projects?' *Scientometrics* 71: 239–69.

Rounsley, Steven (2003). 'Sharing the Wealth: The Mechanics of Data Release from Industry', *Plant Physiology* 133: 438–40.

Sell, Susan (2003). *Private Power, Public Law* (New York: Cambridge University Press).

Shapin, Steven (2003). 'Ivory Trade', *London Review of Books* (11 September): 15–19.

Shapin, Steven (2008). *The Scientific Life: A Moral History of a Late Victorian Vocation* (Chicago: University of Chicago Press).

Sherman, Brad (1996). 'Governing Science: Patents and Public Sector Research', in Michael Power (ed.), *Accounting and Science* (New York: Cambridge University Press): 170–94.

Sismondo, Sergio (2009). 'Ghosts in the Machine', *Social Studies of Science* 39: 109–33.

Slaughter, Sheila & Gary Rhoades (2002). 'The Emergence of a Competitiveness R&D Policy Coalition and the Commercialization of Academic Science', in P. Mirowski & E. Mirjam-Sent (eds.), *Science Bought and Sold* (Chicago, IL: University of Chicago Press): 69–108.

Slaughter, Sheila & Gary Rhoades (2004). *Academic Capitalism and the New Economy* (Baltimore: Johns Hopkins University Press).

Streitz, Wendy & Alan Bennett (2003). 'Material Transfer Agreements: A University Perspective', *Plant Physiology* 133: 10–13.

Thursby, Marie & Jerry Thursby (2003). 'University Licensing and the Bayh-Dole Act', *Science* 301: 1052.

Tyfield, David (2006). 'Neoliberalism and the Knowledge Economy', ESRC paper, University of Sussex.

Tyfield, David (2010). 'Neoliberalism, Intellectual Property and the Global Knowledge Economy', in K. Birch & V. Mykhenko (eds.), *The Rise and Fall of Neoliberalism* (London: Zed).

Varma, Roli (2000). 'Changing Research Cultures in U.S. Industry', *Science, Technology, & Human Values* 25(4): 395–416.

Vogeli, Christine, Recal Yucup, Eran Bendavid, Lisa Jones, Melissa Anderson, Karen Louis et al. (2007). 'Data Withholding and the Next Generation of Scientists: Results of a National Survey', *Academic Medicine* 81(2): 128–36.

CHAPTER 2

■■■

Introduction to Technology

Leo Marx

Does improved technology mean progress? If some variant of this question had been addressed to a reliable sample of Americans at any time since the early nineteenth century, the answer of a majority almost certainly would have been an unequivocal "yes." The idea that technological improvements are a primary basis for—and an accurate gauge of—progress has long been a fundamental belief in the United States. In the last half century, however, that belief has lost some of its credibility. A growing minority of Americans has adopted a skeptical, even negative, view of technological innovation as an index of social progress.

The extent of this change in American attitudes was brought home to me when I spent October 1984 in China. At that time the announced goal of the People's Republic was to carry out (in the popular slogan) "Four Modernizations"—agriculture, science and technology, industry, and the military. What particularly struck our group of Americans was the seemingly unbounded, largely uncritical ardor with which the Chinese were conducting their love affair with Western-style modernization—individualistic, entrepreneurial or "capitalist," as well as scientific and technological. Like early nineteenth-century visitors to the United States, we were witnessing a society in a veritable transport of improvement: long pent-up, innovative energies were being released, everyone seemed to be in motion, everything was eligible for change. It was assumed that any such change almost certainly would be for the better.

Most of the Chinese we came to know best—teachers and students of American studies—explicitly associated the kind of progress represented by the four modernizations with the United States. This respect for American wealth and power was flattering but disconcerting, for we often found ourselves reminding the Chinese of serious shortcomings, even some terrible dangers, inherent in the Western mode of industrial development. Like the Americans whom European travelers met 150 years ago, many of the Chinese seemed to be extravagantly, almost blindly, credulous and optimistic.

Our reaction revealed, among other things, a change in our own culture and, in some cases, in our own personal attitudes. We came face to face with the gulf that separates the outlook of many contemporary Americans from the old national faith in the advance of technology as the basis of social progress.

The standard explanation for this change includes that familiar litany of death and destruction that distinguishes the recent history of the West: two barbaric world wars, the Nazi holocaust, the Stalinist terror, and the nuclear arms race. It is striking to note how many of the fearful events of our time involve the destructive use or misuse, the unforeseen consequences, or the disastrous malfunction of modern technologies: Hiroshima and the nuclear threat; the damage inflicted upon the environment by advanced industrial societies; and spectacular accidents like Three Mile Island.

Conspicuous disasters have helped to undermine the public's faith in progress, but there has also been a longer-term change in our thinking. It is less obvious, less dramatic and tangible than the record of catastrophe that distinguishes our twentieth-century history, but I believe it is more fundamental. Our very conception—our chief criterion—of progress has undergone a subtle but decisive change since the founding of the Republic, and that change is at once a cause and a reflection of our current disenchantment with technology. To chart this change in attitude, we need to go back at least as far as the first Industrial Revolution.

THE ENLIGHTENMENT BELIEF IN PROGRESS

The development of radically improved machinery (based on mechanized motive power) used in the new factory system of the late eighteenth century coincided with the formulation and diffusion of the modern Enlightenment idea of history as a record of progress. This conception became the fulcrum of the dominant American worldview. It assumes that history, or at least modern history, is driven by the steady, cumulative, and inevitable expansion of human knowledge of and power over nature. The new scientific knowledge and technological power was expected to make possible a comprehensive improvement in all the conditions of life—social, political, moral, and intellectual as well as material.

The modern idea of progress, as developed by its radical French, English, and American adherents, emerged in an era of political revolution. It was a revolutionary doctrine, bonded to the radical struggle for freedom from feudal forms of domination. To ardent republicans like the French philosopher Condorcet, the English chemist Priestley, and Benjamin Franklin, a necessary criterion of progress was the achievement of political and social liberation. They regarded the new sciences and technologies not as ends in themselves, but as instruments for carrying out a comprehensive transformation of society. The new knowledge and power would provide the basis for alternatives to the deeply entrenched authoritarian, hierarchical institutions of *l'ancien régime*: monarchical, aristocratic, and ecclesiastical. Thus in 1813 Thomas Jefferson wrote to John Adams describing the combined effect of the new science and the American Revolution on the minds of Europeans:

> Science had liberated the ideas of those who read and reflect, and the American example had kindled feelings of right in the people. An insurrection has consequently begun, of science, talents, and courage, against rank and birth, which have fallen into contempt. . . . Science is progressive.

Admittedly, the idea of history as endless progress did encourage extravagantly optimistic expectations, and in its most extreme form, it fostered some wildly improbable dreams of the "perfectibility of Man" and of humanity's absolute mastery of nature. Yet the political beliefs of the radical republicans of the eighteenth century, such as the principle of making the authority of government dependent upon the consent of the governed, often had the effect of limiting these aspirations to omnipotence.

The constraining effect of such ultimate, long-term political goals makes itself felt, for example, in Jefferson's initial reaction to the prospect of introducing the new manufacturing system to America. "Let our work-shops remain in Europe," he wrote in 1785.

Although a committed believer in the benefits of science and technology, Jefferson rejected the idea of developing an American factory system on the grounds that the emergence of an urban proletariat, which he regarded as an inescapable consequence of the European factory system, would be too high a price to pay for any potential improvement in the American material standard of living. He regarded the existence of manufacturing cities and an industrial working class as incompatible with republican government and the happiness of the people. He argued that it was preferable, even if more costly in strictly economic terms, to ship raw materials to Europe and import manufactured goods. "The loss by the transportation of commodities across the Atlantic will be made up in happiness and permanence of government." In weighing political, moral, and aesthetic costs against economic benefits, he anticipated the viewpoint of the environmentalists and others of our time for whom the test of a technological innovation is its effect on the overall quality of life.

Another instance of the constraining effect of republican political ideal is Benjamin Franklin's refusal to exploit his inventions for private profit. Thus Franklin's reaction when the governor of Pennsylvania urged him to accept a patent for his successful design of the "Franklin stove":

> Governor Thomas was so pleased with the construction of this stove as described in . . . [the pamphlet] that . . . he offered to give me a patent for the sole vending of them for a term of years; but I declined it from a principle which has ever weighed with me on such occasions, namely; viz., *that as we enjoy great advantages from the invention of others, we should be glad of an opportunity to serve others by any invention of ours, and this we should do freely and generously* [emphasis in original].

What makes the example of Franklin particularly interesting is the fact that he later came to be regarded as the archetypal self-made American and the embodiment of the Protestant work ethic. When Max Weber sought out of all the world *the* exemplar of that mentality for his seminal study, *The Protestant Ethic and the Spirit of Capitalism*, whom did he choose but our own Ben? But Franklin's was a principled and limited self-interest. In his *Autobiography*, he told the story of his rise in the world not to exemplify a merely personal success, but rather to illustrate the achievements of a "rising people." He belonged to that heroic revolutionary phase in the history of the bourgeoisie when that class saw itself as the vanguard of humanity and its principles as universal. He thought of his inventions as designed not for his private benefit but for the benefit of all.

THE TECHNOCRATIC CONCEPT OF PROGRESS

With the further development of industrial capitalism, a quite different conception of technological progress gradually came to the fore in the United States. Americans celebrated the advance of science and technology with increasing fervor, but they began to detach the idea from the goal of social and political liberation. Many regarded the eventual attainment of that goal as having been assured by the victorious American Revolution and the founding of the Republic.

The difference between this later view of progress and that of Jefferson's and Franklin's generation can be heard in the rhetoric of Daniel Webster. He and Edward Everett were perhaps the leading public communicators of this new version of the progressive ideology. When Webster decided to become a senator from Massachusetts instead of New Hampshire, the change was widely interpreted to mean that he had become the quasi-official spokesman for the new industrial manufacturing interests. Thus Webster, who was generally considered the nation's foremost orator, was an obvious choice as the speaker at the dedication of new railroads. Here is a characteristic peroration of one such performance in 1847:

> It is an extraordinary era in which we live. It is altogether new. The world has seen nothing like it before. I will not pretend, no one can pretend, to discern the end; but everybody knows that the age is remarkable for scientific research into the heavens, the earth, and what is beneath the earth; and perhaps more remarkable still for the application of this scientific research into the pursuits of life . . . We see the ocean navigated and the solid land traversed by steam power, and intelligence communicated by electricity. Truly this is almost a miraculous era. What is before us no one can say, what is upon us no one can hardly realize. The progress of the age has almost outstripped human belief; the future is known only to Omniscience.

By the 1840s, as Webster's rhetoric suggests, the idea of progress was already being dissociated from the Enlightenment vision of political liberation. He invests the railroad with a quasi-religious inevitability that lends force to the characterization of his language as the rhetoric of the technological sublime. Elsewhere in the speech, to be sure, Webster makes the obligatory bow to the democratic influence of technological change, but it is clear that he is casting the new machine power as the prime exemplar of the overall progress of the age, quite apart from its political significance. Speaking for the business and industrial elite, Webster and Everett thus depict technological innovation as a sufficient cause, *in itself*, for the fact that history assumes the character of continuous, cumulative progress.

At the same time, discarding the radical political ideals of the Enlightenment allowed the idea of technological progress to blend with other grandiose national aspirations. Webster's version of the "rhetoric of the technological sublime" is of a piece with the soaring imperial ambitions embodied in the slogan "Manifest Destiny," and by such tacit military figurations of American development as the popular notion of the "conquest of nature" (including Native Americans) by the increasingly technologized forces of advancing European-American "civilization." These future-oriented themes easily harmonized with the belief in the coming of the millennium that characterized evangelical Protestantism, the most popular American religion at the time. Webster indicates as much when, at the end of his tribute to the new railroad, he glibly brings in "Omniscience" as the ultimate locus of the meaning of progress.

The difference between the earlier Enlightenment conception of progress and that exemplified by Webster is largely attributable to the difference between the groups they represented. Franklin, Jefferson, and the heroic generation of founding revolutionists constituted a distinct, rather unusual social class in that for a short time the same men possessed authority and power in most of its forms: economic, social, political, and intellectual. The industrial capitalists for whom Webster spoke were men of a very different stripe. They derived their status from a different kind of wealth and power, and their conception of progress, like their economic and social aspirations, were correspondingly different. The new technology and the immense profits it generated belonged to them, and since they had every reason to assume that they would retain their property and power, they had a vested interest in technological innovation. It is not surprising, under the circumstances, that as industrialization proceeded these men became true believers in technological improvement as the primary basis for—as virtually tantamount to—universal progress.

This dissociation of technological and material advancement from the larger political vision of progress was an intermediate stage in the eventual impoverishment of that radical eighteenth-century worldview. This subtle change prepared the way for the emergence, later in the century, of a thoroughly technocratic idea of progress. It was "technocratic" in that it valued improvements in power, efficiency, rationality as ends in themselves. Among those who bore witness to the widespread diffusion of this concept at the turn of the century were Henry Adams and Thorstein Veblen, who were critical of it, and Andrew Carnegie, Thomas Edison, and Frederick Winslow Taylor and his followers, who lent expression to it. Taylor's theory of scientific management embodies the quintessence of the technocratic mentality, "the idea," as historian

Hugh Aitken describes it, "that human activity could be measured, analyzed, and controlled by techniques analogous to those that had proved so successful when applied to physical objects."

The technocratic idea of progress is a belief in the sufficiency of scientific and technological innovation as the basis for general progress. It says that if we can ensure the advance of science-based technologies, the rest will take care of itself. (The "rest" refers to nothing less than a corresponding degree of improvement in the social, political, and cultural conditions of life.) Turning the Jeffersonian ideal on its head, this view makes instrumental values fundamental to social progress, and relegates what formerly were considered primary, goal-setting values (justice, freedom, harmony, beauty, or self-fulfillment) to a secondary status.

In this century, the technocratic view of progress was enshrined in Fordism and an obsessive interest in economies of scale, standardization of process and product, and control of the workplace. This shift to mass production was accompanied by the more or less official commitment of the U.S. government to the growth of the nation's wealth, productivity, and global power, and to the most rapid possible rate of technological innovation as the essential criterion of social progress.

But the old republican vision of progress—the vision of advancing knowledge empowering humankind to establish a less hierarchical, more just and peaceful society—did not disappear. If it no longer inspired Webster and his associates, it lived on in the minds of many farmers, artisans, factory workers, shopkeepers, and small-business owners, as well as in the beliefs of the professionals, artists, intellectuals, and other members of the lower and middle classes. During the late nineteenth century, a number of disaffected intellectuals sought new forms for the old progressive faith. They translated it into such political idioms as utopian socialism, the single-tax movement, the populist revolt, Progressivism in cities, and Marxism and its native variants.

THE ROOTS OF OUR ADVERSARY CULTURE

Let me turn to a set of these late-eighteenth-century ideas that was to become the basis for a powerful critique of the culture of advanced industrial society. Usually described as the viewpoint of the "counter-Enlightenment" of the "romantic reaction," these ideas have formed the basis for a surprisingly long-lived adversarial culture.

According to conventional wisdom, this critical view originated in the intellectual backlash from the triumph of the natural sciences we associate with the great discoveries of Galileo, Kepler, Harvey, and Newton. Put differently, this tendency was a reaction against the extravagant claims of the universal, not to say exclusive, truth of "the Mechanical Philosophy." That term derived from the ubiquity of the machine metaphor in the work of Newton and other natural scientists ("celestial mechanics") and many of their philosophic allies, notably Descartes, all of whom tended to conceive of nature itself as a "great engine" and its subordinate parts (including the human body) as lesser machines.

By the late eighteenth century, a powerful set of critical, antimechanistic ideas was being developed by Kant, Fichte, and other German idealists, and by great English poets like Coleridge and Wordsworth. But in their time the image of the machine also was being invested with greater tangibility and social import. The Industrial Revolution was gaining momentum, and as power machinery was more widely diffused in Great Britain, Western Europe, and North America, the machine acquired much greater resonance: it came to represent both the new technologies based on mechanized motive power and the mechanistic mindset of scientific rationalism. Thus the Scottish philosopher and historian Thomas Carlyle, who had been deeply influenced by the new German philosophy, announced in his seminal 1829 essay, "Signs of the Times," that the right name for the dawning era was the "Age of Machinery." It was to be the Age of Machinery, he warned, in every "inward" and "outward" sense of the word, meaning that it would be dominated by mechanical (utilitarian) thinking as well as by actual machines.

In his criticism of this new era, Carlyle took the view that neither kind of "machinery" was inherently dangerous. In his opinion, indeed, they represented *potential* progress as long as neither was allowed to become the exclusive or predominant mode in its respective realm.

In the United States a small, gifted, if disaffected minority of writers, artists, and intellectuals adopted this ideology. Their version of Carlyle's critical viewpoint was labeled "romantic" in reference to its European strains, or "transcendentalist" in its native use. In the work of writers like Emerson and Thoreau, Hawthorne and Melville, we encounter critical responses to the onset of industrialism that cannot be written off as mere nostalgia or primitivism. These writers did not hold up an idealized wilderness, a preindustrial Eden, as preferable to the world they saw in the making. Nor did they dismiss the worth of material improvement as such. But they did regard the dominant view, often represented (as in Webster's speech) by the appearance of the new machine power in the American landscape, as dangerously shallow, materialistic, and one-sided. Fear of "mechanism," in the several senses of that word—especially the domination of the individual by impersonal systems—colored all of their thought. In their work, the image of the machine-in-the-landscape, far from being an occasion for exultation, often seems to arouse anxiety, dislocation, and foreboding. Henry Thoreau's detailed, carefully composed account of the intrusion of the railroad into the Concord woods is a good example; it bears out his delineation of the new inventions as "improved means to unimproved ends."

This critical view of the relationship between technological means and social ends did not merely appear in random images, phrases, and narrative episodes. Indeed, the whole of *Walden* may be read as a sustained attack on a culture that had allowed itself to become confused about the relationship of ends and means. Thoreau's countrymen are depicted as becoming "the tools of their tools." Much the same argument underlies Hawthorne's satire, "The Celestial Railroad," a modern replay of *Pilgrim's Progress* in which the hero, Christian, realizes too late that his comfortable railroad journey to salvation is taking him to hell, not heaven. Melville incorporates a similar insight into his characterization of Captain Ahab, who is the embodiment of the Faustian aspiration toward domination and total control given credence by the sudden emergence of exciting new technological capacities. Ahab exults in his power over the crew, and he explicitly identifies it with the power exhibited by the new railroad spanning the North American continent. In reflective moments, however, he also acknowledges the self-destructive nature of his own behavior: "Now in his heart, Ahab had some glimpse of this, namely, all my means are sane, my motive and my object mad."

Of course there was nothing new about the moral posture adopted by these American writers. Indeed their attitude toward the exuberant national celebration of the railroad and other inventions is no doubt traceable to traditional moral and religious objections to such an exaggeration of human powers. In this view, the worshipful attitude of Americans toward these new instruments of power had to be recognized for what it was: idolatry like that attacked by Old Testament prophets in a disguised, new-fashioned form. This moral critique of the debased, technocratic version of the progressive worldview has slowly gained adherents since the mid-nineteenth century, and by now it is one of the chief ideological supports of an adversary culture in the United States.

The ideas of writers like Hawthorne, Melville, and Thoreau were usually dismissed as excessively idealistic, nostalgic, or sentimental, hence impractical and unreliable. They were particularly vulnerable to that charge at a time when the rapid improvement in the material conditions of American life lent a compelling power to the idea that the meaning of history is universal progress. Only in the late twentieth century, with the growth of skepticism about scientific and technological progress, and with the emergence of a vigorous adversary culture in the 1960s, has the standpoint of that earlier eccentric minority been accorded a certain intellectual respect. To be sure, it is still chiefly the viewpoint of a relatively small minority, but there have been times, like the Vietnam upheaval of the 1960s, when that minority has won the temporary support of, or formed a tacit coalition with, a remarkably large number of other disaffected Americans. Much the same antitechnocratic viewpoint has made itself felt in various dissident movements and intellectual tendencies since the 1960s: the antinuclear movements (against both nuclear power and nuclear weaponry); some branches of the environmental and feminist movements; the "small is beautiful" and "stable-state" economic theories, as well as the quest for "soft energy paths" and "alternative (or appropriate) technologies."

TECHNOCRATIC VERSUS SOCIAL PROGRESS

Perhaps this historical summary will help explain the ambivalence toward the ideal of progress expressed by many Americans nowadays. Compared with prevailing attitudes in the U.S. in the 1840s, when the American situation was more like that of China today, the current mood in this country would have to be described as mildly disillusioned.

To appreciate the reasons for that disillusionment, let me repeat the distinction between the two views of progress on which this analysis rests. The initial Enlightenment belief in progress perceived science and technology to be in the service of liberation from political oppression. Over time that conception was transformed, or partly supplanted, by the now familiar view that innovations in science-based technologies are in themselves a sufficient and reliable basis for progress. The distinction, then, turns on the apparent loss of interest in, or unwillingness to name, the social ends for which the scientific and technological instruments of power are to be used. What we seem to have instead of a guiding political goal is a minimalist definition of civic obligation.

The distinction between two versions of the belief in progress helps sort out reactions to the many troubling issues raised by the diffusion of high technology. When, for example, the introduction of some new labor-saving technology is proposed, it is useful to ask what the purpose of this new technology is. Only by questioning the assumption that innovation represents progress can we begin to judge its worth. The aim may well be to reduce labor costs, yet in our society the personal costs to the displaced workers are likely to be ignored.

The same essential defect of the technocratic mindset also becomes evident when the president of the United States [ed: at the time of this writing, the president was Ronald Reagan] calls upon those who devise nuclear weapons to provide an elaborate new system of weaponry, the Strategic Defense Initiative, as the only reliable means of avoiding nuclear war. Not only does he invite us to put all our hope in a "technological fix," but he rejects the ordinary but indispensable method of international negotiation and compromise. Here again, technology is thought to obviate the need for political ideas and practices.

One final word. I perhaps need to clarify the claim that it is the modern, technocratic worldview of Webster's intellectual heirs, not the Enlightenment view descended from the Jeffersonians, that encourages the more dangerous contemporary fantasies of domination and total control. The political and social aspirations of the generation of Benjamin Franklin and Thomas Jefferson *provided tacit limits to, as well as ends for, the progressive vision of the future.* But the technocratic version so popular today entails a belief in the worth of scientific and technological innovations as ends in themselves.

All of which is to say that we urgently need a set of political, social, and cultural goals comparable to those formulated at the beginning of the industrial era if we are to accurately assess the worth of new technologies. Only such goals can provide the criteria required to make rational and humane choices among alternative technologies and, more important, among alternative long-term policies.

Does improved technology mean progress? Yes, it certainly *could* mean just that. But only if we are willing and able to answer the next question." Progress toward what? What is that we want our new technologies to accomplish? What do we want beyond such immediate, limited goals as achieving efficiencies, decreasing financial costs, and eliminating the troubling human element from our workplaces? In the absence of answers to these questions, technological improvements may very well turn out to be incompatible with genuine, that is to say *social,* progress.

CHAPTER 3

■■■

Engineering and the Problem of Moral Overload

Jeroen Van den Hoven

Gert-Jan Lokhorst

Ibo Van de Poel

INTRODUCTION

Engineers are often confronted with moral dilemmas in their design work because they are presented with conflicting (value) requirements (cf. Van de Poel 2009). They are supposed to accommodate for example both safety and efficiency, security and privacy, accountability and confidentiality. The standard reaction to moral dilemmas was to try and weigh the different moral considerations, establish which values were more important for the engineering task at hand, and think about trade-offs or justifications for giving priority to one of the values at play. It seems only natural to think about moral solutions to moral problems arrived at by moral means. Sometimes this is the only thing we can do. Sometimes, however, our moral dilemmas are amenable to a technical solution. We tend to forget that since a moral dilemma is constituted by a situation in the world that does not allow us to realize all our moral obligations in that situation at the same time, solutions to a dilemma may also be found by changing the situation in such a way that we can satisfy all our value commitments. We argue here that some moral dilemmas may very well have engineering solutions and that certain types of moral dilemmas can be tackled by means of technical innovations. Our analysis draws attention to a special feature of the responsibility of engineers, namely the responsibility to prevent situations that are morally dilemmatic and that must inevitably lead to suboptimal solutions or compromises and trade-offs from a moral point of view. We start our analysis from a familiar place: the analysis of moral dilemmas and the problem of moral overload.

We are repeatedly confronted by situations in which we cannot satisfy all the things that are morally required of us. Sometimes our moral principles and value commitments can simply not all be satisfied at the same time given the way the world is. The result is that we are morally "overloaded." These situations have been extensively studied in moral philosophy, rational choice theory and welfare economics and are referred to as "hard choices," "moral dilemmas" or "conflicting preferences" (e.g., Kuran 1998; Van Fraassen 1970; Levi 1986). The problem that has received most of the attention is the question of how we ought to decide in these dilemmatic cases between the various options and alternatives open to the agent. There is, however, another aspect that has received far less attention and that is sometimes referred to as "the moral residue," i.e., the moral emotions and psychological tensions that are associated with the things that were not done, the road not traveled, the moral option forgone. A moral residue provides those who are exposed to it with an incentive to avoid moral overload in the future. It can therefore function as a motor for improvement, in fact as a motor for technological innovation. We will argue that if an instance of technological innovation successfully reduces moral overload, it constitutes an instance of moral progress.

MORAL OVERLOAD AND MORAL DILEMMAS

Timur Kuran (1998) has referred to situations in which we have different value commitments by which we cannot live simultaneously as situations of "moral overload." The basic idea of moral overload is that an agent is confronted with a choice situation in which different obligations apply but in which it is not possible to fulfill all these obligations simultaneously.

Kuran provides the following more detailed definition of moral overload. An agent A has to make a particular decision in a choice situation in which A can only choose one option. The options she can choose from form together the opportunity set X, which is defined by physical and practical constraints. The agent has a number of values $V_a \ldots V_x$; each of these values requires her to avoid a subset of the options. More specifically the values instruct the agent to keep $v_n > v\underline{n}$, where v_n is the actual realization of value V_n by an option and $v\underline{n}$ a threshold that V_n should at least meet. The set of feasible options that meet all these value thresholds forms the moral opportunity set X^m (see Figure 3.1).

Now in some choice situations, the moral opportunity set is empty: the agent cannot live by her values. This situation is

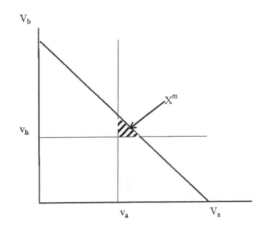

FIGURE 3.1. The Moral Opportunity Set X^m. Under Certain Conditions X^m May Be Empty, So Creating Moral Overload. (The figure is based on Figure 1 in Kuran 1998:235.)

defined as moral overload. In a situation of moral overload the agent is not only confronted with a difficult choice problem, she is also forced to do something that violates her values; moral overload therefore results in a feeling of moral guilt or moral regret.

The notion of moral overload is quite similar to what others have described as a moral dilemma. The most basic definition of a moral dilemma is the following (Williams 1973:180):

1 The agent ought to do a

2 The agent ought to do b

3 The agent cannot do a and b

One available option of action meets one obligation but not the other. The agent again can fulfill the second obligation, but not without violating the first. Conflicting moral obligations create moral dilemmas. The nature, structure and logic of moral dilemmas has been extensively studied and has been discussed by Bas van Fraassen (1970), Bernard Williams (1973) and Ruth Marcus (1980).

William's definition of a moral dilemma is somewhat different from Kuran's definition of moral overload because it is defined in terms of "oughts" instead of "values" and because it is defined over two options a and b instead of over a larger set of options, but the basic deontic structure is obviously the same. For our current purpose, Levi's (1986:5) definition of what he calls "moral struggle" is particularly relevant:

1 The agent endorses one or more value commitments P_1, P_2, . . . , P_n.

2 Value commitment P_i stipulates that in contexts of deliberation of type T_i, the evaluation of feasible options should satisfy constraint C_i.

3 The specific decision problem being addressed is recognized to be of each of the types T_1, T_2, . . . , T_n so that all constraints C_1, C_2, . . . , C_n are supposed to apply.

4 The decision problem currently faced is one where the constraints C_1, C_2, . . . , C_n cannot all be jointly satisfied.

Levi sees his definition of moral struggle, which is almost identical to Kuran's definition of moral overload, as a more general characterization of moral dilemmas. It is not only more general because it applies to a set of options and a set of value commitments instead of just two options and two "oughts," but also because the notion of value commitment is more general than the notion of "ought." According to Levi, value commitments may be represented as moral principles, but also as "expressions of life goals, personal desires, tastes or professional commitments" (Levi, 1986:5). This suggests that we also can have non-moral overload generated by conflicting non-moral value commitments in a choice situation. We may, for example, have a conflict between a prudential and a moral value or between two prudential values or two preferences.

STRATEGIES FOR DEALING WITH MORAL OVERLOAD

There are various strategies for dealing with moral overload or moral dilemmas. In this section we will discuss several such strategies. We will see that although these strategies may be more or less adequate in the individual choice situation, in most cases they do not take away what has been called the "moral residue." Moral residue here refers to the fact that even if we may have made a justified choice in the case of moral overload or moral dilemma, there remains a duty unfulfilled, a value commitment not met.

One way to deal with a moral dilemma is to look for the option that is best, all things considered. Although this can be done in different ways, it will usually imply a trade-off among the various relevant value commitments. The basic idea here is that the fact that an option x does not meet value commitment P_i with respect to value V_i could be compensated by better meeting one or more of the other values. Such a strategy reduces the multidimensional decision problem to a one-dimensional decision problem.

Value commitments can, however, not always be traded off. This is sometimes expressed in terms of value incommensurability, i.e., the fact that values cannot be measured on the same scale (Chang 1997). What makes trade-offs impossible is, however, probably not just formal incommensurability, i.e., the lack of a measurement method to compare (degrees of) values on one scale, but rather substantive incommensurability, i.e., the fact that some values resist trade-offs: less of one value cannot be compensated by having more of another (Tetlock 2003; Raz 1986; Baron and Spranca 1997). No money in the world can compensate the loss of a dear friend. Another way of expressing this idea is that if trade-offs or compensations are tried, there is always some residue that cannot be compensated; it is in fact this residue that creates a feeling of moral guilt or regret that is typical for moral dilemmas and moral overload. This also implies that even if we might be justified in believing that one value commitment is more important than another one in a morally dilemmatic choice, this does not take away the occurrence of a moral residue.

Making value trade-offs is not the only strategy for dealing with moral dilemmas and moral overload. We will focus here on the various strategies, social mechanisms and social institutions that Kuran (1998) discusses. He distinguishes three categories of strategies. The first comprises strategies that allow the agent to lower the threshold for one or more of the value commitments in the particular choice situation while retaining the long-term value commitments. The second category of strategies allows the agent to avoid entering into a choice situation that is characterized by moral overload. The third category is formed by strategies that help to avoid moral overload by reformulating or revising long-term value commitments. All of these strategies can be employed by individuals but all of them also have an institutional component, i.e., they are made possible or made easier through the existence of certain social institutions that help to alleviate value conflict of individuals.

Kuran discusses three strategies of the first category that allow the agent to lower the threshold for one or more value commitment in the particular choice situation while retaining the long-term value commitment: compensation, casuistry and rationalization. Compensation is often not directly possible in the choice situation because the relevant values in a situation of moral overload resist trade-offs and are therefore not amenable to direct compensation. However, agents can and often do—as empirical evidence suggests—compensate a moral loss in one situation by doing more than is required in a next situation. Compensation may then allow agents to live by their values over the course of their life, even if they cannot live up to their value commitments in every choice situation.[1]

Kuran describes casuistry, the second strategy, as "the use of stratagems to circumvent a value without discarding it formally" (Kuran 1998:251). The use of such tricks is obviously one of the things that gave casuistry a bad name in the past (cf. Jonsen and Toulmin 1988). It might indeed strike one as wicked to propose this as a strategy for dealing with moral overload. It might nevertheless have some value because it helps to preserve the value commitment for future choice situations without incurring a feeling of guilt in the current choice situation.

In rationalization, the agent tries to rationalize away the conflict between two values. Take the following example. In choosing a means of transport, one may have the prudential value of "comfort" and the moral value of "taking care of the environment." The values conflict because the most comfortable means of transport, the car, pollutes the environment more than, for example, the train. The agent may now rationalize away the conflict by arguing that the train is more comfortable than a car because you do not have to drive yourself and you have time to read. In this way, rationalization not only alleviates the felt tension between the two values, but it also affects the choice made. In the example given, the agent in effect restrained her prudential value in favor of the moral value at play.

The second category of strategies aims at avoiding moral overload. Kuran suggests two strategies for doing so: escape and compartmentalization. Escape is a strategy in which an agent tries to prevent moral overload by avoiding choices. Compartmentalization refers to the splitting up of an individual's life or of society in different contexts to which different values apply. In as far as compartmentalization is successful it avoids the need to choose between two or more values in a specific choice context.

The third category comprises strategies in which the agent revises her value commitments in order to avoid moral overload. Kuran refers to this as "moral reconstruction." Obviously, moral reconstruction only makes sense if an agent is repeatedly not able to live by her value commitments or if there are independent reasons to revise a value commitment, for example, because it was mistaken in the first place or has become outdated due to historical developments. In the absence of such independent reasons, moral reconstruction to avoid moral dilemmas is often dubious. As Hansson writes:

> More generally, dilemma-avoidance by changes in the code always takes the form of weakening the code and thus making it less demanding. There are other considerations that should have a much more important role than dilemma-avoidance in determining how demanding a moral code should be. In particular, the major function of a moral code is to ensure that other-regarding reasons are given sufficient weight in human choices. The effects of a dilemma per se are effects on the agent's psychological state, and to let such considerations take precedence is tantamount to an abdication of morality (Hansson 1998:413).

Nevertheless, a milder form of moral reconstruction, not mentioned by Kuran, might sometimes be acceptable. In some cases, it is possible to subsume the conflicting values under a higher order value. Kantians, for example, tend to believe that all value conflicts can eventually be solved by having recourse to the only value that is unconditionally good: the good will. One need not share this optimism to see that it makes sometimes perfect sense to try to redefine the conflicting values in terms of one higher-order value. A good example is the formulation of the value "sustainable development" in response to the perceived conflict between the value of economic development and the abatement of poverty on the one hand, and environmental care and care for future generations on the other hand. In 1987, sustainable development was defined by the Brundtland Commission of the UN as "development that meets the needs of the present without compromising the ability of future generations to meet their own needs" (WCED 1987).

Although higher order values, like sustainability, may be useful to decide how to act in a moral dilemma, they often do not just dissolve the dilemma. Often the overarching value may refer to or contain a range of more specific component values and norms that are conflicting and incommensurable (cf. Chang 1997:16; Richardson 1997:131). This means that even if a justified choice may be made in a dilemmatic situation on the basis of an overarching value, a moral residue, in the sense of a moral value or norm not (fully) met, may still occur.

As we have seen, there are different ways in which people can react to moral overload. Not all replies are, however, equally morally acceptable. Casuistry and rationalization, for example, may be psychologically functional, but they may well lead to morally unacceptable choices. Trying to avoid entering into a moral dilemma by escape or compartmentalization may sometimes be morally desirable but are certainly not always morally praiseworthy. In some circumstances, these choices may also be interpreted as a way of neglecting one's moral responsibilities. As we have also seen, moral reconstruction, while sometimes adequate, may in other circumstances be unacceptable. Moreover, even if there is a morally justified choice in a dilemmatic situation, this choice as such does not usually take away the occurrence of a moral residue.

The occurrence of a moral residue or moral guilt is thus typical for choice under moral overload. The moral residue or guilt is, however, not just an unfortunate by-product we have to live with, but will motivate the agent to organize her life in such a way that in the future moral overload is reduced. Marcus (1980) has in fact suggested that we have a second-order duty to avoid moral dilemmas: "One ought to act in such a way that, if one ought to do X and one ought to do Y, then one can do both X and Y." This principle is regulative; the second order "ought" does not imply "can." The principle applies to our individual lives, but also entails a collective responsibility (Marino 2001) to create the circumstances in which we as a society can live by our moral obligations and our moral values. One way in which we can do so is by developing new technologies.

MORAL RESIDUES AS MOTORS FOR TECHNOLOGICAL INNOVATION

Ruth Marcus (1980) has put forward the following second-order regulatory principle:

(BF1) One ought to act in such a way that, if one ought to do x and one ought to do y, then one can do both x and y.

To understand this principle, it is useful first to revisit the question of whether, and in what sense, "ought" implies "can." If OA (it is obligatory that A), then PA (it is permitted that A), and therefore MA (it is logically possible that A). In this sense, OA → MA is valid. But in many other senses, OA does not entail MA. For example, if M means "economically possible," "politically possible," "physically possible," "biologically possible," "possible without losing your life," "astrologically possible," "using only your bare hands and not any instrument whatsoever," or "possible with your left thumb," then OA → MA is invalid. In such cases, it makes sense to say that OA *should* imply MA:

1 O(OA → MA).

According to standard deontic logic with a possibility operator, (1) is a theorem if and only if (2) is a theorem (indeed, both (1) and (2) are theorems of that system):

2 $O(OA\&OB \rightarrow M(A\&B))$.

Formula (2) expresses principle BF1, while (1) expresses the following principle, which seems weaker but in fact has the same force:

(BF2) One ought to act in such a way that if one ought to do x, one can do x.

We will refer to "principle (BF1/BF2)" to refer to the principles (BF1) and (BF2), which can be derived from each other. In cases in which $OA\& \sim MA$, there is what Ruth Marcus calls a "moral residue" because OA cannot be fulfilled. This may cause anxiety and distress. What can one do in such cases?

One approach in such situations is to try to avoid entering into a moral dilemma or situation of moral overload in the first place. Principle BF1/BF2, for example, implies that one should not make two promises that cannot be fulfilled simultaneously. More generally, the second category of strategies discussed by Kuran, which includes the strategies of escape and compartmentalization, are relevant here (see previous section).

However, principle BF1/BF2 can also be fulfilled by a set of strategies that seems to be missing in Kuran's overview: strategies that help to avoid moral overload by expanding the opportunity set, i.e., by changing the world in such a way that we can live by all our values. We may refer to this set of strategies as "innovation." Innovation can be institutional or technical in nature. We are here primarily interested in innovation that has its origin in engineering, technology and applied science. Our thesis to be defended here is that technical innovation and engineering design are important, though often neglected, means for reducing or even avoiding moral overload on a collective level and dealing with dilemmatic situations and their moral tensions on an individual level. We argue that technical innovation and engineering design sometimes offer genuine ways out of moral mazes and provide opportunities to obviate moral dilemmas and reduce the regret, guilt and moral residues that are inevitably linked to them.

The crucial point is that innovation can make the impossible possible, not in the sense of "logically possible," of course, but in the sense of "feasible" or "physically realizable." Given technologies S and T, where S is less advanced than T, it may be the case that $\sim M^S A \& M^T A$: A is not possible with technology S but

A is possible with technology T. Here M^TA may be explicated as $MA\&N(MA \rightarrow T)$, where N means "necessarily": it is possible that A, but only in the presence of T. Seen from this perspective, (BF1/BF2) admonishes us to look for more advanced technology in cases in which we cannot fulfill our obligations on the basis of current technology. If $N(MA \rightarrow T)$ is true, then principle (BF1/BF2) implies $O(OA \rightarrow T)$ and $O(OA \rightarrow OA\&M^TA)$. In other words, if OA, then we should look for technology T such that $OA\&M^TA$. It is in this sense that moral residues in combination with principle (BF1/BF2) can promote technological innovation.

We provide the following examples.

1 Suppose that your new neighbors have invited you for their house-warming party and you feel obliged to attend (OA). But you also have to look after your baby (OB). Suppose also that there is no baby-sitter available. If your actions were limited to those that were available in Ancient Greece you would have a problem because $\sim M^G(A\&B)$, where G is Greek technology. However, we now have the baby phone. It enables you to take care of your baby during your visit to the neighbors. As a result, M(A&B) is now true and both O(A&B) and (BF1/BF2) can be fulfilled. It is in this way that technology may lead to empowerment. If technology such as the baby phone did not exist, somebody should invent it.

2 *Trade-off between security and privacy.* As a society we value privacy, but at the same time we value security and the availability of information about citizens. This tension is exemplified in the debates about ubiquity of CCTV cameras in public places. We either hang them everywhere and have the desired level of security (OA) in that area but give up on our privacy (~OB), or out of respect for privacy we do not hang them everywhere (OB), but settle for less security (~OA). Respect for our privacy may pull us in the direction of reticence, whereas security pushes us in the direction of making more information about individual citizens available to the outside world. Smart CCTV systems allow us to have our cake and eat it, in the sense that their smart architecture allows us to enjoy the functionality and at the same time realize the constraints on the flow and availability of personal data that respect for privacy requires ($M^T(A\&B)$). These applications are referred to as Privacy Enhancing Technologies (PET).

3 *Trade-off between economic growth and sustainability.* Environmental technology in Germany is among the most advanced in the world. One of the reasons why this is the case is because in Germany in the sixties the Green Party was very influential and articulated the obligation to reconcile economic growth with the protection of the environment. It is only because this tension between desirable production and economic growth (OA) was explicitly contrasted with cherished environmental values (OB) that an opportunity was created to find ways in which the two could be reconciled. Environmental technology is exactly the sort of smart technology that changes the world in such a way as to allow us to produce and grow without polluting the environment $(M^T(A\&B))$.

4 *Trade-off between military effectiveness and proportionality.* We are sometimes under an obligation to engage in military interventions that satisfy the universally accepted principles of *ius cogens* or *ius ad bellum* (OA). At the same time, we foresee that these military operations may cause the death of innocent non-combatants (OB). Here we find ourselves torn between two horns of a dilemma in a particular case of a mission or on a collective level. We are morally overloaded since we have two values that we cannot satisfy at the same time, i.e., destroy the enemies' weapons of mass destruction, or prevent innocent deaths $(\sim M(A\&B))$. Non-lethal weapons or precision/smart weapons ideally allow us to satisfy both obligations $(M^T(A\&B))$ (cf. Cummings 2006). This example only serves to exhibit the logic of military thinking concerning advanced weapons technology. Whether the envisaged technology really delivers the goods needs to be established independently.

The list of examples of this type is extensible *ad lib*. For this reason, we propose the following hypothesis: moral residues in combination with principle (BF1/BF2) can—and often do—act as motors of technological progress.

MORAL PROGRESS AND TECHNOLOGICAL INNOVATION

Meeting principle (BF1/BF2) can be described as moral progress because it allows us to better fulfill our moral obligations (Marino 2001). We have shown that technical innovation can be a means to fulfill principle (BF1/BF2). This implies that technological innovation can result in moral progress.

The reason why technical innovation can entail moral progress is that it enlarges the opportunity set. In the examples mentioned, technical innovation moved the boundary of the opportunity set

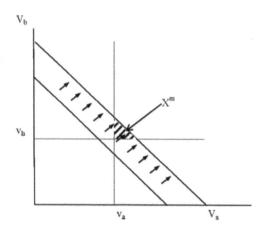

FIGURE 3.2. By Extending the Opportunity Set, the Moral Opportunity Set X^m May Become Non-empty.

in the upper right direction (see Figure 3.2). As an effect, the moral opportunity set, which was empty in the case of (moral) overload, became non-empty. Even if the moral opportunity set does not become non-empty, the degree of moral overload is reduced by moving the boundary of the opportunity set in the upper right direction.

Of course, not all instances of technological innovation entail moral progress. While technical innovation may result in progress in some respects, it may at the same time represent a decline in other important value dimensions. Due to agricultural innovations, grain output in many western countries has significantly increased per area of land cultivated, but it has *decreased* per unit of energy consumed (Pacey 1983:14). Another reason why technical innovation does not necessarily result in moral progress is that it may result in a "technological fix," i.e., a technical solution to a problem that is social in nature (Weinberg 1966). Technological fixes are not always undesirable or inadequate, but there is a danger that what is addressed is not the real problem but the problem in as far as it is amendable to technical solutions (see also Sarewitz 1996, especially Chapter 8). It can, for example, be argued that world hunger is not primarily a problem of production capacity, which can be enlarged by technical innovation, but rather a problem of distribution of food, income and land, which is far less amendable to technical solutions.

Despite such reservations, we still think that it can be claimed that technical innovation results in moral progress in those cases in which it means an improvement in *all* relevant value dimensions. There is, nevertheless, another possible objection to this view: it assumes a static notion of the relevant value dimensions. It has been argued that technological innovation does not only change the opportunity set but also morality, and thus the value dimensions along which we judge moral progress (Swierstra et al. 2009).

Although it is true that technology can change morality—think about the change in sexual morals due to the availability of anticonceptives—we think that technology-induced moral change at the level of fundamental values is the exception rather than the rule. In many cases, we can therefore simply assess moral progress by the standard of current values. Nevertheless, technical innovation may sometimes make new value dimensions *relevant* that were not considered in the design of a technology. We can think of two reasons why this might occur.

One reason is that technical innovation not only enlarges the range of options but that new options also bring new side effects and risks. This may introduce new value dimensions that should be considered in the choice situation and these new value dimensions may create new forms of moral overload. Nuclear energy may help to decrease the emission of greenhouse gases and at the same time provide a reliable source of energy, but it also creates long-term risks for future generations due to the need to store the radioactive waste for thousands of years. It thus introduces the value dimension of intergenerational justice and creates new moral overload. The design of new reactor types and novel fuel cycles is now explored to deal with those problems (Taebi and Kadak 2010).

Second, technical innovation may introduce choice in situations in which there was previously no choice. An example is prenatal diagnostics. This technology creates the possibility to predict that an unborn child will have a certain disease with a certain probability. This raises the question whether it is desirable to abort the fetus in certain circumstances. This choice situation is characterized by a conflict between the value of life (even if this life is not perfect) and the value of avoiding unnecessary suffering. Given that prenatal diagnostic technologies introduce such new moral dilemmas, one can wonder whether the development of such technologies meets principle (BF1/BF2). The same applies to the technologies for human enhancement that are now foreseen in the field of nanotechnology and converging technologies.

IMPLICATIONS FOR THE RESPONSIBILITY OF ENGINEERS

We have seen that while technological innovation might be a means to fulfill principle (BF1/BF2), not all innovations meet principle (BF1/BF2). We think this has direct implications for the responsibility of engineers that develop new technology. We suggest that engineers, and other actors involved in technological development, have a moral responsibility to see to it that the technologies they develop meet principle (BF1/BF2).

This higher order moral obligation can be construed as an important aspect of an engineer's task responsibility. This has been described as a meta-task responsibility (Van den Hoven 1998; Rooksby 2009), or an obligation to see to it (by designing an artifact) that oneself or others (users or clients) can do what ought to be done.

An interesting way to fulfill this responsibility is the approach of Value Sensitive Design. In Value Sensitive Design, the focus is on incorporating moral values into the design of technical artifacts and systems by looking at design from an ethical perspective concerned with the way moral values, such as freedom from bias, trust, autonomy, privacy and justice, are facilitated or constrained (Friedman et al. 2006; Flanagan et al. 2008; Van den Hoven 2005). Value Sensitive Design focuses primarily and specifically on addressing values of *moral* import. Other frameworks tend to focus more on functional and instrumental values, such as speed, efficiency, storage capacity or usability. Although building a user-friendly technology might have the side effect of increasing a user's trust or sense of autonomy, in Value Sensitive Design the incorporation of moral values into the design is a primary goal instead of a by-product. According to Friedman, Value Sensitive Design is primarily concerned with values that center on human well-being, human dignity, justice, welfare and human rights (Friedman et al. 2006). It requires that we broaden the goals and criteria for judging the quality of technological systems to include explicitly moral values. Value Sensitive Design is at the same time, as pointed out by Van den Hoven (2005), "a way of doing ethics that aims at making moral values part of technological design, research and development." More specifically it looks at ways of reconciling different and opposing values in engineering design or innovations, so that we may have our cake and eat it (Van den Hoven 2008). Value Sensitive Design may thus be an excellent way to meet principle (BF1/BF2) through technical innovation.

CONCLUSION

In discussions about technology, engineering and ethics, technology and engineering are usually treated as the source of ethical problems, and ethics is treated as a constraint on engineering and technological development. We have shown that a quite different relation also exists between these realms. Ethics can be the source of technological development rather than just a constraint, and technological progress can create moral progress rather than just moral problems. We have shown this by a detailed analysis of how technology can contribute to the solution of so-called moral overload or moral dilemmas. Such dilemmas typically create a moral residue that is the basis of a second-order principle that tells us to reshape the world so that we can meet all our moral obligations. We can do so, among other things, through guided technological innovation. We have suggested Value Sensitive Design as a possible approach to guide the engineering design process in the right direction.

Note

1. Compensation may be made easier by social institutions in several ways. Kuran mentions redemption or the absolution from sins in Christianity as one institution. The modern welfare state also provides compensation mechanisms, e.g., social workers compensate in taking care of the elderly and those who need assistance when family and relatives lack the time to assist as a result of their other value commitments.

References

Baron, J., & Spranca, M. (1997). Protected values. *Organizational Behavior and Human Decision Processes, 70*(1), 1–16.

Chang, R. (Ed.). (1997). *Incommensurability, incomparability, and practical reasoning.* Cambridge, Mass: Harvard University Press.

Cummings, M. L. (2006). Integrating ethics in design through the value-sensitive design approach. *Science and Engineering Ethics, 12,* 701–715.

Flanagan, M., Howe, D. C., & Nissenbaum, H. (2008). Embodying values in technology. Theory and practise. In J. Van den Hoven, & J. Weckert (Eds.), *Information technology and moral philosophy* (pp. 322–353). Cambridge: Cambridge University Press.

Friedman, B., Kahn, P. H. J., & Borning, A. (2006). Value sensitive design and information systems. In P. Zhang & D. Galletta (Eds.), *Human-computer interaction in management information systems: Foundations (Vol. 5, pp. 348–372, Advances in mangement information systems).* Armonk, NY: M.E, Sharpe.

Hansson, S. O. (1998). Should we avoid moral dilemmas? *The Journal of Value Inquiry, 32*, 407–416.

Jonsen, A. R., & Toulmin, S. (1988). *The abuse of casuistry. A history of moral reasoning.* Berkeley: University of California Press.

Kuran, T. (1998). Moral overload and its alleviation. In A. Ben-Ner & L. Putterman (Eds.), *Economics, values, organization* (pp. 231–266). Cambridge: Cambridge University Press.

Levi, I. (1986). *Hard Choices. Decion making under unresolved conflict.* Cambridge: Cambridge University Press.

Marcus, R. B. (1980). Moral dilemmas and consistency. *Journal of Philosophy, 77*, 121–136.

Marino, P. (2001). Moral dilemmas, collective responsibility, and moral progress. *Philosophical Studies, 104*, 203–225.

Pacey, A. (1983). *The culture of technology.* Oxford, England: Blackwell.

Raz, J. (1986). *The morality of freedom.* Oxford: Oxford University Press.

Richardson, H. S. (1997). *Practical reasoning about final ends.* Cambridge: Cambridge University Press.

Rooksby, E. (2009). How to be a responsible slave: Managing the use of expert information systems. *Ethics and Information Technology, 11*(1), 81–90.

Sarewitz, D. R. (1996). *Frontiers of illusion: Science, technology, and the politics of progress.* Philadelphia: Temple University Press.

Swierstra, T., Stemerding, D., & Boenink, M. (2009). Exploring techno-moral change. The case of the obesity pill. In P. Sollie & M. Düwell (Eds.), *Evaluating new technologies* (pp. 119–138). Dordrecht: Springer.

Taebi, B., & Kadak, A. C. (2010). Intergenerational considerations affecting the future of nuclear power: Equity as a framework for assessing fuel cycles. *Risk Analysis, 30*(9), 1341–1362, doi:10.1111/j.1539-6924.2010.01434.x.

Tetlock, P. E. (2003). Thinking the unthinkable: Sacred values and taboo cognitions. *Trends in cognitive sciences, 7*(7), 320–324.

Van de Poel, I. (2009). Values in engineering design. In A. Meijers (Ed.), *Handbook of the philosophy of science. Volume 9: Philosophy of technology and engineering sciences* (pp. 973–1006). Oxford: Elsevier.

Van den Hoven, J. (1998). Moral responsibility, public office and information technology. In Snellen & Van de Donk (Eds.), *Public administration in an information age.* Amsterdam: IOS Press.

Van den Hoven, J. (2005). Design for values and values for design. *Information Age,* 4–7.

Van den Hoven, J. (2008). Moral methodology and information technology. In H. Tavani & K. Himma (Eds.), *Handbook of computer ethics.* Hoboken, NJ: Wiley.

Van Fraassen, B. (1970). Values and the heart's command. *Journal of Philosophy, 70*(1), 5–19.

WCED. (1987). *Our common future. Report of the world commission on environment and development.* Oxford: Oxford University Press.

Weinberg, A. M. (1966). Can technology replace social engineering? In A. H. Teich (Ed.), *Technology and the future* (Vol. 59, pp. 55–64). New York: St. Martin's Press.

Williams, B. (1973). *Problems of the self. Philosophical papers 1956–1972.* Cambridge: Cambridge University Press.

CHAPTER 4

■ ■ ■

Vision for Inclusion: An LGBT Broadband Future

Jessie Daniels, PhD
Professor, City University of New York—CUNY

Mary L. Gray, PhD
Senior Researcher, Microsoft Research
Associate Professor, Media School, Indiana University

PART I. INTRODUCTION

Demographics

Approximately 3.5% of adults in the United States identify as lesbian, gay, or bisexual and an estimated 0.3% of adults identify as transgender (Gates, 2011). This means that there are approximately 9 million LGBT people in the country, a figure roughly equivalent to the population of New Jersey (Gates, 2011). Of course, a variety of factors, including continuing stigma, changing identification over the course of a lifetime, and methodological challenges of accurately recording sexual and gender identities, make it difficult to know if these are low population estimates. Yet we do know that there are an increasing number of families led by LGBT-identifying people (Ryan, 2012) and there remain consistent shared experiences of this population (Pew Research, 2013) that suggest that their specific individual and community-wide needs warrant attention.

A report published in October 2012 by the Williams Institute found that people of color were more likely to identify as non-heterosexual than whites (4.6% of blacks, 4.0% of Hispanics and 3.2% of whites identified as LGBT). In addition, people between the ages of 18–29 were three times more likely to identify as LGBT than those over the age of 65.

LGBT individuals vary in race, religion, age and gender. Thus, the LGBT community is not a monolith but rather contains multiple, intersection communities. There are several characteristics of modern life that make the Internet particularly important for LGBT communities.

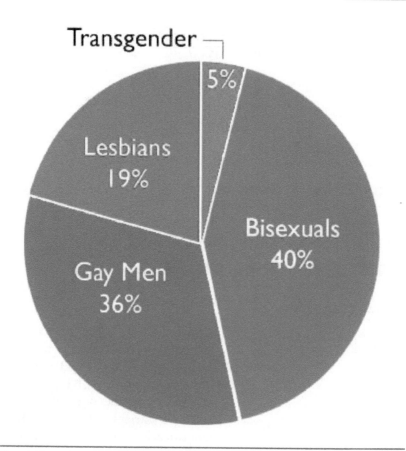

The LGBT Population

Source: Pew Research Center, 2013

Despite enormous advancements in LGBT rights in recent years, discrimination and stigma persist, and many LGBT people remain cautious about to whom they reveal their identity. A 2013 Pew survey of a nationally representative sample of LGBT adults found that 39% have been rejected by friends or family because of their sexual or gender identity; 30% have been physically attacked or threatened; 58% have been the target of slurs or jokes; and 21% have been treated unfairly by an employer. In fact, it still remains legal to fire someone in 29 states based merely on their LGBT status (HRC, 2013). The survey also found that a large proportion of LGBT people have not disclosed their identity to their parents—just 56% say they have told their mother about their sexual or gender identity, and 39% have told their father. Studies show that most young people—both gay and heterosexual—first become aware of being sexually attracted to another person around age 10, with most realizing they were LGBT around 13 years old (Ryan, C., 2009). Many of those

Lisa Howe

(Tennessee)

This former Belmont University soccer coach was fired in December 2010 after she came out to her soccer team that she is a lesbian and announced that she and her partner were expecting their first child. While the university's official statement at first said that she had resigned, it was soon amended to say that the decision had been mutual, and that her continuing to work for Belmont would not be beneficial to her or the university.

Demonstrators protested Howe's termination, as she was a highly successful and popular coach, and they called for an official apology, which they never received. Although Belmont had terminated its ties with the Tennessee Baptist Church in 2007, chairman of Belmont's board of trustees Marty Dickens told *The Tennessean* that, "We expect people to commit themselves to high moral and ethical standards within a Christian context."

(Williams Institute, 2012)

surveyed realized they were gay around ages 7 or 9 but do not reveal the information because by that age most had learned that being gay was shameful and wrong from family, friends and other people in their community.

Given this ongoing context of stigma, along with the related risks of employment security and safety that surround the disclosure of one's sexual and/or gender identity, the Internet proves particularly important to LGBT-identifying people and their communities. Specifically, the Internet offers a key means for LGBT people to explore their identities without risking physical harm; connect to other people in and beyond their own neighborhoods and communities; and, seek out information about an array of LGBT-specific issues, ranging from safe places to live to health information.

As this report makes clear, LGBT people are dependent on the Internet to meet a range of individual and social needs because supportive resources are not widely and readily available offline. Paradoxically, this reliance also makes them particularly vulnerable to the threats and limitations posed by our current Internet policies. The Federal Communications Commission dedicated a significant amount of time to examining the state of broadband and its unique impact on vulnerable populations, from disabled communities to communities of color (National Broadband Plan, 2010). Representatives of LGBT communities were not at the table at that time to contribute to this framework. This report aims to build on that framework and add LGBT communities' needs to a more inclusive vision for the future of Internet access.

The Internet has the potential to help LGBT people navigate around the threats that they face in their everyday lives. It provides them with extraordinarily powerful tools to mitigate some of the discrimination, stigma, and isolation that have historically limited their livelihoods and full participation in society. Even as younger generations may be less likely to identify with any one sexual category (Savin-Williams, 2005), the need for information and community-specific support remains (Stephen Russell, 2001). However, for this vision to become a reality, policymakers must make deliberate choices that account for the unique needs of LGBT online users.

Adoption and Use

According to a recent study by the Pew Research Center, LGBT people are core users of the Internet, with 80% of LGBT respondents saying they participate in a social networking site, such as Facebook or Twitter, compared to just 58% of the general public (Pew Research, 2013).

Experts suggest that part of the reason for the larger adoption and use of social media among LGBT people has to do with age cohort. The LGBT population is younger than the general population. When young LGBT adults are compared with their age cohorts, the proportion using social networking sites is almost the same, for example 89% of LGBT adults ages 18 to 29 compared to 90% of all adults ages 18 to 29.

Another part of the reason that LGBT people are such significant users of the Internet is a powerful need to connect with others to foster a healthy sense of self and realistic understanding of LGBT lives and communities. Young people in the United States turn to social media for many reasons but central among them is to connect with peers and the broader world. Unlike their parents, many of today's teens no longer have easy access to the private and public spaces that made traditional social identity formation possible. Concerns for their physical safety, increased pressures among middle class families to focus on academics, and economic pressures to work have left most teens reliant on the Internet for basic social interaction and camaraderie (Gray, 2009; boyd, 2014). LGBT-identifying youth, and, especially those questioning their sexual and gender identities in their early teens, arguably have an even greater need for seeking out alternative representations of themselves. As Larry Gross and other communication scholars have argued, LGBT and questioning young people, like the greater population, turn to popular and digital media to see reflections of themselves (Gross, 2001, 2007; Walters, 2001; Gray, 2009). While popular media representations of LGBT people have increased dramatically in the past two decades, they fail to reflect the diversity (or reality) of LGBT communities (Walters, 2002). Yet LGBT-identifying young people are more dependent on these media types to understand what it means to be an LGBT-identifying adult because of the relative absence of a visible, diverse range of LGBT-identifying adults in their schools, families, churches, and public life (Walters, 2001; Gross, 2002).

These two factors combined—the importance of the Internet for today's generation and the pressing need for realistic reflections and connections to diverse communities of LGBT-identifying people—place even greater value and social importance on digital technologies for LGBT and questioning young people.

Identity, Community and Relationship Formation

The Internet is an important site for identity and community formation for LGBT people (Driver, 2007; Gray, 2009). For many LGBT people, the Internet is their main source of information about LGBT issues. They often use the Internet to connect to local groups or organizations that serve LGBT people and connect to vital online community spaces (DeHaan, et al., 2013).

LGBT young people use the Internet differently than their heterosexual peers. The differences in the LGBT communities Internet uses mirror similar areas that we know LGBT young people are often invisible in their offline lives: finding safe spaces to explore their sexuality, finding other young people negotiating their identities, accepting and supportive friendships, same-sex romance, and information about same-sex relationships and safe sex (Hillier, Mitchell, & Ybarra, 2012). For example, Franssens (et al., 2010) found that many young gay and bisexual men are active on the Internet and that many—but not all—meet their first same-sex partner online. Similarly, DeHaan (et al., 2013) found that for many LGBT youth, the Internet is their main source of information about their emerging identities. Many young people also used the anonymity of the Internet to experiment with their sexuality and to create peer and romantic relationships. The authors found that use of the Internet gave these young people confidence to make more informed decisions offline. In part due to the historical marginalization and stigmatization of LGBT communities, the privacy, security and confidentiality needs for LGBT communities online are significant. The range of issues and the complexity of online privacy and confidentiality go beyond the scope of this report, but warrant further research.

Considering adult behavior, Ashford (2009) posits that the Internet provides a safe virtual space for the exploration of sexual or gender identities that is unprecedented for marginalized communities. The Internet can be especially useful for those who are beginning to understand their sexual identity (Alexander, 1997, 2002; Maczewski, 2002). Roughly half (43%) of LGBT adults have revealed their sexual or gender identities on a social networking site (Pew Research, 2013). Some research indicates that blogging can help to foster the experience of a healthy coming out process through a combined identity and community formation, in which a blogger and readers engage in dialogue online (George, 2011). What a growing body of research has made clear is that LGBT people, particularly young people, are heavily reliant on the Internet, not only for information, but also for the important tasks of identity formation, peer connection, and partner identification.

In particular, the Internet provides LGBT people with a greater range of social connections. Among all LGBT adults, 55% say they have met new LGBT friends online or through a social networking site. Gay men are the most likely to say they have done so (69%). By contrast, about half of lesbians (47%) and bisexuals (49%) say they have met a new LGBT friend online (Pew Research, 2013).

Mobile Technology

Increasingly, adults access the Internet through mobile devices. Globally, 91% of people own mobile phones and use them to access the Internet rather than through desktop or laptop computers. In the U.S., 57% of adults use their mobile phone to go online and 34% of mobile phone owners say they mostly access the Internet using their mobile device (Pew Internet, 2013).

While there is not yet reliable national data on the rate of mobile phone ownership among LGBT people, a May 2013 survey by the marketing firm Digitas found that LGBT mobile owners use their devices for shopping and travelling at higher rates than the larger population (Marketing Charts, 2013). The Digitas

---

"A member of our SPRY seniors program is an immigrant from Mexico. Because he is low income, he has been unable to stay in contact with his family back home and has felt isolated. Through the help of the Montrose Center (LGBT Center in Houston, TX) volunteers and our Cyber Center funded by the David Bohnett Foundation, he learned how to email and Skype with his family back home and has been doing so with the resources at the Montrose Center. He has seen pictures of the village where he grew up and met nieces and nephews he has never seen. The ability to communicate with his family has done more for his mental health than any counseling session could."

Ann Robison, PhD, Executive Director the Montrose Center, Houston, TX.

The Myth of the Wealthy Gay

As poverty rates for nearly all populations increased during the recession, lesbian, gay, and bisexual (LGB) Americans remained more likely to be poor than heterosexual people.

Gender, race, education and geography all influence poverty rates among LGB populations, and children of same-sex couples are particularly vulnerable to poverty.

(Williams Institute, 2013)

survey also found that a large number of LGBT-identifying people live in a post-PC world, with 56% choosing to use a mobile device over a "desktop" or "laptop" compared to 2012. About 51% of LGBT-identifying adults have used a smartphone or tablet for three years or more, nearly twice as much as compared to those who do not identify as LGBT (28%). Another finding in the Digitas survey is the increased use of mobile technology by LGBT older adults (65+), with 21% having used a smartphone or tablet for five years or more. On the other end of the age spectrum, the survey found that 35% of LGBT individuals ages 18–24 have used a mobile device in their coming out process. Again, beyond the Digitas survey, research is limited around LGBT and mobile but we can hypothesize that mobile devices play a particularly vital and important role in the lives of LGBT-identifying adults because of their unique need to find resources and places that will be welcoming and supportive to them as they develop and express their identities.

Vandy Beth Glenn

(Georgia)

In 2005, Vandy Beth Glenn began working as the legislative editor of the Georgia General Assembly while still presenting as a man, Glenn Morrison. Glenn was fired in October 2007 for revealing to her supervisor that she planned to transition from male to female. Her boss, legislative counsel Sewell Brumby, allegedly told her that "her gender transition and presentation of herself as a woman would be seen as immoral, could not happen appropriately in the workplace in which Glenn worked and would make other employees uncomfortable." This story has a happy ending, however: Glenn sued, and U.S. District Court Judge Story ruled that she was illegally fired based on sex discrimination. The judge ordered that she be compensated for wages during the appeals process. Finally, in December 2011, the appeals court ruled that she should be allowed to return to work.

(Williams Institute, 2012)

Peter TerVeer

(District of Columbia)

This case is playing out as we speak. Until April 2012, TerVeer was a management analyst for the Library of Congress. He claims that he was harassed and fired because of his sexual orientation, and he has filed a discrimination complaint. WJLA reported that he received emails in 2009 from his boss referencing bible passages that speak against homosexuality, and that "he stated that as a homosexual I could never succeed because it was against God's law." The trouble apparently all started when TerVeer "liked" a page on Facebook called Two Dads.

(Williams Institute, 2012)

PART II. PARTICULAR NEEDS

Health Benefits of the Internet for LGBT People

The Internet offers a set of health benefits for LGBT people, including the ability to search for health information online, a greater range of social connections (which is beneficial for overall health), as well as increased access to preventive health services, such as mental health and HIV prevention. In addition, many LGBT people make use of the Internet to navigate a sometimes hostile healthcare system to find healthcare providers who understand the needs of LGBT clients and patients (Schwartz, et al., 2006; Magee et al., 2012).

The Internet provides an ideal forum for LGBT people to seek health information without having to disclose their sexual or gender identity. Indeed, LGBT people, especially youth, are more likely to use the Internet to search for health information than their non-LGBT counterparts (Detlefsen, 2004; Gray, Klein, & Noyce, 2005; Kanuga & Rosenfeld, 2004; Magee, Bigelow, DeHaan & Mustanski, 2012). A 2013 study by GLSEN found that a large majority (81%) of LGBT youth have searched for health information online as compared to just 46% of non-LGBT youth (GLSEN, 2013). Other research indicates that searching for health information online may be particularly meaningful for lesbians whose health needs are often ignored or overlooked (Lindley, Friedman, & Struble 2012; Polonijo & Hollister, 2011).

Homophobia among healthcare providers is well documented (GLMA reports). Many LGBT people either fail to disclose their sexual or gender identity to medical professionals or seek out LGBT and LGBT-sensitive providers. For example, one study found that as many as 45% of lesbian and bisexual women are not out to their providers (GLMA report). The Internet can provide a means for LGBT people to locate providers who are either LGBT themselves or who are sensitive to their needs. For instance, the Gay & Lesbian Medical Association offers an online service to help LGBT people find friendly doctors. Similarly, the Human Rights Campaign offers a rating of healthcare facilities against the Healthcare Equality Index, which measures a facility's commitment to providing high-quality, equitable care to LGBT people.

Social support, in turn, is linked to improved health and increased longevity (Brody, J., 2012. Some research indicates there is a link between overall Internet use and seeking HIV/AIDS–related information online to community involvement.

GLSEN

The (Gay, Lesbian and Straight Education Network) is the nation's largest homosexual advocacy group focused entirely on reaching public school students as young as kindergarten age.

GLMA

The (Gay and Lesbian Medical Association) is an international organization of approximately 1,000 lesbian, gay, bisexual, and transgender (LGBT) physicians, medical students, and their supporters in all 50 U.S. states, as well as twelve countries.

Further, those with more community involvement tend to acquire more HIV/AIDS information online. And, these people tend to see that information as more relevant, and have more knowledgeable peers in their networks with whom they may discuss that information (Veinot et al., 2013).

Policy makers need to take a look at laws as they relate to telemedicine, so LGBT communities can gain access to health and mental health services regardless of state lines. For example, a transgender youth should be able to easily and confidentially gain access to a medical professional who is familiar with transgender medical and health issues.

Health Risks of the Internet

Usage of Terms

Men who have sex with men (**MSM**), also known as males who have sex with males, are male persons who engage in sexual activity.

While LGBT people clearly benefit from Internet access, there are health risks associated with this access, a small portion of LGBT individuals turn to places online that could put them at higher risk for damaging health outcomes. For example, research indicates that seeking sexual partners online may put one at higher risk for STDs and HIV. Research about the health risks of the Internet for LGBT people is limited and has focused almost exclusively on HIV risk among men who have sex with men (MSM). There is no data to suggest that lesbians experience the same level of health risks associated with MSM. The data indicate that MSM who use the Internet to find sexual partners have an especially high risk for HIV transmission and other STDs (Benotsch, et al., 2011; Chew, et al., 2013; Jenness, et al., 2010; McKirnan, Houston, & Tolou-shams, 2006). However, McKirnan (et al., 2006) found that men who have sex with men who reported any Internet use were more sexually active—but not more risky—than men who had never been on the Internet. Indeed, some researchers have found no strong evidence of greater exposure to health risks from seeking online partners (Grov, et al., 2007). Some researchers have posited a "self-selection hypothesis" that higher rates of unprotected sex among Internet users merely reflects risks that were already there (Jenness et al., 2010). What is clearly indicated is that there is a need for greater education about the potential health risks associated with meeting people online, and there is an opportunity for policy makers to support such educational efforts.

Research on how other groups and other health risks are mitigated or facilitated by the Internet is sorely needed. But whether or not the Internet facilitates health risks, it is clearly a critical avenue for health information and interventions.

Access to Prevention Services and Healthcare

Public health professionals and community activists are also using the Internet to promote access to healthcare and prevention services among hard-to-reach populations. There are a plethora of efforts to reach gay men and other men who have sex with men with information about preventing STDs and HIV (Bull, McFarlane, Lloyd & Rietmeiler, 2004; Conner, et al., 2005; Fields, et al., 2006; Jenkins & Wold, 2012; Moskowitz, Melton, & Owczarzak, 2009; Muessig, et al., 2013; Nguyen, et al., 2013; Rosenberger, et al., 2011). Those working in HIV/AIDS-related services for those who test positive are also making use of the Internet for social support (Peterson, 2009).

LGBT people have particular needs when it comes to mental health services. There is strong evidence indicating that LGBT individuals report higher rates of suicide ideation and attempts from their late teens through early twenties than their heterosexual counterparts (Silenzio, et al., 2007). The fact that 89% of young LGBT people use social media suggests that social networking sites offer a novel opportunity to reach them with mental health interventions or services (Silenzio, et al., 2009; Benson, 2013). However, to date, this remains a missed opportunity. A recent study of college counseling center web sites found that these online portals to mental health services often overlook the needs of LGBT college students (Wright & McKinley, 2010). Only 11% of those sites surveyed made any mention of the capacity to counsel LGBT clients (Wright & McKinley, 2010).

There is a well-documented pattern of reluctance to seek medical care among LGBT people due to social stigma and physician prejudice (Hinchliff, Gott, & Galena, 2005; Kelly & Robinson, 2011; Steele, Tinmouth, & Lu, 2006). Given this context, the Internet has been identified as a valuable resource for navigating social stigma in the doctor-patient relationship by LGBT people seeking healthcare providers (Gee, 2006; Hoffman, Freeman, & Swann, 2009; Mulligan & Heath, 2007; Sánchez, Hailpern, Lowe, & Calderon, 2007; Seçkin, 2010).

Lastly, recent evidence that mobile texting technologies may also offer a route to better support young people could give policy makers new motivation to make bandwidth and spectrum improvements to areas such as the rural United States, where mental healthcare resources are sparse (Kaufman, 2014).

Cyberbullying, Education, LGBT Youth and the Internet

Schools are often a setting where young people who identify as LGBT encounter stigma, harassment, bullying, and even physical violence (Hong & Espeage, 2012; GLSEN, 2010; Greytak, Kosciw, & Diaz, 2009; Pascoe, 2007). We cannot divorce the increased reports of cyberbullying directed at LGBT-identifying youth or those perceived to be LGBT from the larger context of anti-LGBT violence and harassment that pervades school environments (Pascoe, 2007; Marwick & Boyd, 2011; Bazelon, 2013). However, bullying—verbal threats and harassment online—clearly presents a new challenge to educators and parents concerned about the mental health and welfare of all young people. A recent report found that 42% of LGBT youth report experiencing bullying and harassment online as compared to just 15% of non-LGBT youth, according to a national survey of 5,680 students in 6th–12th grade (GLSEN, 2013). The same report finds that 27% of LGBT youth were bullied via text message as compared to just 13% of non-LGBT youth. Experiences with cyberbullying contributed to negative self-esteem, higher depression and lower grade point averages (Donnerstein, 2012; Varjas, Meyers, Kiperman, & Howard, 2013). Indeed, like bullying on the playground, any young person can become a target of social media and text-based slurs that use anti-LGBT sentiment. But, in the case of cyberbullying, there are rarely clear routes for bystanders or responsible adults to intervene. In addition, unlike playground bullying which is geographically limited, cyberbullying offers opportunities to scale and compound bullying efforts, even anonymously.

In the context of an Internet in which privacy is very hard to maintain, LGBT individuals—both youth and adults—are even more vulnerable to cyberbullying when their name, face, and identity can be so easily tracked through multiple online accounts. Educators can do much to help create welcoming environments for LGBT youth and their families, even for students at young ages (Burt, Gelnaw, & Lesser, 2010).

Schools are, simultaneously, the primary place where LGBT youth are likely to use the Internet for learning across all ages and grade levels. Such Internet-based learning can contribute to identity formation, finding community and lessening the impact of homophobic stigma for LGBT youth. While there is no research on LGBT-positive Internet curricula in elementary or middle schools, there is some emerging research about high schools and colleges. For high school students, the Internet makes possible exercises and role-playing games that can allow young people room to experiment in ways that help reduce the impact of stigma and homophobia (Alexander, 1997). In college, educators may use the Internet as an instructional tool for writing exercises that focus on LGBT issues (Burnes, 2007). Such an Internet-enabled and LGBT-focused pedagogy may reduce prejudice in those students who identify as heterosexual and can help young people who are trying to understand their sexual or gender identity, or who may be looking for communities of other people like them in settings where they are visibly in the minority.

The presence of openly identifying LGBT instructors can be extremely important for the well-being of LGBT students (Depalma & Atkinson, 2007); this may be particularly crucial for those attending colleges or universities in rural areas (D'Augelli, 2006). In keeping with an ethical stance that embraces educational equity for LGBT students (MacGillivray, 2000), some educational researchers have advanced the idea of a 'queer pedagogy' that incorporates the knowledge base of LGBT students themselves in creating teacher education programs (Peters & Swanson, 2004; Strauss, 2005; Zacko-Smith & Smith, 2010). Such an Internet-enabled and LGBT-focused pedagogy can help young people who are trying to understand their sexual or gender identity, or who may be looking for community of other people like themselves. Critical to making schools healthy learning environments for all youth is a reassessment of Internet access and filtering that may

---

"The Trevor Project cannot underscore enough the importance of broadband in the lives of LGBTQ youth, especially when it comes to the prevention of suicide. Access to the Internet allows LGBTQ young people to know they are not alone, reducing the overall sense of isolation especially in rural environments.

This access allows them to find safe spaces to explore their sexual orientation and gender identity, and find other young people who are also trying to figure out their own identities. Access to the Internet also provides access to critical mental health and healthcare information, one of the many things that LGBTQ youth seek out when going online.

When suicide is the second leading cause of death among youth as young as 10 through age 24, and more than 41 percent of youth who need mental healthcare do not have access to it, something has to change. We must find ways to make it easier for vulnerable youth to access mental healthcare services and other protective factors that can reduce their risk for suicide. Because young people often lack access to transportation or their own income, going to the doctor, meeting friends, or joining a community center—three factors that can reduce a young person's risk for suicide—can be next to impossible. Providing broadband access to the Internet can eliminate these barriers to seeking and finding help, safety, and care.

As an example, our social networking site, TrevorSpace.org provides a safe space for LGBTQ youth ages 13 to 24 to create meaningful connections with each other in a monitored way, and provides them direct access to suicide prevention help.

As a result it is important that public policy makers, company leaders and anyone who may influence youth understand the need for LGBTQ teens and young adults to be able to gain access to the Internet through high speed broadband, be it through the library, at school, via cellphone, or another location in their communities, regardless of whether they live in an urban or rural setting."

Abbe Land, Executive Director & CEO, The Trevor Project

limit the knowledge base of LGBT-identifying and questioning young people.

Filtering, Libraries, E-Rate

Young LGBT people looking for information about their own identities or a community of friends who are like themselves are often blocked from accessing the open, public Internet due to the presence of filters. For example, in response to widespread, illegal censoring of Internet content in Tennessee, the American Civil Liberties Union launched its "Do Not Block" initiative to help students identify school computers unlawfully blocking appropriate LGBT content from students. Issues having to do with filters, libraries and "e-Rate" are pertinent, even crucial to the discussion of LGBT youth in educational settings.

Commonly used filters—that is, software designed to block "objectionable" content—can also, either inadvertently or intentionally, block LGBT-specific content. In 1998, the U.S. Congress passed The Child Online Protection Act (COPA). COPA prohibits the transmission of any material over the Internet deemed "harmful to minors," if the communication was made for a commercial purpose. The Children's Internet Protection Act (CIPA), passed in 2000, requires libraries and K–12 schools to install filters on

"High-speed Internet is a valuable tool for the LGBT community, especially LGBT youth and the elderly, and access to the most rural members of the community is not currently available. With 18.1% of the Wyoming population either unserved or underserved by Internet providers, including a disproportionally high percentage of the people over the age of 55, the expansion of broadband service must be a priority.

When LGBT youth communicate on our resources website MatthewsPlace.com, they engage with their peers who are passionate about making their community a better, safer place. For rural youth especially, high-speed Internet access facilitates that conversation when they do not know any LGBT people in their area and need help living happier, healthier lives.

MatthewsPlace.com Youth Blogger Jake Stallman writes about being from rural Iowa and the challenges he faces being the only openly gay student at his school. Over the last year blogging for Matthew's Place, he has grown as a person, as a leader in his area and as an activist for the LGBT community.

Crook County, Wyoming's least-served county, has only 0.3% of the population connected at the national standard for wired broadband. LinkWyoming, the state's initiative to increase access to broadband Internet service, is a first step, but nationally, more must be done to enhance this expansion."

Jason Marsden, Executive Director, Matthew Shepard Foundation

The stats all come from LinkWyoming. You can see that report at http://www.linkwyoming.org/lwy/docs/WY%20Phase%202%20Report_Final.pdf

their Internet computers to retain federal funding—known as the "e-Rate"—and discounts for computers and computer access. (American Library Association, http://www.ala.org/offices/oif/ifissues/issuesrelatedlinks/cppacopacipa).

Some filtering software does a commendable job blocking egregious and harmful materials, such as violent depictions of child abuse. Unfortunately, in the absence of policy guidelines that explicitly support the rights of young people to seek out information about LGBT identities and sexual health, the vast majority of filters often block LGBT-specific content, as well as much sexual and reproductive health content (ACLU, 2011).

The COPA and CIPA laws have unintentionally blocked access to information and LGBT-themed content of all kinds. For example, websites that provide information about LGBT health issues are blocked by filtering software (Holt, 2009; Jones, 2003; Keegan, 2006). In the absence of clearly articulated guidelines, COPA and CIPA leave the definition of content deemed both "objectionable" and "harmful to minors" to those, ultimately, marketing and setting up the software itself. This jeopardizes the fundamental rights to free speech not only for young people, but also adult users of publicly funded Internet access. The lack of explicit support for the rights of people to information about sexual health and LGBT communities presents an additional burden for youth who are trying to access LGBT-specific content on the Internet from school or a library. Research indicates that Internet filtering impairs construction of online communities, identity formation, and access to health information for LGBT youth (Holt 2007, 2009).

Librarians are often crucial guides, especially for adolescent LGBT patrons, who want to navigate through filters for information related to sexuality, gender identity, or health information (Storts-Brinks, 2010). For their part, schools and libraries are reluctant to remove filters because the funding they receive from the e-rate program requires these strict filters be in place. Removing the filter mandated by the e-rate program would cost these schools and libraries millions of dollars in much needed revenue (Jones, 2004). Given the reality of filters, the role of librarians becomes even more significant.

Librarians often serve both as guides in the information age and as LGBT role models. There are reference resources on the web for lesbian, gay, bisexual and transgender people that may not be easily located without the guidance of a skilled librarian (Watstein, Gales, & Stratton, 2001). Reference librarians who are attuned to the specific needs of gay (Hamer, 2003), lesbian (Rothbauer, 2004) and transgender (Taylor, 2002) individuals can prove to be helpful. Librarians, like openly LGBT or accepting teachers, can be important role models and guides for young people (Ciszek, 2011; Greenblatt, 2011; Mehra & Braquet, 2011). Finally, libraries provide crucial public spaces and access to online portals for LGBT people who want to access the Internet (Kapitzke, 2001).

Economic Opportunity, the Internet and LGBT People

Approximately 3.8% of the U.S. workforce identifies as lesbian, gay, bisexual or transgender (Williams Institute, 2011). At the present time in the U.S., there is no nationwide federal employment protection for LGBT people. Instead, there is a patchwork of protections at the state level, with only 21 states offering explicit protection for LGBT employees from losing their jobs because they identify as or are perceived to be LGBT. This variation in legal status leaves LGBT people vulnerable to discrimination in hiring and firing, as well as to on-the-job harassment (Chung, 2001). According to a study from the Williams Institute (2011), 21% of LGB employees report having been discriminated against in hiring, promotions and pay, while 47% of transgender employees report similar discrimination at work. Another report, "Injustice at Every Turn," from The Gay and Lesbian Task Force (2011) presents an in-depth account of the difficulties faced by transgender individuals in the labor market, including that 27% have been fired from jobs and 96% have been harassed at their jobs. Additionally, transgender people of color are more likely to experience such discrimination than their white counterparts (Whitfield, et al., 2014).

Some companies welcome LGBT employees and this has been good for their business. According to the same Williams Institute study, 96% of Fortune 500 companies that have LGBT workplace protections say such policies have boosted their businesses. Fortune 500 executives, including Apple CEO Tim Cook, have said such workplace policies boost productivity, increase retention rates and attract talent. Among the sectors where LGBT people find work, the multimedia, online and Internet industries are among the most accepting workplaces (Politics & Government Business, Nov. 29, Dec. 6, 2012).

Given this context of less than full equality, the Internet can be a valuable tool for finding information about LGBT-friendly employment opportunities and organizing for greater protection under the law.

According to a recent study, 32% of people in the U.S. credit social media for their current job (2012 Social Job Seeker Survey, http://web.jobvite.com/rs/jobvite/images/Jobvite_JobSeeker_FINAL_2012.pdf). While there is no separate national data on the job-seeking strategies of LGBT people, it is reasonable to assume based on previous research that this population is making use of the Internet to find employment at similar or even higher rates than the larger population (Kirk, 2000; Mehra, Merkel, & Bishop, 2004). By comparison, there is a recent study of African American jobseekers that found that this group is more likely than the general population to use the Internet for their search (Horrigan, 2013). Until we have a coherent federal policy protecting the rights of LGBT-identifying people in the workplace, there is a clear need for both expanding online resources that identify employment opportunities and workplaces supportive of LGBT communities and individuals as well as an awareness that those individuals drawn to online work may very well be seeking refuge from otherwise hostile work environments. Employers in the IT sector would do well to know that they may have a disproportionately high number of LGBT-identifying people in their applicant pool and would be best positioned to attract the strongest candidates by adopting LGBT-supportive hiring and employment policies, ranging from transgender health support to legal counsel for employees adopting their same-sex partner's children from a previous relationship.

Civic and Community Engagement

The form that civic engagement takes is changing. Traditionally, civic engagement meant activities like joining a club or community group where people discussed politics. Now, people are just as likely to find community online and discuss politics with far-flung others as they are with neighbors living in the same zip code (de Zúñiga, et al., 2010). This is especially true for LGBT people who may find community at online LGBT affinity websites or apps in a study of Gay.com, Campbell examined a variety of discussion forums and found that these constituted emerging forms of civic engagement (Campbell, 2007). In a majority of the forums that he examined, online discussions led to calls for offline political activism, such as voting, boycotting, letter writing or protest marching. In this way, the Internet, and LGBT-specific sites like Gay.com, function as a kind of public sphere for LGBT people (Mowlabocus, 2008; Rhoades, 2011; Shapiro, 2004).

A recent study indicates that LGBT youth have high rates of civic engagement online (GLSEN, 2013). In this study, 77% of LGBT youth reported taking part in an online community that supports a cause or issue. A large majority, 68%, said they had written a blog post or posted comments on another blog about a cause or an issue, while 51% said they had used the Internet to participate in or recruit people for an offline event or activity (GLSEN, 2013).

Public Safety

LGBT people continue to face serious threats to their safety on a daily basis even as there have been gains in public recognition of same-sex marriage and the repeal of harmful legislation (e.g., DOMA, DADT). A 2013 report by the National Coalition of Anti-Violence Programs reported 25 anti-LGBTQ homicides in the United States. This is the 4th highest yearly total ever recorded by NCAVP. Given the persistence of racism in the contemporary U.S., LGBT people of color are at an increased risk for threats to their personal safety. The same NCAVP report found that 73% of all anti-LGBTQ homicide victims in 2012 were people of color. Of the 25 known homicide victims in 2012 whose race/ethnicity was disclosed, 54 percent were Black/African American, 15 percent Latino, 12 percent white and 4 percent Native American. Transgender women of color are nearly 3 times more likely to be victims of violence as compared to their lesbian, gay or bisexual counterparts.

The Internet, and specifically, mobile technology can provide a form of 'safety net' for LGBT people because it increases connection to safety and supportive others (Hillier, Mitchell, & Ybarra, 2012) This, however, does not eliminate the need for continued awareness of the types of messaging that is created, transmitted, and disseminated.

For LGBT people of color, contact with police can be an occasion for harassment and brutality rather than assistance and safety. One study finds that LGBT people of color are using their mobile phones regularly to either record police misconduct or to avoid contact with police; for both, respondents reported using their mobile phones this way: daily—14%, several times a week—6%, and at least once a week—8%. (Daniels & Battle, 2012). For vulnerable LGBT youth such as those who are marginally housed, mobile technology provides emotional support, access to social services, and a connection to legitimate employment opportunities (Daniels, 2011). The research suggests that Internet access and civic media and technologies could play a key role in mitigating the disproportional violence directed at LGBT communities and individuals perceived to be a part of these communities.

PART III. RECOMMENDATIONS

1. *Thoughtful and responsible filtering software that respects civil liberties and rights to free speech*

Access to knowledge and information in a networked, information economy is fundamental to all other forms of access. For LGBT people, access to knowledge about their own identity, communities and health is often blocked when they search in public libraries and, for youth, in public schools.

We recommend policy changes that would redefine the "e-rate" benefits for Federally-funded IT so that they do not block LGBT-specific content and allow access to LGBT information in public libraries and schools.

2. *Increase the deployment of licensed and unlicensed spectrum available for broadband Internet services*

The Internet has become a critical tool for civic engagement and public service. As more and more government services move online, reliable, safe, and unfettered broadband access to the Internet becomes more critical to vibrant civic participation and community engagement. Addressing the specific needs of LGBT communities and individuals may be a route to better support a broad base of people who would benefit from access to Internet networks that stand to be improved with an infusion of additional spectrum. All people deserve and require reliable Internet access for the health of our democracy.

And, unlike the trend for LGBT individuals to move to urban centers (e.g., Greenwich Village, The Castro) decades ago to find community support, research from a large national survey suggests that more and more LGBT-identifying people are living and raising families beyond traditional gay enclaves (Kastanis & Williams, 2014). LGBT people of color, in particular, tend to "come out" and remain in the same geographical area. For many, this means living in rural areas. For LGBT people living in rural areas, the Internet is a vital mechanism for youth negotiating a LGBT identity in the rural United States (Gray, 2009).

Given the important role of access to the Internet and resources in the lives of LGBT-identifying people, it is clear this community would benefit greatly from policies that allocate additional licensed and unlicensed spectrum for usage. Additional spectrum would alleviate network congestion and increase the capacity of both cellular and WiFi-based networks for all users. The increase in spectrum will help ensure Internet connections to these networks are reliable, robust and widely available. In addition,

Usage of Terms

Licensed and Unlicensed Spectrum

Licensed—Spectrum that is licensed by the government for one company to use.

Unlicensed—Spectrum that is open for use by anyone as long as they follow as set of rules.

increases in spectrum should also allow for Internet availability to be economically accessible for all LGBT people.

3. Support and training for educators and librarians working with LGBT youth and adults

Education about usage, being good online digital citizens, privacy, confidentiality and online bullying are just a few but important components of digital literacy.

For LGBT youth, educators and librarians are often their first guides to information about their own identity and finding others like themselves. Yet, teachers and librarians often lack adequate training and digital literacy tools to be able to guide LGBT young people to the appropriate information. Similarly, older LGBT adults often turn to libraries not only for training, connection and basic classes, but also to find safe, accepting spaces.

We recommend developing and providing training in LGBT-specific digital literacy information for librarians, K–12 teachers and community leaders.

As our population continues to age we recommend that libraries, schools, community centers and LGBT centers continue to train staff and volunteers about LGBT-specific needs. We also emphasize the need for local community resources to support the LGBT individuals in their community by providing safe and welcoming spaces, programs and partnerships with LGBT organizations.

4. Expand mental health support via mobile-Internet

Given the LGBT community's predilection to use the Internet to identify preventive health information, service providers and community resources, policy makers, medical providers, corporations, and social service and information providers should make sure that their services meet the needs of LGBT communities searching for health related information online and via mobile/smart phones. These information and service providers should be keenly aware of the unique characteristics of the LGBT community and understand the community is not a monolith but rather comprised of nearly every other community be it race, religion, age, class or geographic location. It is also important to note that each of the different communities within the LGBT community has unique needs, especially around healthcare.

5. Call on public and private sector commitments to Internet users' right to privacy, equal access, and anonymous use of the Internet

In an ideal world, it would not matter if someone identified as or was perceived to be lesbian, gay, bisexual, or transgender.

Unfortunately, there are still very real, negative consequences for identifying as or being perceived as LGBT. As long as diverse communities of LGBT people need spaces and resources to address the discrimination they potentially face at school, in their homes, or at the workplace, they will need the privacy and anonymity to seek out support and information that could be, literally, the difference between life and death.

We call on the Public and Private Sectors, from educators managing school records to companies that monetize private user data across commercial social media, to prioritize the right of citizens to use the Internet, as we do other modes of private communication, to share information freely and confidentially. Recent revelations of the National Security Agency's breach of U.S. citizens' rights to privacy are an opportunity to call on both the Public and Private Sector to grant users explicit rights to the data and content that they generate online and to commit to supporting the right to privacy and opportunities for anonymous use of the Internet. A policy that supports individuals and communities turning to the Internet to share ideas and assemble in private is fundamental to the health of our democracy and must take precedence over the commercial value of selling people's private communication with others. To do less would have a chilling effect on the value of the Internet as a source for democratic participation and exchange, not just in the United States but around the world. We call on government entities and commercial enterprises to request the right to use individuals' content and to be transparent when data is generated through individual use in one context is connected to data use in another.

6. Expand research initiatives with and about the LGBT community

From our research, what is most apparent is the general lack of research on LGBT communities. We implore public policy makers, companies and academic institutions to make funds available for greater research on LGBT issues and ensure that LGBT communities are included and a part of any trials, programs and studies. Specifically, these research initiatives should include studies of:

1. The specific privacy, confidentiality and security needs of LGBT communities;
2. On what LGBT individuals and communities are accessing when seeking online resources;

3 Health information and how LGBT communities, particularly youth and seniors can gain access to salient, timely and relevant health information and providers;

4 How filtering standards can be revised to ensure that LGBT communities have access to important and relevant information;

5 How International LGBT communities are affected by various Internet polices;

6 How a free cell phone program would impact LGBT youth and older adults; and

7 Online shaming, stigmatization and marginalization.

7. Explicit consideration of LGBT specific needs in future public policy conversations

For too long LGBT communities have not been at the table with other communities as technological policy decisions are being made. As a result, how those policy decisions will affect the broad array of LGBT communities is not taken into account. Public policy makers at the Federal, State and local levels need to ensure that the specific needs and concerns of LGBT communities be taken into account when considering policy decisions.

References

ACLU, March 28, 2011. "ACLU Demands That Schools Stop Unconstitutional Web Filtering of LGBT Content." Available online at: https://www.aclu.org/lgbt-rights/aclu-demands-schools-stop-unconstitutional-web-filtering-lgbt-content

Alexander, Jonathan. "Out of the Closet and into the Network: Sexual Orientation and the Computerized Classroom." *Computers and Composition* 14, no. 2 (1997): 207–216.

Ashford, J., & LeCroy, C. (2009). *Human behavior in the social environment: A multidimensional perspective.* Cengage Learning.

Baams, L., K. J. Jonas, S. Utz, H. M. W. Bos, and L. van der Vuurst. "Internet Use and Online Social Support among Same Sex Attracted Individuals of Different Ages." *Computers in Human Behavior* 27, no. 5 (September 2011): 1820–1827.

Battle, Juan, Antonio Jay Pastrana, and Jessie Daniels. "Social Justice Sexuality Project: 2010 National Survey, including Puerto Rico." (2013).

Benotsch, Eric G., Aaron M. Martin, Flint M. Espil, Christopher D. Nettles, David W. Seal, and Steven D. Pinkerton. "Internet Use, Recreational Travel, and HIV Risk Behaviors in Men Who Have Sex With Men." *Journal of Community Health* 36, no. 3 (June 2011): 398–405.

Benson, Kristen E. "Seeking Support: Transgender Client Experiences with Mental Health Services." *Journal of Feminist Family Therapy* 25, no. 1 (January 2013): 17–40.

Boellstorff, Tom. "But do not identify as gay: a proleptic genealogy of the MSM category." *Cultural Anthropology* 26, no. 2 (2011): 287–312.

Blumenfeld, Warren J., and R. M. Cooper. "LGBT and Allied Youth Responses to Cyberbullying: Policy Implications." *The International Journal of Critical Pedagogy* 3, no. 1 (July 21, 2010): 112.

Bull, S. S., M. McFarlane, L. Lloyd, and C. Rietmeijer. "The Process of Seeking Sex Partners Online and Implications for STD/HIV Prevention." *AIDS Care* 16, no. 8 (2004): 1012–1020.

Burnes, Theodore R. "Queering College Writing: Writing Students' Learning of LGB Issues Using the Internet as an Instructional Tool." *Journal of Gay & Lesbian Issues in Education* 4, no. 2 (2007): 75–88.

Burt, Tracy, Aimee Gelnaw, and Lee Klinger Lesser. "Creating Welcoming and Inclusive Environments for Lesbian, Gay, Bisexual, and Transgender (LGBT) Families in Early Childhood Settings." *YC Young Children* 65, no. 1 (January 2010): 97–102.

Campbell, John Edward. "Virtual Citizens or Dream Consumers: Looking for Civic Community on Gay. com." *Queer online: media technology & sexuality* 40 (2007): 197.

Cassels, Peter. "LGBT Youth Singled out with Cyber Bullying." *Bay Windows* 21, no. 2 (December 19, 2002): 14–15.

Chew Ng, Rilene A., Michael C. Samuel, Terrence Lo, Kyle T. Bernstein, Getahun Aynalem, Jeffrey D. Klausner, and Gail Bolan. "Sex, Drugs (Methamphetamines), and the Internet: Increasing Syphilis Among Men Who Have Sex With Men in California, 2004–2008." *American Journal of Public Health* 103, no. 8 (August 2013): 1450–1456.

Chung, Y. Barry. "Work discrimination and coping strategies: Conceptual frameworks for counseling lesbian, gay, and bisexual clients." *The Career Development Quarterly* 50, no. 1 (2001): 33–44.

Ciszek, Matthew P. "Out on the Web: The Relationship between Campus Climate and GLBT-Related Web-Based Resources in Academic Libraries." *The Journal of Academic Librarianship* 37, no. 5 (September 2011): 430–436.

Clark, Taylor, Carina Marquez, C. Bradley Hare, Malcolm D. John, and Jeffrey D. Klausner. "Methamphetamine Use, Transmission Risk Behavior and Internet Use Among HIV-Infected Patients in Medical Care, San Francisco, 2008." *AIDS and Behavior* 16, no. 2 (December 30, 2010): 396–403.

Conner, Ross F., Lois Takahashi, Eloy Ortiz, Eduardo Archuleta, Juan Muniz, and Julio Rodriguez. "The SOLAAR HIV Prevention Program for Gay and Bisexual Latino Men: Using Social Marketing to Build Capacity for Service Provision and Evaluation." *AIDS Education and Prevention* 17, no. 4 (2005): 361–374.

Cooper, Robyn M., and Warren J. Blumenfeld. "Responses to Cyberbullying: A Descriptive Analysis of the Frequency of and Impact on LGBT and Allied Youth." *Journal of LGBT Youth* 9, no. 2 (April 2012): 153–177.

Cox, Nele, Alexis Dewaele, Mieke van Houtte, and John Vincke. "Stress-Related Growth, Coming Out, and Internalized Homonegativity in Lesbian, Gay, and Bisexual Youth. An Examination of Stress-Related Growth Within the Minority Stress Model." *Journal of Homosexuality* 58, no. 1 (December 30, 2010): 117–137.

Cox, Nele, Wim Vanden Berghe, Alexis Dewaele, and John Vincke. "Acculturation Strategies and Mental Health in Gay, Lesbian, and Bisexual Youth." *Journal of Youth and Adolescence* 39, no. 10 (October 2010): 1199–210.

D'Augelli, Anthony R. "Coming Out, Visibility, and Creating Change: Empowering Lesbian, Gay, and Bisexual People in a Rural University Community." *American Journal of Community Psychology* 37, no. 3–4 (June 2006): 203–10.

Daniels, Jessie. "LGBT Homeless Youth and Mobile Technology: Data from New York City," Paper presented at Social Science History Association Meetings, Boston, MA, (November 18, 2011).

Daniels, Jessie and Battle, Juan. "SJS Project: House and Ball Community Data," Paper presented at Creating Change, Baltimore, MD, (February 4, 2012).

DeHaan, S., Kuper, L. E., Magee, J. C., Bigelow, L., & Mustanski, B. S. (2013). "The interplay between online and offline explorations of identity, relationships, and sex: A mixed-methods study with LGBT youth." *Journal of sex research,* 50(5), 421–434.

DeLonga, Kathryn, Hector L. Torres, Charles Kamen, Stephanie N. Evans, Susanne Lee, Cheryl Koopman, and Cheryl Gore-Felton. "Loneliness, Internalized Homophobia, and Compulsive Internet Use: Factors Associated with Sexual Risk Behavior among a Sample of Adolescent Males Seeking Services at a Community LGBT Center." *Sexual Addiction & Compulsivity* 18, no. 2 (April 2011): 61–74.

Depalma, Renee, and Elizabeth Atkinson. "Strategic Embodiment in Virtual Spaces: Exploring an On-Line Discussion about Sexualities Equality in Schools." *Discourse: Studies in the Cultural Politics of Education* 28, no. 4 (2007): 499–514.

Detlefsen, Ellen Gay. "Where am I to go? Use of the Internet for consumer health information by two vulnerable communities." *Library Trends* 53, no. 2 (2004): 283–300.

Digitas, LBi. "Digitas Unveils Industry's First Large-Scale Research on LGBT Mobile Device Behavior." (June 2013)

Donnerstein, Ed. "Internet Bullying." *Pediatric Clinics of North America* 59, no. 3 (June 2012): 623–633.

Eichhorn, Kate. "Re-In/citing Linguistic Injuries: Speech Acts, Cyberhate, and the Spatial and Temporal Character of Networked Environments." *Computers and Composition* 18, no. 3 (January 3, 2001): 293–304.

Fields, Sheldon D., Mitchell J. Wharton, Anita I. Marrero, Avril Little, Kraig Pannell, and John H. Morgan. "Internet Chat Rooms: Connecting With a New Generation of Young Men of Color at Risk for HIV Infection Who Have Sex With Other Men." *Journal of the Association of Nurses in AIDS Care* 17, no. 6 (November 2006): 53–60.

Fogg-Davis, Hawley G. "Theorizing Black Lesbians within Black Feminism: A Critique of Same-Race Street Harassment." *Politics and Gender* 2, no. 1 (2006): 57–76.

Gates, Gary J. "How many people are lesbian, gay bisexual and transgender?" Los Angeles, CA: The Williams Institute at UCLA School of Law, (April 2011). http:// williamsinstitute.law.ucla.edu/ wp-content/uploads/Gates-How-Many-People-LGBT-Apr-2011.pdf.

Gay, Gale Horton. "Vulnerabilities in Cyber Security Mean Opportunities Too." *U.S. Black Engineer & Information Technology* 35, no. 4 (Winter 2011): 68–69.

Gay Times, "When 16-Year-Old Ed Johnson Was Bullied He Started a Website to Help Other Gay Kids." no. 382 (July 2010): 62–63.

Gee, Royal. "Primary Care Health Issues among Men Who Have Sex with Men." *Journal of the American Academy of Nurse Practitioners* 18, no. 4 (April 2006): 144–153.

GLSEN. "Out Online: The Experiences of LGBT Youth on the Internet." (July 10, 2013). Available online at: http://glsen.org/press/study-finds-lgbt-youth-face-greater-harassment-online.

GLSEN. The 2009 National School Climate Survey: Key Findings on the Experiences of Lesbian, Gay, Bisexual and Transgender Youth in Our Nation's Schools. Executive Summary. Gay, Lesbian and Straight Education Network (GLSEN). New York, NY, 2010.

Grant, Jaime M., Mottet, Lisa, and Tanis, Justin. "Injustice at Every Turn: A Report of the National Discrimination Survey." National Center for Transgender Equality and National Gay and Lesbian Task Force, Washington, D.C., 2011. Available online at: http://www.thetaskforce.org/ downloads/reports/reports/ntds_full.pdf.

Gray, Mary L. *Out in the Country: Youth, Media, and Queer Visibility in Rural America.* New York: NYU Press, 2009.

Gray, Mary L. "Coming of Age in a Digital Era: Youth Queering Technologies in Small Town, USA." Ph.D dissertation, University of California, San Diego, 2004.

Gray, Nicola J., Jonathan D. Klein, Peter R. Noyce, Tracy S. Sesselberg, and Judith A. Cantrill. "Health Information-Seeking Behaviour in Adolescence: The Place of the Internet." *Social Science & Medicine* 60, no. 7 (April 2005): 1467–1478.

Greenblatt, Ellen. "The Internet and LGBTIQ communities." Serving LGBTIQ library and archives users: Essays on outreach, service, collections and access (2011): 42–50.

Greytak, Emily A., Joseph G. Kosciw, and Elizabeth M. Diaz. Harsh Realities: The Experiences of Transgender Youth in Our Nation's Schools. Gay, Lesbian and Straight Education Network (GLSEN). 121 West 27th Street Suite 804, New York, NY 10001, 2009.

Grundy, John, and Miriam Smith. "Activist Knowledges in Queer Politics." *Economy and Society* 36, no. 2 (2007): 294–317.

Hamer, Judah S. "Coming-out: Gay males' information seeking." School Libraries Worldwide (2003): 73–89.

Harrison, Richard, and Michael Thomas. "Identity in Online Communities: Social Networking Sites and Language Learning." *International Journal of Emerging Technologies and Society* 7, no. 2 (2009): 109–124.

Hillier, Lynne, Kimberly J. Mitchell, and Michele L. Ybarra. "The Internet As a Safety Net: Findings From a Series of Online Focus Groups With LGB and Non-LGB Young People in the United States." *Journal of LGBT Youth* 9, no. 3 (July 2012): 225–246.

Hinchliff, Sharron, Merryn Gott, and Elisabeth Galena. "'I daresay I might find it embarrassing': general practitioners' perspectives on discussing sexual health issues with lesbian and gay patients." *Health & Social Care in the Community* 13, no. 4 (2005): 345–353.

Hoffman, Neal D., Katherine Freeman, and Stephanie Swann. "Healthcare Preferences of Lesbian, Gay, Bisexual, Transgender and Questioning Youth." *Journal of Adolescent Health* 45, no. 3 (2009): 222–229.

Holt, David. "LGBTIQ Teens-Plugged in and Unfiltered: How Internet Filtering Impairs Construction of Online Communities, Identity Formation, and Access to Health Information." *Identity Formation, and Access to Health Information* (December 22, 2009) (2011).

Holt, David Brian. "Internet filtering and the adolescent gay/lesbian patron." *Library Student Journal* (2007).

Hong, Jun Sung, and Dorothy L. Espelage. "A Review of Research on Bullying and Peer Victimization in School: An Ecological System Analysis." *Aggression and Violent Behavior* 17, no. 4 (July 2012): 311–322.

Hooper, Simon, B. R. Simon Rosser, Keith J. Horvath, J. Michael Oakes, and Gene Danilenko. "An Online Needs Assessment of a Virtual Community: What Men Who Use the Internet to Seek Sex with Men Want in Internet-Based HIV Prevention." *AIDS and Behavior* 12, no. 6 (2008): 867–875.

Horrigan, John. "Broadband and Jobs: African Americans Rely Heavily on Mobile Access and Social Networking in Job Search." Joint Center for Political and Economic Studies (November, 2013). Available online at: http://www.jointcenter.org/sites/default/files/upload/research/files/ Broadband%20and%20Jobs.pdf.

Huang, Zjennifer, Na He, Eric J. Nehl, Tony Zheng, Brian D. Smith, Jin Zhang, Sarah McNabb, and Frank Y. Wong. "Social Network and Other Correlates of HIV Testing: Findings from Male Sex Workers and Other MSM in Shanghai, China." *AIDS and Behavior* 16, no. 4 (2012): 858–871.

Human Rights Campaign (HRC). Employment Non-Discrimination Act and The Number of States it is Still Legal to be Fired for by Identifying as LGBT. Available online at: http://www.hrc.org/laws-and-legislation/federal-legislation/employment-non-discrimination-act.

Itz, Caspar A. "The Internet: GLBT Campuslife on the Web." *Journal of Homosexuality* 40, no. 1 (November 30, 2000): 189.

Jenkins, Wiley D., and Brittany Wold. "Use of the Internet for the Surveillance and Prevention of Sexually Transmitted Diseases." *Microbes and Infection* 14, no. 5 (May 2012): 427–437.

Jenness, Samuel M., Alan Neaigus, Holly Hagan, Travis Wendel, Camila Gelpi-Acosta, and Christopher S. Murrill. "Reconsidering the Internet as an HIV/STD Risk for Men Who Have Sex with Men." *AIDS and Behavior* 14, no. 6 (July 28, 2010): 1353–1361.

Jones, Jeremy. "Censorship or Protection?" *Weekly News: South Florida's Gay Community Newspaper* 26, no. 43 (July 3, 2003): 12.

Jones, Jeremy. "Refusal to Install Porn Filters Could Cost Library Millions." *Weekly News: South Florida's Gay Community Newspaper* 27, no. 26 (March 4, 2004): 10–10.

Kakietek, Jakub, Patrick S. Sullivan, and James D. Heffelfinger. "You've Got Male: Internet Use, Rural Residence, and Risky Sex in Men Who Have Sex With Men Recruited in 12 U.S. Cities." *AIDS Education and Prevention* 23, no. 2 (April 2011): 118–127.

Kanuga, Mansi, and Walter D. Rosenfeld. "Adolescent Sexuality and the Internet: The Good, the Bad, and the URL." *Journal of Pediatric and Adolescent Gynecology* 17, no. 2 (April 2004): 117–124.

Kapitzke, Cushla. "Ceremony and Cybrary: Digital Libraries and the Dialectic of Place and Space." *Social Alternatives* 20, no. 1 (January 2001): 33–40.

Kaufman, Leslie. "In Texting Era, Crisis Hotlines Put Help at Youths' Fingertips," *New York Times,* February 4, 2014, Available online at: http://www.nytimes.com/2014/02/05/us/in-texting-era-crisis-hotlines-put-help-at-youths-fingertips.html

Keegan, Andrew. "Feds Yank Gay Health Site." *Southern Voice* 19, no. 5 (March 10, 2006): 29–29.

Kelly, Rebecca J., and Gregory C. Robinson. "Disclosure of Membership in the Lesbian, Gay, Bisexual, and Transgender Community by Individuals With Communication Impairments: A Preliminary Web-Based Survey." *American Journal of Speech-Language Pathology* (Online) 20, no. 2 (May 1, 2011): 86–94A.

Kienzel, Olivia. "Federal Judge Issues Restraining Order Against Right-Wing Group Using Gay Wedding Photo." *Frontiers Newsmagazine* 23, no. 26 (April 13, 2005): 33.

Kilman, Carrie. "This Is Why We Need a GSA." *Teaching Tolerance* no. 31 (2007): 30–36.

Kirk, James J. "Web Assisted Career Counseling." *Journal of Employment Counseling* 37, no. 3 (2000): 146–159.

Koch, Nadine S., and H. Eric Schockman. *Democratizing Internet Access in the Lesbian, Gay, and Bisexual Communities.* Praeger, 1998.

Kubicek, Katrina, Julie Carpineto, Bryce McDavitt, George Weiss, and Michele D. Kipke. "Use and Perceptions of the Internet for Sexual Information and Partners: A Study of Young Men Who Have Sex with Men." *Archives of Sexual Behavior* 40, no. 4 (August 31, 2010): 803–816.

LaFee, Scott. "The Political and Cultural Complications of Bullying." *School Administrator* 69, no. 4 (April 2012): 26–31.

LGBT in Changing Times: Attitudes, Experiences and Growing Acceptance. Washington, DC: Pew Social & Demographic Trends, June 13, 2013.

Lindley, Lisa L., Daniela B. Friedman, and Corrie Struble. "Becoming Visible: Assessing the Availability of Online Sexual Health Information for Lesbians." *Health Promotion Practice* 13, no. 4 (2012): 472–480.

MacGillivray, Ian K. "Educational Equity for Gay, Lesbian, Bisexual, Transgendered, and Queer/questioning Students." *Education and Urban Society* 32, no. 3 (May 2000): 303–323.

Maczewski M. Exploring Identities Through the Internet: Youth Experiences Online. Child and Youth Care Forum. 2002; 31(2):111–129.

Magee, Joshua C., Louisa Bigelow, Samantha DeHaan, and Brian S. Mustanski. "Sexual Health Information Seeking Online: A Mixed-Methods Study Among Lesbian, Gay, Bisexual, and Transgender Young People." *Health Education & Behavior* 39, no. 3 (2012): 276–289.

Mapuva, Jephias. "Confronting Challenges to E-Learning in Higher Education Institutions." *International Journal of Education and Development Using Information and Communication Technology* 5, no. 3 (2009): J1–J14.

Marketing Charts, "LGBT Mobile Owners Use Actively Use Devices for Shopping, Travel," June, 2013. Available online at: http://www.marketingcharts.com/wp/interactive/lgbt-mobile-owners-actively-use-devices-for-shopping-travel-30184/.

McBride, Tim. "Filtering Madness." *Echo Magazine* 15, no. 26 (September 9, 2004): 28.

McKirnan, David, Eric Houston, and Marina Tolou-Shams. "Is the Web the Culprit? Cognitive Escape and Internet Sexual Risk among Gay and Bisexual Men." *AIDS and Behavior* 11, no. 1 (June 16, 2006): 151–160.

Mehra, Bharat, Cecelia Merkel, and Ann Peterson Bishop. "The internet for empowerment of minority and marginalized users." *New Media & Society* 6, 6 (2004): 781–802.

Mehra, Bharat, and Donna Braquet. "Progressive LGBTQ reference: coming out in the 21st century." Reference Services Review 39, no. 3 (2011): 401–422.

Moskowitz, David A., Dan Melton, and Jill Owczarzak. "PowerON: The Use of Instant Message Counseling and the Internet to Facilitate HIV/STD Education and Prevention." *Patient Education and Counseling* 77, no. 1 (2009): 20–26.

Mowlabocus, S. "Revisiting Old Haunts through New Technologies: Public (homo)sexual Cultures in Cyberspace." *International Journal of Cultural Studies* 11, no. 4 (December 1, 2008): 419–439.

Muessig, Kathryn E., Emily C. Pike, Beth Fowler, Sara LeGrand, Jeffrey T. Parsons, Sheana S. Bull, Patrick A. Wilson, David A. Wohl, and Lisa B. Hightow-Weidman. "Putting Prevention in Their Pockets: Developing Mobile Phone-Based HIV Interventions for Black

Men Who Have Sex with Men." *AIDS Patient Care and STDs* 27, no. 4 (April 2013): 211–222.

Mulligan, Ea, and Mary Heath. "Seeking open minded doctors—how women who identify as bisexual, queer or lesbian seek quality healthcare." *Australian family physician* 36, no. 6 (2007): 469–471.

"Multimedia, Online, Internet; Comcast and NBCUniversal Named Among America's 'Best Places To Work' For LGBT People." *Politics & Government Business* (November 29, 2012).

Nguyen, Phuong, Judy Gold, Alisa Pedrana, Shanton Chang, Steve Howard, Olivia Ilic, Margaret Hellard, and Mark Stoove. "Sexual Health Promotion on Social Networking Sites: A Process Evaluation of the FaceSpace Project." *Journal of Adolescent Health* 53, no. 1 (July 2013): 98–104.

O'Riordan, Kate, and David J. Phillips, eds. *Queer online: Media technology and sexuality.* Vol. 40. Peter Lang, 2007.

Oswald, Ramona Faith, and Linda S. Culton. "Under the Rainbow: Rural Gay Life and Its Relevance for Family Providers*." *Family Relations* 52, no. 1 (2003): 72–81.

Peters, Brad, and Diana Swanson. "Queering the Conflicts: What LGBT Students Can Teach Us in the Classroom and Online." *Computers and Composition* 21, no. 3 (September 2004): 295–313.

Peterson, Jennifer L. "'You Have to Be Positive.' Social Support Processes of an Online Support Group for Men Living with HIV." *Communication Studies* 60, no. 5 (November 2009).

Pew Research Center. A Survey of LGBT Americans: Attitudes, Experiences and Values in Changing Times. Washington, DC: Pew Social & Demographic Trends, June 13, 2013. http://www.pewsocialtrends.org/2013/06/13/a-survey-of-lgbt-americans/.

Poeter, Damon. "Ex-Rutgers Student Sentenced to 30 Days for Webcam Cyberbullying." *PC Magazine* (May 2012): 1.

Polonijo, Andrea N., and Brooke A. Hollister. "Normalcy, Boundaries, and Heterosexism: An Exploration of Online Lesbian Health Queries." *Journal of Gay & Lesbian Social Services* 23, no. 2 (April 2011): 165–187.

Quillen, Ian. "ACLU Files First School Suit Over LGBT Website Filtering." *Education Week* 31, no. 1 (August 24, 2011).

Quillen, Ian. "ACLU: Campaign Against LGBT Filtering Is Effective." *Education Week* 31, no. 7 (October 12, 2011).

Rhoades, Mindi. "Disrupting Discourses Digitally for LGBTQ Rights." *Journal of Cultural Research in Art Education* 29 (2011): 47–64.

Ring, Niamh. "Gay Financial Network Landing Big-Name Allies." *American Banker* 164, no. 141 (July 26, 1999): 10.

Rosenberger, Joshua G., Michael Reece, David S. Novak, and Kenneth H. Mayer. "The Internet as a Valuable Tool for Promoting a New Framework for Sexual Health among Gay Men and Other Men Who Have Sex with Men." *AIDS and Behavior* 15, no. S1 (February 18, 2011): 88–90.

Rothbauer, Paulette. "The Internet in the Reading Accounts of Lesbian and Queer Young Women: Failed Searches and Unsanctioned Reading." *Canadian Journal of Information & Library Sciences* 28, no. 4 (December 2004): 89–110.

Sánchez, John Paul, Susan Hailpern, Carla Lowe, and Yvette Calderon. "Factors Associated with Emergency Department Utilization by Urban Lesbian, Gay, and Bisexual Individuals." *Journal of Community Health* 32, no. 2 (April 2007): 149–56.

Sanlo, Ronni. "Lesbian, Gay, and Bisexual College Students: Risk, Resiliency, and Retention." *Journal of College Student Retention* 6, no. 1 (2004): 97–110.

Seçkin, Gül. "Cyber Patients Surfing the Medical Web: Computer-Mediated Medical Knowledge and Perceived Benefits." *Computers in Human Behavior* 26, no. 6 (November 2010): 1694–1700.

Shapiro, Eve. "'Trans'cending Barriers: Transgender Organizing on the Internet." *Journal of Gay & Lesbian Social Services* 16, no. 3/4 (July 2004): 165–179.

Silenzio VM, Pena JB, Duberstein PR, Cerel J, Knox KL. Sexual orientation and risk factors for suicidal ideation and suicide attempts among adolescents and young adults. *American Journal of Public Health*. 2007; 97(11): 2017–2019.

Silenzio, Vincent M. B., Paul R. Duberstein, Wan Tang, Naiji Lu, Xin Tu, and Christopher M. Homan. "Connecting the Invisible Dots: Reaching Lesbian, Gay, and Bisexual Adolescents and Young Adults at Risk for Suicide through Online Social Networks." *Social Science & Medicine* 69, no. 3 (August 2009): 469–474.

Steele, Leah S., Jill M. Tinmouth, and Annie Lu. "Regular healthcare use by lesbians: a path analysis of predictive factors." *Family Practice* 23, no. 6 (2006): 631–636.

Storts-Brinks, Karyn. "Censorship Online: One School Librarian's Journey to Provide Access to LGBT Resources." *Knowledge Quest* 39, no. 1 (2010): 22–28.

Strauss, Sarah A. "The Legacy of Brown: Implications for Equal Educational Opportunities for Gay, Lesbian, and Bisexual Students." *Teachers College Record* 107, no. 3 (March 2005): 424–452.

Taylor, Jami Kathleen. "Targeting the Information Needs of Transgender Individuals." *Current Studies in Librarianship* 26, no. 1/2 (Spring/Fall 2002): 85–110.

Treat, Alena R., and Becky Whittenburg. "Gifted Gay, Lesbian, Bisexual, and Transgender Annotated Bibliography: A Resource for Educators of Gifted Secondary GLBT Students." *Journal of Advanced Academics* 17, no. 4 (Summer 2006): 230–243, 285.

Varjas, Kris, Joel Meyers, Sarah Kiperman, and Alice Howard. "Technology Hurts? Lesbian, Gay, and Bisexual Youth Perspectives of Technology and Cyberbullying." *Journal of School Violence* 12, no. 1 (January 2013): 27–44.

Veinot, Tiffany Christine, Chrysta Cathleen Meadowbrooke, Jimena Loveluck, Andrew Hickok, and Jose Artruro Bauermeister. "How

'Community' Matters for How People Interact With Information: Mixed Methods Study of Young Men Who Have Sex With Other Men." *Journal of Medical Internet Research* 15, no. 2 (2013): 180–200.

Watstein, Sarah Barbara, Melinda Gales, and Stephen E. Stratton. "Reference on the Web: Gay, Lesbian, Bisexual, and Transgendered E-Reference Sources." *The Booklist* 97, no. 19/20 (June 1, 2001): 1922–1926.

"Wells Fargo & Company; Wells Fargo Named on 'Best Places to Work for LGBT Equality' List by the Human Rights Campaign." *Politics & Government Business* (December 6, 2012).

Wright, Paul J., and Christopher J. McKinley. "Mental Health Resources for LGBT Collegians: A Content Analysis of College Counseling Center Web Sites." *Journal of Homosexuality* 58, no. 1 (December 30, 2010): 138–147.

Zacko-Smith, Jeffrey D., and Pritchy G. Smith. "Recognizing and Utilizing Queer Pedagogy: A Call for Teacher Education to Reconsider the Knowledge Base on Sexual Orientation for Teacher Education Programs." *Multicultural Education* 18, no. 1 (2010): 2–9.

Zapalska, Alina, and Dallas Brozik. "Learning Styles and Online Education." *Campus-Wide Information Systems* 24, no. 1 (2007): 6.

METHODOLOGY

Because the make-up of LGBT communities is diverse, from the start of this project, it was the goal of this research to be as inclusive as possible. The researchers performed an exhaustive review of available research, data and information about the intersection of LGBT communities and technology. The research was also refined to identify the most salient points that overlapped with the National Broadband Plan, the potential impacts on public policy and LGBT communities. Drafts of the initial research were circulated among additional academics and scholars for additional input. A draft of the paper was then opened for public comments on the Internet from March 21 until April 7th. Announcements were made on Twitter and Facebook to broadly solicit input, comments and feedback from all organizations and individuals. The comments and feedback were incorporated as appropriate. The final release of the paper was made on June 26, 2014 on Capitol Hill where the authors discussed their work.

APPENDIX A. DEMOGRAPHICS: GENDER, AGE, RACE, EDUCATION.

Demographic Profiles of Recent LGBT Survey Samples and the Adult Population of the United States

% among those ages 18 or older

	LGBT Respondents			U.S. Population
	Pew Research/ GfK Knowledge Panel 2013	Gallup Daily Tracking Survey 2012	General Social Survey 2008, 2010,2012	American Community Survey 2011
Men	50	48	41	49
Women	49	52	59	51
Age group				
18-29	30	37	36	22
30-49	39	32	44	35
50-64	23	20	16	25
65 or older	9	10	3	17
Race/Ethnicity				
White	66	67	66	66
Black	10	15	14	12
Hispanic	17	14	16	15
Other	7	4	4	7
Educational attainment				
High school or less	33	40	31	43
Some college	36	32	30	31
Bachelor's degree or more	32	27	39	26

PEW Research Center

APPENDIX A. DEMOGRAPHICS: INCOME, REGION, POLITICAL PARTY

Demographic Profiles of Recent LGBT Survey Samples and the Adult Population of the United States *(Cont.)*

% among those ages 18 or older

	LGBT Respondents			U.S. Population
	Pew Research/ GfK Knowledge Panel 2013	**Gallup Daily Tracking Survey 2012**	**General Social Survey 2008, 2010,2012**	**American Community Survey 2011**
Annual family income				
Less than $30,000	39	---	39	28
$30,000-$74,999	39	---	32	35
$75,000 or more	20	---	25	34
Annual household income				
Less than $36,000	---	45	---	---
$36,000-$89,999	---	31	---	---
$90,000 or more	---	16	---	---
Region of residence				
Northeast	20	19	14	18
Midwest	20	22	23	22
South	34	34	38	37
West	27	25	24	23
Party identification				
Republican	8	11	5	24*
Democrat	56	42	44	32*
Independent/other	36	47	51	44*
Sample size	1,197	6,004	188	2,436,714

Notes. Whites, blacks and others include only non-Hispanics; Hispanics are of any race. The GSS includes respondents who self-identify as gay, lesbian or bisexual only. Family income includes income from non-family households; "Independent/other" party affiliation includes independents, those who lean toward Democrat or Republican, but don't identify fully with either one of those parties, and those who did not supply an answer. Some totals may not add to 100% due to rounding and the exclusion of "Don't know" and "Refused" responses.

Sources: Pew Research Center 2013 LGBT survey; Gallup Daily Tracking Survey June-December 2012; Gallup data regarding race/ethnicity are derived from June-August 2012 Daily Tracking Survey, n=2,669; Pew Research Center analysis of the 2008, 2010 and 2012 General Social Survey and the 2011 American Community Survey (1% IPUMS); *U.S. population numbers for party identification are from Pew Research Center for the People & the Press 2013 aggregated polls (N=6,011)

PEW Research Center

CHAPTER 5

■ ■ ■

Women and Girls in Science, Technology, Engineering, and Mathematics

Definition of Science, Technology, Engineering, and Mathematics (STEM)

STEM is defined in many ways (for example, see U.S. government definitions at http://nces.ed.gov/pubs2009/2009161.pdf). In this report the term "STEM" refers to the physical, biological, and agricultural sciences; computer and information sciences; engineering and engineering technologies; and mathematics. The social and behavioral sciences, such as psychology and economics, are not included, nor are health workers, such as doctors and nurses. College and university STEM faculty are included when possible, but high school teachers in STEM subjects are not. While all of these workers are part of the larger scientific and engineering workforce, their exclusion is based on the availability of data. In this report the terms "STEM," "science, technology, engineering, and mathematics," and "scientific and engineering fields" are used interchangeably.

Science, technology, engineering, and mathematics (STEM) are widely regarded as critical to the national economy. Concern about America's ability to be competitive in the global economy has led to a number of calls to action to strengthen the pipeline into these fields (National Academy of Sciences, Committee on Science, Engineering & Public Policy, 2007; U.S. Government Accountability Office, 2006; U.S. Department of Education, 2006). Expanding and developing the STEM workforce is a critical issue for government, industry leaders, and educators. Despite the tremendous gains that girls and women have made in education and the workforce during the past 50 years, progress has been uneven, and certain scientific and engineering disciplines remain overwhelmingly male. This report addresses why there are still so few women in certain scientific and engineering fields and provides recommendations to increase the number of women in these fields.

The National Science Foundation estimates that about five million people work directly in science, engineering, and technology— just over 4 percent of the workforce.[1] This relatively small group of workers is considered to be critical to economic innovation and productivity. Workers in science and engineering fields tend to be well paid and enjoy better job security than do other workers. Workforce projections for 2018 by the U.S. Department of Labor show that nine of the 10 fastest-growing occupations that require at least a bachelor's degree will require significant scientific or mathematical training. Many science and engineering occupations are predicted to grow faster than the average rate for all occupations, and some of the largest increases will be in engineering- and computer-related fields—fields in which women currently hold one-quarter or fewer positions (Lacey & Wright, 2009; National Science Board, 2010).

Attracting and retaining more women in the STEM workforce will maximize innovation, creativity, and competitiveness. Scientists and engineers are working to solve some of the most vexing challenges of our time—finding cures for diseases like cancer and malaria, tackling global warming, providing people with clean drinking water, developing renewable energy sources, and understanding the origins of the universe. Engineers design many of the things we use daily—buildings, bridges, computers, cars, wheelchairs, and X-ray machines. When women are not involved in the design of these products, needs and desires unique to women may be overlooked. For example, "some early voice-recognition systems were calibrated to typical male voices. As a result, women's voices were literally unheard. . . . Similar cases are found in many other industries. For instance, a predominantly male group of engineers tailored the first generation of automotive airbags to adult male bodies, resulting in avoidable deaths for women and children" (Margolis & Fisher, 2002, pp. 2–3). With a more diverse workforce, scientific and technological products, services, and solutions are likely to be better designed and more likely to represent all users.

The opportunity to pursue a career in science, technology, engineering, and mathematics is also a matter of pay equity. Occupational segregation accounts for the majority of the wage gap (AAUW Educational Foundation, 2007), and although women still earn less than men earn in science and engineering fields, as they do on average in the overall workforce, women in science and engineering tend to earn more than women earn in other sectors of the workforce. According to a July 2009 survey, the average starting salary for someone with a bachelor's degree in mechanical engineering, for example, was just over $59,000. By comparison, the average starting salary for an individual with a bachelor's degree in economics was just under $50,000 (National Association of Colleges and Employers, 2009).

PREPARATION OF GIRLS FOR STEM FIELDS

Math skills are considered essential to success in STEM fields. Historically, boys have outperformed girls in math, but in the past few decades the gender gap has narrowed, and today girls are doing as well as boys in math on average (Hyde et al., 2008). Girls are earning high school math and science credits at the same rate as boys and are earning slightly higher grades in these classes (U.S. Department of Education, National Center for Education Statistics, 2007) (see Figures 5.1 and 5.2).

On high-stakes math tests, however, boys continue to outscore girls, albeit by a small margin. A small gender gap persists on the mathematics section of the SAT and the ACT examinations (Halpern, Benbow, et al., 2007; AAUW, 2008). Fewer girls than boys take advanced placement (AP) exams in STEM-related subjects such as calculus, physics, computer science, and chemistry (see Figure 5.3), and girls who take STEM AP exams earn

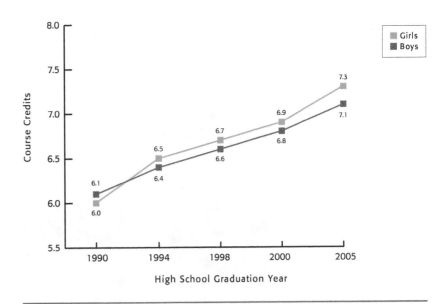

FIGURE 5.1. High School Credits Earned in Mathematics and Science, by Gender, 1990–2005.

Source: U.S. Department of Education, National Center for Education Statistics, 2007, *The Nation's Report Card: America's high school graduates: Results from the 2005 NAEP High School Transcript Study,* by C. Shettle et al. (NCES 2007–467) (Washington, DC: Government Printing Office).

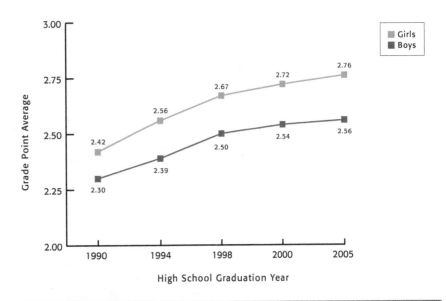

FIGURE 5.2. Grade Point Average in High School Mathematics and Science (Combined), by Gender, 1990–2005.

Source: U.S. Department of Education, National Center for Education Statistics, 2007, *The Nation's Report Card: America's high school graduates: Results from the 2005 NAEP High School Transcript Study,* by C. Shettle et al. (NCES 2007–467) (Washington, DC: Government Printing Office).

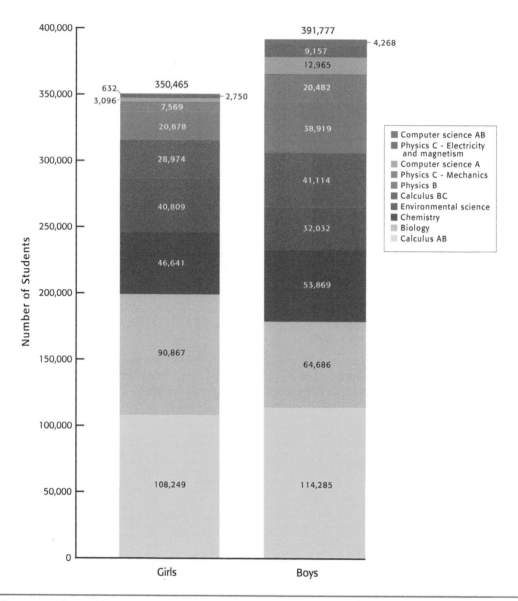

FIGURE 5.3. Students Taking Advanced Placement Tests in Mathematics and Science, by Gender, 2009.

Source: Retrieved November 11, 2009, from the College Board website at www.collegeboard.com.

lower scores than boys earn on average (see Figure 5.4). Research on "stereotype threat" sheds light on the power of stereotypes to undermine girls' math test performance and may help explain the puzzle of girls' strong classroom performance and relatively weaker performance on high-stakes tests such as these.

One notable gain is girls' increased representation in the ranks of the highest achievers in mathematics. Among students

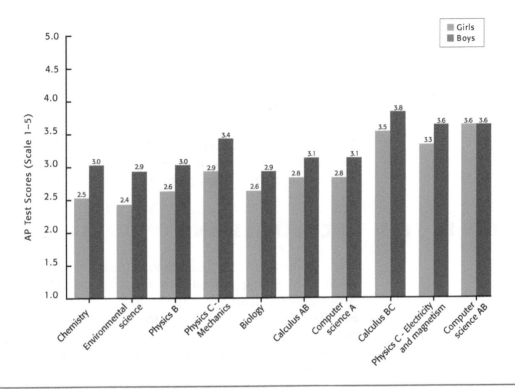

FIGURE 5.4. Average Scores on Advanced Placement Tests in Mathematics and Science Subjects, by Gender, 2009.

Source: Retrieved November 11, 2009, from the College Board website at www.collegeboard.com.

with very high scores on math tests, boys continue to outnumber girls (Lubinski & Benbow, 1992, 2006; Hedges & Nowell, 1995); however, the proportion of girls among the highest math achievers has greatly increased during the past few decades. The Study of Mathematically Precocious Youth identifies seventh and eighth graders who score greater than 700 on the SAT math section (the top 0.01 percent or 1 in 10,000 students). Since the early 1980s the ratio of boys to girls in this extremely select group has dramatically declined from 13:1 (Benbow & Stanley, 1983) to around 3:1 in recent years (Brody & Mills, 2005; Halpern, Benbow, et al., 2007).

Students from historically disadvantaged groups such as African American and Hispanic students, both female and male, are less likely to have access to advanced courses in math and science in high school, which negatively affects their ability to enter and successfully complete STEM majors in college (May & Chubin, 2003; Frizell & Nave, 2008; Tyson et al., 2007; Perna et al., 2009). In 2005, 31 percent of Asian American and 16 percent of white high school graduates completed calculus, compared with 6 percent and 7 percent of African American and Hispanic high school graduates, respectively. Additionally, one-quarter of Asian American and one-tenth of white high school graduates took either the AP or International Baccalaureate exam in calculus, compared with just 3.2 percent of African American and 5.6 percent of Hispanic graduates (National Science Board, 2008). Yet even among underrepresented racial-ethnic groups, a growing number of girls are leaving high school well prepared in math and science and capable of pursuing STEM majors in college.

WOMEN IN STEM IN COLLEGES AND UNIVERSITIES

The transition between high school and college is a critical moment when many young women turn away from a STEM career path. Although women are the majority of college students, they are far less likely than their male peers to plan to major in a STEM field (see Figure 5.5).

Almost one-third of all male freshmen (29 percent), compared with only 15 percent of all female freshmen, planned to major in a STEM field in 2006 (National Science Foundation, 2009b). The gender disparity in plans to major is even more significant when the biological sciences are not included. Just over one-fifth of male freshmen planned to major in engineering, computer science, or the physical sciences, compared with only about 5 percent of female freshmen (ibid.).

Women who enter STEM majors in college tend to be well qualified. Female and male first-year STEM majors are equally likely to have taken and earned high grades in the prerequisite math and science classes in high school and to have confidence in their math and science abilities (Brainard & Carlin, 1998; U.S. Department of Education, National Center for Education Statistics, 2000; Vogt et al., 2007). Nevertheless, many of these academically capable women leave STEM majors early in their college careers, as do many of their male peers (Seymour & Hewitt, 1997). For example, in engineering the national rate of retention from entry into the major to graduation is just under 60 percent for women and men (Ohland et al., 2008). Although the overall retention of female undergraduates in STEM is similar to the retention rate for men and has improved over time (U.S. Department of Education, National Center for Education Statistics, 2000; Xie & Shauman, 2003), understanding why women leave STEM majors is still an important area of research. Women make up a smaller number of STEM students from the

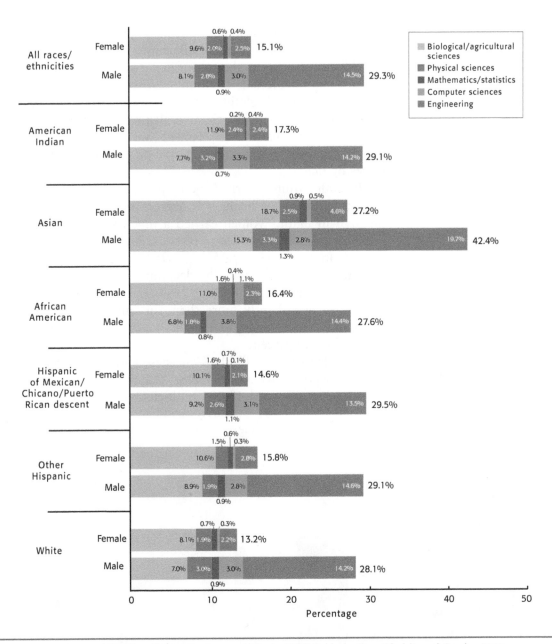

FIGURE 5.5.   Intent of First-Year College Students to Major in STEM Fields, by Race-Ethnicity and Gender, 2006.

Source: Higher Education Research Institute, 2007, *Survey of the American freshman: Special tabulations* (Los Angeles, CA), cited in National Science Foundation, Division of Science Resources Statistics, 2009, *Women, minorities, and persons with disabilities in science and engineering: 2009* (NSF 09-305) (Arlington, VA) Table B-8.

start, so the loss of women from these majors is of special concern. The work of researchers Barbara Whitten, Jane Margolis, and Allan Fisher, show the role of departmental culture in attracting and retaining female computer science and physics majors.

Despite the still relatively small percentages of women majoring in some STEM fields, the overall proportion of STEM bachelor's degrees awarded to women has increased dramatically during the past four decades, although women's representation varies by field.

In 2006, women earned the majority of bachelor's degrees in biology, one-half of bachelor's degrees in chemistry, and nearly one-half in math. Women earned a much smaller proportion of bachelor's degrees awarded in physics, engineering, and computer science. In fact, as Figure 5.6 shows, women's representation in computer science is actually declining—a stark reminder that women's progress cannot be taken for granted. In the mid-1980s women earned slightly more than one-third (36 percent) of the bachelor's degrees in computer science; by 2006 that number had dropped to 20 percent.

The size of the STEM disciplines, and, therefore, the number of degrees awarded, varies dramatically. As Figure 5.7 shows, women earned 48,001 biological science degrees in 2007,

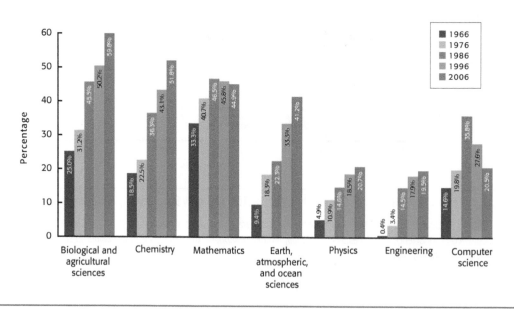

FIGURE 5.6. Bachelor's Degrees Earned by Women in Selected Fields, 1966–2006.

Source: National Science Foundation, Division of Science Resources Statistics, 2008, *Science and engineering degrees: 1966–2006* (Detailed Statistical Tables) (NSF 08-321) (Arlington, VA), Table 11, Author's analysis of Tables 34, 35, 38, & 39.

compared with only 7,944 computer science degrees, 2,109 electrical engineering degrees, and 1,024 physics degrees. In comparison, men earned 31,347 biological science degrees, 34,652 computer science degrees, 16,438 electrical engineering degrees, and 3,846 physics degrees.

Trends in bachelor's degrees earned by women from underrepresented racial-ethnic groups (African American, Hispanic, and Native American/Alaskan Native) generally mirror the overall

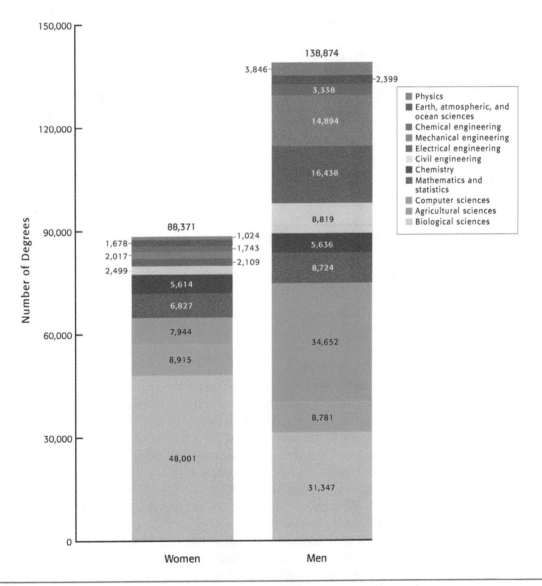

FIGURE 5.7. Bachelor's Degrees Earned in Selected Science and Engineering Fields, by Gender, 2007.

Source: National Science Foundation, Division of Science Resources Statistics, 2009, *Women, minorities, and persons with disabilities in science and engineering: 2009* (NSF 09-305) (Arlington, VA), Tables C-4 and C-5.

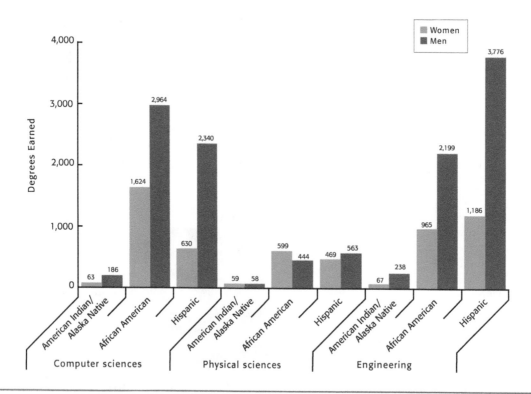

FIGURE 5.8. Bachelor's Degrees Earned by Underrepresented Racial-Ethnic Groups in Selected STEM Fields, by Gender, 2007.

Note: Racial-ethnic groups include U.S. citizens and permanent residents only. Data based on degree-granting institutions eligible to participate in Title IV federal financial aid programs.

Source: National Science Foundation, Division of Science Resources Statistics, 2009, *Women, minorities, and persons with disabilities in science and engineering: 2009* (NSF 09-305) (Arlington, VA), Table C-14.

pattern; however, in some cases the gender gap in degrees earned by African American and Hispanic women and men is much smaller or even reversed (see Figure 5.8). For example, African American women earned 57 percent of physical science degrees awarded to African Americans in 2007; still, the overall number of African American women earning physical science bachelor's degrees was less than 600.

Women's representation among doctoral degree recipients in STEM fields also has improved in the last 40 years (see Figure 5.9). In 1966, women earned about one-eighth of the doctorates in the biological and agricultural sciences, 6 percent of the doctorates in chemistry and mathematics, and 3 percent or less of the doctorates in earth, atmospheric, and ocean sciences; physics; engineering; and computer science. Forty years later, in 2006, women earned almost one-half of the doctorates in the biological

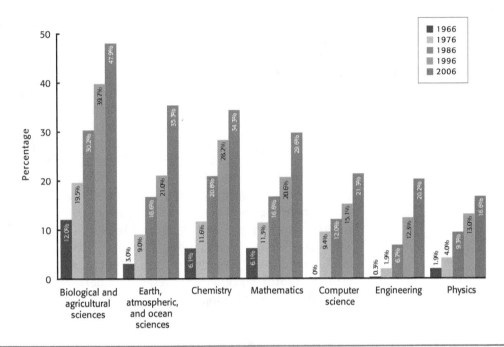

FIGURE 5.9. Doctorates Earned by Women in Selected STEM Fields, 1966–2006.

Source: National Science Foundation, Division of Science Resources Statistics, 2008. *Science and engineering degrees: 1966–2006* (Detailed Statistical Tables) (NSF 08-321) (Arlington, VA), Table 25, Author's analysis of Tables 34, 35, 38, & 39.

Title IX and Gender Equity in STEM

Title IX of the Education Amendments of 1972 prohibits sex discrimination in education programs and activities that receive federal financial assistance. The law states, "No person in the United States shall, on the basis of sex, be excluded from participation in, be denied the benefits of, or be subjected to discrimination under any educational program or activity receiving federal financial assistance" (20 U.S. Code § 1681). Title IX covers nearly all colleges and universities. To ensure compliance with the law, Title IX regulations require institutions that receive any form of federal education funding to evaluate their current policies and practices and adopt and publish grievance procedures and a policy against sex discrimination.

When Congress enacted Title IX, the law was intended to help women achieve equal access to all aspects of education at all levels. During the last 37 years, however, Title IX has been applied mostly to sports. Recent efforts by Congress have brought attention to how Title IX could be used to improve the climate for and representation of women in STEM fields.

Critics argue that women do not face discrimination in STEM fields but rather that women are less interested than men in certain STEM fields and that enforcement of Title IX could lead to a quota system in the sciences (Tierney, 2008; Munro, 2009). Title IX requires neither quotas nor proportionality, and it cannot address gender gaps in participation due to personal choices; however, Title IX reviews can help identify institutional policies and practices that negatively, and in some cases inadvertently, affect personal choices in gender-specific ways (Pieronek, 2005). Simply put, Title IX can help create a climate where women and men of similar talent who want to be scientists or engineers have equal opportunity to do so.

A report by the U.S. Government Accountability Office (2004) focused on Title IX in STEM disciplines and concluded that federal agencies need to do more to ensure that colleges and universities receiving federal funds comply with Title IX. In response to these findings, federal agencies, including NASA and the Department of Energy in conjunction with the Department of Education and the Department of Justice, have begun to conduct Title IX compliance reviews more regularly (Pieronek, 2009).

and agricultural sciences; around one-third of the doctorates in earth, atmospheric, and ocean sciences, chemistry, and math; and approximately one-fifth of the doctorates in computer science, engineering, and physics.

In general the number of doctoral degrees in STEM disciplines earned by women from underrepresented racial-ethnic backgrounds also increased during the past four decades but still remains a small proportion of the total. For example, in 2007, African American women earned 2.2 percent of the doctorates awarded in the biological sciences and less than 2 percent of those awarded in engineering, computer sciences, the physical sciences, and mathematics and statistics. The proportions were similar for Hispanic women and even smaller for Native American women (National Science Foundation, 2009b). Although women have clearly made great progress in earning doctorates in STEM fields, at the doctoral level women remain underrepresented in every STEM field except biology.

WOMEN IN THE STEM WORKFORCE

Consistent with the increased representation of women among STEM degree recipients, women's representation in the STEM workforce has also improved significantly in recent decades; yet, as Figure 5.10 shows, women are still underrepresented in many STEM professions.

In fields such as the biological sciences, women have had a sizeable presence as far back as 1960, when women made up about 27 percent of biologists. Forty years later, in 2000, women made up about 44 percent of the field. On the other end of the spectrum, women made up a mere 1 percent of engineers in 1960 and only about 11 percent of engineers by 2000 (see Figure 5.11). This is an impressive increase, but women still make up only a small minority of working engineers. Overall, progress has been made, but women remain vastly outnumbered in many STEM fields, especially engineering and physics.

Among workers who hold doctorates, men represent a clear majority in all STEM fields. Figures 5.12A and 5.12B show that men far outnumber women, even in the biological sciences.

In the academic workforce, women's representation varies by discipline as well as tenure status. Forty percent of the full-time faculty in degree-granting colleges and universities in the United States in 2005 were women; however, women's representation in STEM disciplines was significantly lower. Women made up less

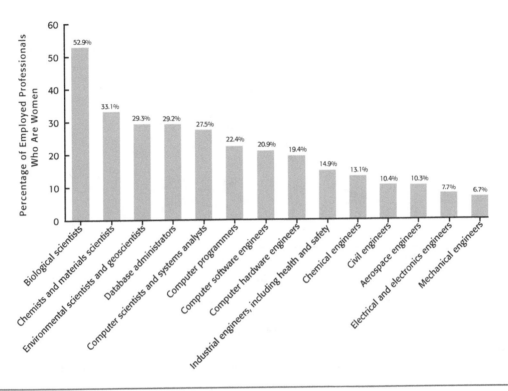

FIGURE 5.10. Women in Selected STEM Occupations, 2008.

Note: Occupations are self-reported.

Source: U.S. Department of Labor, Bureau of Labor Statistics, 2009, *Women in the labor force: A databook* (Report 1018) (Washington, DC), Table 11.

than one-quarter of the faculty in computer and information sciences (22 percent), math (19 percent), the physical sciences (18 percent), and engineering (12 percent). In the life sciences, an area in which many people assume that women have achieved parity, women made up only one-third (34 percent) of the faculty. In all cases women were better represented in lower faculty ranks than in higher ranks among STEM faculty in four-year colleges and universities (Di Fabio et al., 2008).

The situation is even more severe for women from under-represented racial-ethnic backgrounds. Of the more than 7,000 computer-science doctoral faculty in 2006, only 60 were African American women; numbers for Hispanic and Native American women were too low to report. African American women also made up less than 1 percent of the 17,150 postsecondary teachers in engineering. Even in the biological sciences the number of African American and Hispanic female faculty was low. Of the nearly

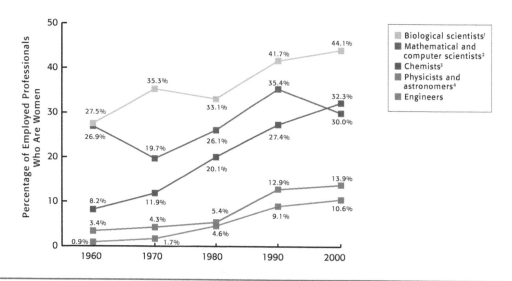

FIGURE 5.11. Women in Selected STEM Occupations, 1960–2000.

Note: Data on postsecondary teachers by field of instruction were not gathered in the 2000 census, so postsecondary teachers are not included here. When postsecondary teachers were included from 1960 to 1990, the general trends remained the same.

[1] In the 1980 and 1990 censuses, data include life scientists as well as biological scientists.

[2] In the 1960 census, no category for computer scientists was included; in the 1970 census, the category was titled "mathematicians and computer specialists."

[3] In the 1980 and 1990 censuses, the category was titled "chemists except biochemists"; in the 2000 census, the category was titled "chemists and material scientists."

[4] In the 1960 census, the category was titled "physicists."

Source: U.S. Census Bureau, 1960, 1970, 1980, 1990, & 2000, Census of the population (Washington, DC).

25,000 postsecondary teachers in the biological sciences, 380 were African American women and 300 were Hispanic women (ibid.).

Women's representation among tenured faculty is lower than one would expect based on the supply of female science and engineering doctoral degree recipients in recent decades (Kulis et al., 2002). The path from elementary school to a STEM career has often been compared to a pipeline. This metaphor suggests that as the number of girls who study STEM subjects in elementary, middle, and secondary school increases (more girls go into the pipeline), the number of women who become scientists and engineers will also increase (more women come out of the pipeline), and gender disparities in representation will disappear. This has not happened at the expected rate, especially at the tenured faculty level in science and engineering. If we compare the percentage of tenured female faculty in 2006 with the percentage of STEM doctorates awarded to women in 1996 (allowing 10 years for an individual to start an academic job and earn tenure), in most STEM fields the drop-off is pronounced. For example, women

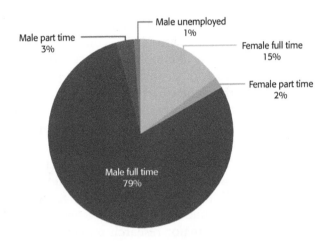

FIGURE 5.12A. Workers with Doctorates in the Computer and Information Sciences Workforce, by Gender and Employment Status, 2006.

Note: The number of female unemployed workers was not available due to small sample size.

Source: National Science Foundation, Division of Science Resources Statistics, 2009, *Characteristics of doctoral scientists and engineers in the United States: 2006* (Detailed Statistical Tables) (NSF 09-317) (Arlington, VA), Authors' analysis of Table 2.

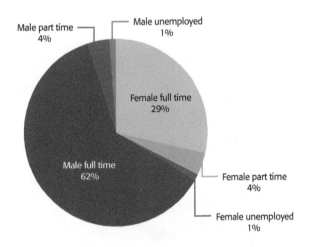

FIGURE 5.12B. Workers with Doctorates in the Biological, Agricultural, and Environmental Life Science Workforce, by Gender and Employment Status, 2006.

Note: The percentages do not equal 100 due to rounding.

Source: National Science Foundation, Division of Science Resources Statistics, 2009, *Characteristics of doctoral scientists and engineers in the United States: 2006* (Detailed Statistical Tables) (NSF 09-317) (Arlington, VA), Authors' analysis of Table 2.

earned 12 percent of the doctorates in engineering in 1996 but were only 7 percent of the tenured faculty in engineering in 2006. Even in fields like biology, where women now receive about one-half of doctorates and received 42 percent in 1996, women made up less than one-quarter of tenured faculty and only 34 percent of tenure-track faculty in 2006 (National Science Foundation, 2008, 2009a). Women make up larger percentages of the lower-paying, nontenured STEM faculty positions (see Figure 5.13).

Several studies have found a gender difference in hiring in STEM academic disciplines (Bentley & Adamson, 2003; Nelson & Rogers, n.d.; Ginther & Kahn, 2006). Although recent research found that when women do apply for STEM faculty positions at major research universities they are more likely than men to be hired, smaller percentages of qualified women apply for these positions in the first place (National Research Council, 2009). Improving women's position among STEM faculty will apparently require more than simply increasing the pool of female STEM degree holders (Valian, 1998; Kulis et al., 2002).

Cathy Trower and her colleagues at the Collaborative on Academic Careers in Higher Education (COACHE) at Harvard University found that female STEM faculty express lower job satisfaction than do their male peers. Lower satisfaction leads to

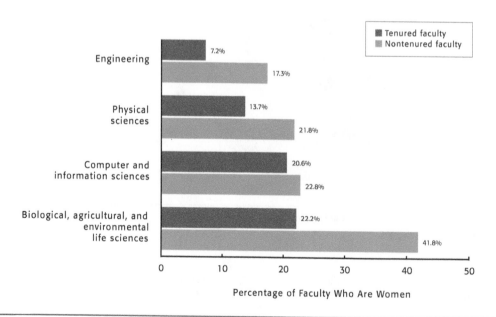

FIGURE 5.13. Female STEM Faculty in Four-Year Educational Institutions, by Discipline and Tenure Status, 2006.

Source: National Science Foundation, Division of Science Resources Statistics, 2009, *Characteristics of doctoral scientists and engineers in the United States: 2006* (Detailed Statistical Tables) (NSF 09-317) (Arlington, VA), Authors' analysis of Table 20.

higher turnover and a loss of talent in science and engineering. Trower's research suggests that the climate of science and engineering departments is closely related to satisfaction of female faculty and that providing effective mentoring and work-life policies can help improve job satisfaction and, hence, the retention of female STEM faculty.

Women working in STEM fields tend to have higher earnings than do other women in the workforce, although a gender pay gap exists in STEM occupations as in other fields. For example, in 2009 the average starting salary for bachelor's degree recipients in marketing was just over $42,000 a year, and bachelor's degree recipients in accounting received starting salaries averaging around $48,500 a year. In comparison, starting salaries for bachelor's degree holders in computer science averaged around $61,500, and average starting salaries were just under $66,000 for individuals holding bachelor's degrees in chemical engineering (National Association of Colleges and Employers, 2009). As these numbers indicate, many STEM careers can provide women increased earning potential and greater economic security.

Recent studies of scientists, engineers, and technologists in business and the high-tech industry have found that women in these fields have higher attrition rates than do both their male peers and women in other occupations (Hewlett et al., 2008; Simard et al., 2008). The studies highlight midcareer as a critical time for these women. Hewlett et al. (2008) at the Center for Work-Life Policy at Harvard University found that female scientists, engineers, and technologists are fairly well represented at the lower rungs on corporate ladders (41 percent). More than half (52 percent), however, quit their jobs by midcareer (about 10 years into their careers). High-tech companies in particular lost 41 percent of their female employees, compared with only 17 percent of their male employees. In engineering, women have higher attrition rates than their male peers have, despite similar levels of stated satisfaction and education. The Society of Women Engineers (2006) conducted a retention study of more than 6,000 individuals who earned an engineering degree between 1985 and 2003. One-quarter of female engineers surveyed were either not employed at all or not employed in engineering or a related field, while only one-tenth of men surveyed had left the engineering field.

WHY SO FEW?

Academic research on this topic is prolific, with three themes emerging from the literature. First, the notion that men are mathematically superior and innately better suited to STEM fields than women are remains a common belief, with a large number of articles addressing cognitive gender differences as an explanation for the small numbers of women in STEM. A second theme revolves around girls' lack of interest in STEM. A third theme involves the STEM workplace, with issues ranging from work-life balance to bias. The remainder of this chapter summarizes and examines these themes.

Cognitive Sex Differences

As noted earlier, a difference in average math performance between girls and boys no longer exists in the general school population (Hyde et al., 2008). Nevertheless, the issue of cognitive sex differences, including mathematical ability, remains hotly contested. Lynn and Irwing (2004) found small or no differences in average IQ between the sexes; that is, neither girls nor boys are the "smarter sex."[2] Other researchers have found, however, that girls and boys tend to have different cognitive strengths and weaknesses. Generally, boys perform better on tasks using spatial orientation and visualization and on certain quantitative tasks that rely on those skills. Girls outperform boys on tests relying on verbal skills, especially writing, as well as some tests involving memory and perceptual speed (Hedges & Nowell, 1995; Kimura, 2002; Halpern, Aronson, et al., 2007).

One of the largest gender gaps in cognitive skills is seen in the area of spatial skills and specifically on measures of mental rotation, with boys consistently outscoring girls (Linn & Petersen, 1985; Voyer et al., 1995). Many people consider spatial skills to be important for success in fields like engineering, although the connection between spatial abilities and success in STEM careers is not definitive (Ceci et al., 2009). Whether or not well-developed spatial skills are necessary for success in science and engineering, research shows that spatial skills can be improved fairly easily with training (Baenninger & Newcombe, 1989; Vasta et al., 1996). Among the most promising research findings in this field are those of Sheryl Sorby. Sorby and Baartmans (2000) and their colleagues designed and implemented a successful course to improve the spatial-visualization skills of first-year engineering students who had poorly developed spatial skills. More than three-quarters of female engineering students who took the course remained in the school of engineering, compared with about one-half of the female students who did not take the course. Poor or underdeveloped spatial skills may deter girls from pursuing math or science courses or careers, but these skills can be improved fairly easily.

Methodology

Using multiple databases, including Web of Science, ProQuest, Social Science Citation Index, and J-Stor, AAUW reviewed hundreds of academic articles written during the past 25 years on the topic of women in science and engineering. Articles from the fields of psychology, sociology, education, economics, neuroscience, and endocrinology were examined. The literature review informed this chapter. These projects were chosen because they each address an important issue with the potential to influence public understanding. The profiled findings are well respected in the research community, as measured by publication in peer-reviewed journals, number of citations, and other forms of public recognition. These projects were conducted within the past 15 years.

Biology Is Not Destiny

Ceci et al. (2009) reviewed more than 400 articles exploring the causes of women's underrepresentation in STEM fields, including biological as well as social factors, and concluded that the research on sex differences in brain structure and hormones is inconclusive. Female and male brains are indeed physically distinct, but how these differences translate into specific cognitive strengths and weaknesses remains unclear. Likewise, evidence for cognitive sex differences based on hormonal exposure is mixed. Ceci et al. found that hormonal exposure, especially in gestation, does have a role in cognitive sex differences. Overall, however, the researchers concluded, "Evidence for a hormonal basis of the dearth of female scientists" is "weaker than the evidence for other factors," such as gender differences in preferences and sociocultural influences on girls' performance on gatekeeper tests (p. 224).

Differences in the representation of women in science and math fields cross-culturally and over time also support the role of sociocultural factors for explaining gender gaps in these fields (Andreescu et al., 2008). As discussed earlier, the ratio of boys to girls among children identified as mathematically precocious has decreased dramatically in the last 30 years, far faster than it would take a genetic change to travel through the population. Also, while in the vast majority of countries more boys than girls scored above the 99th percentile in mathematics on the 2003 Program for International Student Assessment, in Iceland and Thailand more girls than boys scored above the 99th percentile (Guiso et al., 2008). Differences between countries and over time illustrate the importance of culture in the development of mathematical skills.

Scientists and Engineers Are Not Necessarily the Highest Math Achievers

Boys outnumber girls at the very high end of the math test score distribution. Some researchers have suggested that this gender difference accounts for the small number of women in certain STEM fields. This logic has two main flaws. First, as mentioned above, girls have made rapid inroads into the ranks of children identified as "mathematically gifted" in the past 30 years, while women's representation in mathematically demanding fields such as physics, computer science, and engineering has grown slowly. That is, fewer women pursue STEM careers than would be expected based on the number of girls who earn very high math scores. Second, Weinberger (2005) found that the science and engineering workforce is not populated primarily by the highest-scoring math students, male or female. Less than one-third of college-educated white men in the engineering, math, computer science, and physical science workforce scored higher than 650 on the SAT math exam, and more than one-third had SAT math scores below 550—the math score of the average humanities major. Even though a correlation exists between high school math test scores and later entry into STEM education and careers, very high math scores are not necessarily a prerequisite for success in STEM fields.

"Just Not Interested"

Many girls and women report that they are not interested in science and engineering. In a 2009 poll of young people ages 8–17 by the American Society for Quality, 24 percent of boys but only 5 percent of girls said they were interested in an engineering career. Another recent poll found that 74 percent of college-bound boys ages 13–17 said that computer science or computing would be a good college major for them compared with 32 percent of their female peers (WGBH Education Foundation & Association for Computing Machinery, 2009). From early adolescence, girls express less interest in math or science careers than boys do (Lapan et al., 2000; Turner et al., 2008). Even girls and women who excel in mathematics often do not pursue STEM fields. In studies of high mathematics achievers, for example, women are more likely to secure degrees in the humanities, life sciences, and social sciences than in math, computer science, engineering, or the physical sciences; the reverse is true for men (Lubinski & Benbow, 2006).

Interest in an occupation is influenced by many factors, including a belief that one can succeed in that occupation (Eccles [Parsons] et al., 1983; Correll, 2004; Eccles, 2006). The work of Shelley Correll shows that girls assess their mathematical ability lower than do boys with equivalent past mathematical achievement. At the same time, girls hold themselves to a higher standard in subjects like math, where boys are considered to excel. Because of this, girls are less likely to believe that they will succeed in a STEM field and, therefore, are less likely to express interest in a STEM career.

Pajares (2005) found that gender differences in self-confidence in STEM subjects begin in middle school and increase in high school and college, with girls reporting less confidence than boys do in their math and science ability. In part, boys develop greater confidence in STEM through experience developing relevant skills. A number of studies have shown that gender differences in self-confidence disappear when variables such as previous achievement or opportunity to learn are controlled (Lent et al., 1986; Zimmerman & Martinez-Pons, 1990; Cooper & Robinson, 1991; Pajares, 1996, 2005). Students who lack confidence in their math or science skills are less likely to engage in tasks that require those skills and will more quickly give up in the face of difficulty. Girls and women may be especially vulnerable to losing confidence in STEM areas. The research of Carol Dweck has implications for improving self-confidence. Dweck's research shows that when a girl believes that she can become smarter and learn what she needs to know in STEM subjects—as opposed to believing that a person is either born with science and math ability or not—she is more likely to succeed in a STEM field.

A belief that one can succeed in a STEM field is important but is not the only factor in establishing interest in a STEM career. Culturally prescribed gender roles also influence occupational interest (Low et al., 2005). A review of child vocational development by Hartung et al. (2005) found that children—and girls especially—develop beliefs that they cannot pursue particular occupations because they perceive them as inappropriate for their gender.

Jacquelynne Eccles, a leading researcher in the field of occupational choice, has spent the past 30 years developing a model and collecting evidence about career choice. Her work suggests that occupational choice is influenced by a person's values as well as expectancy for success (Eccles [Parsons] et al., 1983; Eccles, 1994, 2006). Well-documented gender differences exist in the value that women and men place on doing work that contributes to society, with women more likely than men to prefer work with a clear social purpose (Jozefowicz et al., 1993; Konrad et al., 2000; Margolis et al., 2002; Lubinski & Benbow, 2006; Eccles, 2006). The source of this gender difference is a subject of debate: Some claim that the difference is innate, while others claim that it is a result of gender socialization. Regardless of the origin of the difference, most people do not view STEM occupations as directly benefiting society or individuals (National Academy of Engineering, 2008; Diekman et al., 2009). As a result, STEM careers often do not appeal to women (or men) who value making a social contribution (Eccles, 1994; Sax, 1994). Certain STEM subdisciplines with a clearer social purpose, such as biomedical engineering and environmental engineering, have succeeded in attracting higher percentages of women than have other subdisciplines like mechanical or electrical engineering (Gibbons, 2009).

Despite girls' lower stated interest in science and engineering compared with boys, recent research suggests that there are ways to increase girls' interest in STEM areas (Turner & Lapan, 2005; Eisenhart, 2008; Plant et al., 2009). Plant et al. (2009) reported an increase in middle school girls' interest in engineering after the girls were exposed to a 20-minute narrative delivered by a computer-generated female agent describing the lives of female engineers and the benefits of engineering careers. The narrative included positive statements about students' abilities to meet the demands of engineering careers and counteracted stereotypes of engineering as an antisocial, unusual career for women while emphasizing the people-oriented and socially beneficial aspects of engineering. Another ongoing study and outreach project is focusing on educating high-achieving, mostly minority, high school girls about what scientists and engineers actually do and how they contribute to society. Although the girls knew almost nothing about engineering at the start of the study, of the 66 percent of girls still participating after two years, 80 percent were seriously considering a career in engineering (Eisenhart, 2008). The Engineer Your Life website (www.engineeryourlife.com), a project of the WGBH Educational Foundation and the National Academy of Engineering, has also been shown to increase high school girls' interest in pursuing engineering as a career. In a survey by Paulsen and Bransfield (2009), 88 percent of 631 girls said that the website made them more interested in engineering as a career, and 76 percent said that it inspired them to take an engineering course in college. Although these studies generally relied on small samples and in a number of cases no long-term follow-up has been done with participants, the results are promising.

Research on interest in science and engineering does not usually consider gender, race, and ethnicity simultaneously. Of course, gender and race do interact to create different cultural roles and expectations for women (and men) from different racial-ethnic backgrounds. Assumptions about the mismatch between women's interests and STEM often are based on the experiences of white women. In the African American community, for example, many of the characteristics that are considered appropriate for African American women, such as high self-esteem, independence, and assertiveness, can lead to success in STEM fields (Hanson, 2004). Young African American women express more interest in STEM fields than do young white women (Hanson, 2004; Fouad & Walker, 2005). The number of African American women in STEM remains low, however, suggesting that other barriers are important for this community (ibid.).

Workplace Environment, Bias, and Family Responsibilities

As mentioned above, women leave STEM fields at a higher rate than do their male peers (Society of Women Engineers, 2006; Hewlett et al., 2008; Frehill et al., 2009). Workplace environment, bias, and family responsibilities all play a role.

Workplace Environment

In the study of STEM professionals in the private sector described earlier, Hewlett et al. (2008) found that many women appear to encounter a series of challenges at midcareer that contribute to their leaving careers in STEM industries. Women cited feelings of isolation, an unsupportive work environment, extreme work schedules, and unclear rules about advancement and success as major factors in their decision to leave. Although women and men in industry and business leave STEM careers at significantly different rates, the situation in academia is somewhat more nuanced. In a recent study on attrition among STEM faculty, Xu (2008) showed that female and male faculty leave at similar rates; however, women are more likely than men to consider changing jobs within academia. Women's higher turnover intention in academia (which is the best predictor of actual turnover) is mainly due to dissatisfaction with departmental culture, advancement opportunities, faculty leadership, and research support. Goulden et al. (2009) compared men and women in the sciences who are married with children and found that the women were 35 percent less likely to enter a tenure-track position after receiving a doctorate.

Bias

Women in STEM fields can experience bias that negatively influences their progress and participation. Although instances of explicit bias may be decreasing, implicit bias continues to have an adverse effect. Implicit biases may reflect, be stronger than, or in some cases contradict explicitly held beliefs or values. Therefore, even individuals who espouse a belief of gender equity and equality may harbor implicit biases about gender and, hence, negative gender stereotypes about women and girls in science and math (Valian, 1998). Nosek et al. (2002a) found that majorities of both women and men of all racial-ethnic groups hold a strong implicit association of male with science and female with liberal arts.

Research has also pointed to bias in peer review (Wenneras & Wold, 1997) and hiring (Steinpreis et al., 1999; Trix & Psenka, 2003). For example, Wenneras and Wold found that a female postdoctoral applicant had to be significantly more productive than a male applicant to receive the same peer review score. This meant that she either had to publish at least three more papers in a prestigious science journal or an additional 20 papers in lesser-known specialty journals to be judged as productive as a male applicant. The authors concluded that the systematic underrating of female applicants could help explain the lower success rate of female scientists in achieving high academic rank compared with their male counterparts.

Trix and Psenka (2003) found systematic differences in letters of recommendation for academic faculty positions for female and male applicants. The researchers concluded that recommenders (the majority of whom were men) rely on accepted gender schema in which, for example, women are not expected to have significant accomplishments in a field like academic medicine. Letters written for women are more likely to refer to their compassion, teaching, and effort as opposed to their achievements, research, and ability, which are the characteristics highlighted for male applicants. While nothing is wrong with being compassionate, trying hard, and being a good teacher, arguably these traits are less valued than achievements, research, and ability for success in academic medicine. The authors concluded, "Recommenders unknowingly used selective categorization and perception, also known as stereotyping, in choosing what features to include in their profiles of the female applicants" (p. 215).

When women are acknowledged as successful in arenas that are considered male in character, women are less well liked and more personally derogated than are equivalently successful men. Being disliked can affect career outcomes, leading to lower evaluations and less access to organizational rewards. These results suggest that gender stereotypes can prompt bias in evaluative judgments of women in male-dominated environments, even when these women have proved themselves to be successful and demonstrated their competence (Heilman et al., 2004).

Biases do change. Today the fields viewed as stereotypically male have narrowed considerably compared with even 30 years ago. Life and health sciences are seen as more appropriate for women, while the physical or hard sciences and engineering fields are still considered masculine domains (Farenga & Joyce, 1999).

Family Responsibilities

Many people think that women leave STEM academic careers because they cannot balance work and family responsibilities (Mason et al., 2009; Xie & Shauman, 2003); however, research evidence by Xu (2008) points to a more nuanced relationship between family responsibilities and academic STEM careers. Research shows that being single is a good predictor that a woman will be hired for a tenure-track job and promoted. Research also shows, however, that marriage is a good predictor for both women and men of being hired as an assistant professor (Xie & Shauman, 2003; Ginther & Kahn, 2006). Married women in STEM appear to have a disadvantage compared with married men in relation to tenure and promotion decisions only if the married women have children (Xie & Shauman, 2003). So while marriage does not appear to hurt women, having young children does affect their chances for advancement. Having young children in the home may affect women's productivity since child-care responsibilities fall disproportionately on women (Stack, 2004).

Some telling statistics point to the difficulties that mothers still face in an academic environment. Mason and Goulden (2002) found that among tenured faculty in the sciences 12 to 14 years after earning a doctorate, 70 percent of the men but only 50 percent of the women had children living in their home. The same study found that among science professors who had babies within the first five years after receiving a doctorate, 77 percent of the men but only 53 percent of the women had achieved tenure 12 to 14 years after earning a doctorate. These disparities were not unique to, and not always worse in, STEM fields. In another Mason and Goulden study (2004), more than twice as many female academics (38 percent) as male academics (18 percent) indicated that they had fewer children than they had wanted.

In business and industry both women and men identify family responsibilities as a possible barrier to advancement, but women are affected differently than men by this "family penalty" (Simard et al., 2008, p. 5). Although both women and men feel that having a family hinders their success at work, women are more likely than men to report foregoing marriage or children and delaying having children. Among women and men with families, women are more likely to report that they are the primary caregiver and have a partner who also works full time. A recent retention study found that most women and men who left engineering said that interest in another career was a reason, but women were far more likely than men to also cite time and family-related issues (Society of Women Engineers, 2006; Frehill et al., 2008). Additionally, women in STEM are more likely to have a partner who is also in STEM and faces a similarly demanding work schedule. In a situation where a "two body problem" exists, the man's career is often given priority (Hewlett et al., 2008).

WHERE DO WE GO FROM HERE?

Multiple factors contribute to the underrepresentation of women and girls in STEM and, therefore, multiple solutions are needed to correct the imbalance. The remainder of this report profiles eight research findings, each of which offers practical ideas for helping girls and women reach their potential in science, technology, engineering, and mathematics. Selected for their relevance to public debate and their scientific credibility, these case studies provide important insights into the question of why so few women study and work in many STEM fields.

These findings provide evidence on the nurture side of the nature-nurture debate, demonstrating that social and environmental factors clearly contribute to the underrepresentation of women in science and engineering. The findings are organized into three areas: social and environmental factors that shape girls' achievements and interest in math and science; the college environment; and the continuing importance of bias, often operating at an unconscious level, as an obstacle to women's success in STEM fields.

Girls' Achievements and Interest in Math and Science Are Shaped by the Environment around Them

This report profiles four research projects that demonstrate the effects of societal beliefs and the learning environment on girls' achievements and interest in science and math. Chapter 2 profiles research showing that when teachers and parents tell girls that their intelligence can expand with experience and learning, girls do better on math tests and are more likely to want to continue to study math.

Research shows that negative stereotypes about girls' abilities in math are still relevant today and can lower girls' test performance and aspirations for science and engineering careers. When test administrators tell students that girls and boys are equally capable in math, the difference in performance disappears, illustrating the importance of the learning environment for encouraging girls' achievement and interest in math.

Research on self-assessment finds that girls assess their mathematical abilities lower than do boys with similar past mathematical achievements. At the same time, girls hold themselves to a higher standard than boys do in subjects like math, believing that they have to be exceptional to succeed in "male" fields. One result of girls' lower self-assessment of their math ability— even in the face of good grades and test scores—and their higher standard for performance is that fewer girls than boys aspire to STEM careers.

One of the most consistent, and largest, gender differences in cognitive abilities is found in the area of spatial skills, with boys and men consistently outperforming girls and women. Research documents that individuals' spatial skills consistently improve dramatically in a short time with a simple training course. If girls are in an environment that enhances their success in science and math with spatial skills training, they are more likely to develop their skills as well as their confidence and consider a future in a STEM field.

At Colleges and Universities, Little Changes Can Make a Big Difference in Attracting and Retaining Women in STEM

As described earlier, many girls graduate from high school well prepared to pursue a STEM career, but few of them major in science or engineering in college. Small improvements in the culture of computer science and physics departments, such as changing admissions requirements, presenting a broader overview of the field in introductory courses, and providing a student lounge, can add up to big gains in female student recruitment and retention.

Likewise, colleges and universities can attract more female science and engineering faculty if they improve the integration of female faculty into the departmental culture. Research provides evidence that women are less satisfied with the academic workplace and more likely to leave it earlier in their careers than their male counterparts are. College and university administrators can recruit and retain more women by implementing mentoring programs and effective work-life policies for all faculty members.

Bias, Often Unconscious, Limits Women's Progress in Scientific and Engineering Fields

Research shows that most people continue to associate science and math fields with "male" and humanities and arts fields with "female," including individuals who actively reject these stereotypes. Implicit bias may influence girls' likelihood of identifying with and participating in math and science and also contributes to bias in education and the workplace—even among people who support gender equity. Taking the implicit bias test at https://implicit.harvard.edu can help people identify and understand their own implicit biases so that they can work to compensate for them.

People not only associate math and science with "male" but also often hold negative opinions of women in "masculine" positions, like scientists or engineers. This research shows that people judge women to be less competent than men in "male" jobs unless women are clearly successful in their work. When a woman is clearly competent in a "masculine" job, she is considered to be less likable. Because both likeability and competence are needed for success in the workplace, women in STEM fields can find themselves in a double bind.

Women have made impressive gains in science and engineering but are still a distinct minority in many science and engineering fields. The following eight research findings, taken together, suggest that creating environments that support girls' and women's achievements and interest in science and engineering will encourage more girls and women to pursue careers in these vital fields.

Notes

1. Defined by occupation, the United States science and engineering workforce totaled between 4.3 and 5.8 million people in 2006. Those in science and engineering occupations who had bachelor's degrees were estimated at between 4.3 and 5.0 million. The National Science Foundation includes social scientists but not medical professionals in these estimates (National Science Board, 2010). Estimates of the size of the scientific, engineering, and technological workforce are produced using different criteria by several U.S. government agencies including the Census Bureau, the National Science Foundation, and the Bureau of Labor Statistics. Defined more broadly, the size of the STEM workforce has been estimated to exceed 21 million people.

2. Some research suggests that women and men achieve similar IQ results using different parts of the brain (Haier et al., 2005).

UNIT 2

Technology at the Moment

CHAPTER 6

■■■

Gaming in the Classroom: Gender Considerations and Promoting STEM Careers

Lorraine C. Beaudin, PhD
Beaulc@uleth.ca

Gail Bailey
Gail.bailey@uleth.ca

ABSTRACT

Given the potential for gaming to enhance collaboration and student learning, it comes as no surprise that education and learning theorists are suggesting that gaming could be useful in education (Kinzie & Joseph, 2008). As research in game-based learning continues to expand, discussions examining the potential for gaming to influence student participation in STEM have also risen. Past research has found that there is a gender gap in science, technology, engineering, and math (STEM) careers (Arnold & Niederman, 2001). Accordingly, when considering the use of video games in the classroom there must be some attention paid to gender differences. This paper will provide a brief overview of the potential benefits of gaming in education, highlight some of the gender issues in gaming; and discuss the importance of game design for both enhancing learning and influencing students' future participation in STEM careers.

INTRODUCTION

Across the world, gaming has become a cultural and commercial sensation (Schrader, Archambault, & Oh-Young, 2011). It comes as no surprise that education and learning theorists are suggesting that gaming could be useful in education (Kinzie & Joseph, 2008). As research in game-based learning continues to expand, discussions examining the potential for gaming to enhance student participation in science, technology, engineering, and math (STEM) have also risen. Past research has found that there is a gender gap in (STEM) careers (Arnold & Niederman, 2001). While there has been growth in the female population of game players in recent years, the majority of those involved in the gaming world are male (Ivory, 2006). Accordingly, when considering the use of games in the classroom there must be some attention paid to gender differences. This paper suggests that there is a need to consider three areas of research relating to gaming in education before integrating gaming in the classroom. These areas include the potential benefits of gaming; gender issues in gaming; and the influence of gaming on STEM career selection.

DEFINITIONS

Educational gaming is typically defined as individual or group games that have cognitive, social, behavioral, and/or emotional dimensions relating to curriculum objectives. The Horizon Report (2010) broadly groups educational games into three categories: games that are not digital; games that are digital, but that are not collaborative; and collaborative digital games. For the purpose of this paper, we are referring to any type of digital game used in the classroom to enhance learning.

POTENTIAL BENEFITS OF GAMING FOR EDUCATION

Historically, there have been strong links between play and learning. In addition to academic gains, life skills such as collaboration, teamwork, problem solving, and communication can also be developed through the integration of educational gaming into classroom practice (Childress and Braswell, 2006; Dickey, 2007; Schrader, et al., 2011). Kenny and Gunter (2011) identify two reasons why gaming is an effective tool for student learning: (1) they (games) provide an opportunity for active learning, having students learn by doing rather than simply reading or listening; and (2) students become engaged and motivated by games. If teachers are to use digital games successfully in the classroom, the games must teach the required knowledge and enable the students to translate this knowledge into higher levels of understanding, without losing the entertainment value (Kenny & Gunter, 2011).

Dickey (2007) identified four different types of knowledge that can be strengthened through the use of quest type games: declarative, procedural, strategic, and metacognitive. These types of knowledge can help students become more proficient in skills such as fact finding and data collection, understanding of how to perform tasks, and how to apply these to novel situations (Dickey, 2007). Spence and Feng (2010) found that video games exercise most cognitive and social skills and that certain genres of games will improve spatial cognition. Games that improve spatial cognition include: action, maze, and puzzle (Spence and

Feng, 2010). Massively Multiplayer Online Role Playing Games (MMORPGs), also offer the benefit of realism and 360-degree perspectives (Dickey, 2007). MMORPGs have become increasingly popular in recent years, not only offering benefits to spatial cognition but also being a highly motivating game in areas such as problem solving and socializing (Dickey, 2007). Royle (2008) suggests that there are three main factors that engage players in a game. These include creating a desire and motivation in the player to want to solve problems, creating a backstory that makes the game believable and authentic, and finally letting the player create a character so that they can become fully engaged. Increased student engagement and motivation are valid reasons for incorporating games into classroom teaching.

GENDER AND STEM CONSIDERATIONS

Gaming has shown to be particularly useful in promoting the skills required for STEM careers—careers that typically have had lower female participation. The number of females enrolling in IT at the post secondary level has dropped in the last ten years (NCWIT Scorecard, 2010). Gender issues in gaming are not simply about the number of females gaming, it is also about differences in interests and the negative reinforcements that games can have on young women. Annetta et al. (2009) found that once female students were given the opportunity to take part in gaming their interest in science and technology was improved. This is significant for educators. Studies have shown that girls used computers more than boys, but that boys used them more for games than girls (Annetta, Mangnum, Holmes, Collazo, & Cheng, 2009; Tan et al., 2013). Further, Cherney (2008) reported that males' previous experiences with video games benefited them, while female participants exhibited higher trait and state anxiety during the experiment. This is consistent with Tan et al. (2013) who reported that girls found games more challenging while the boys more readily achieved flow. These findings suggest that outside game play could influence the classroom experience of gaming and that girls may need more practice or encouragement in order to benefit to the same degree from educational games. The idea of flow is especially important for educators to understand. If girls experience less flow in educational gaming, the benefit might be minimized for them. In general, well-designed games—as with well-designed education experiences—are challenging but achievable (McClarty et al., 2012).

Sàinz & Eccles (2012) found male students reported higher self-concept of computer abilities compared to females, whose self-concept decreased over time. Females decrease in self-concept could possibly be explained by negative stereotypes about women and technology. Self-concept of computer ability was also linked to intention to pursue Information and Technology careers. Lower female self-concept could be one potential link to the existing gender gap in technology careers. In this way, integrating gaming in the classroom without attending to the different needs of students could widen the gender gap.

There has been concern over the years that females are over sexualized and underrepresented in games. One of the first key motivators in MMORPGs is character development (Dickey, 2007). Players will spend hours developing their character and in turn become somewhat emotionally attached (Dickey, 2007). The traits and assets that one's character possesses play an important role in their social capital in the virtual world (Dickey, 2007). In turn, players become motivated to maintain high social status as it can either help or hinder one's advancement in the game. In a study by Kinzie & Joseph (2008) nearly all children chose to create a character of the same gender as themselves. Unfortunately, as found by Beasley, & Collins Standley (2002) there are far fewer female characters available in video games and those that do exist are often provocatively dressed, passive, nonactive characters (Beasley, & Collins Standley, 2002; Haninger, & Thompson, 2002).

It seems that we can gain some insight into why many girls may not pursue gaming as a pastime by exploring the concerns of the women who do participate. Lack of character choice could potentially be a cause for less motivation for female players. It is clear that in order to have girls engage in gaming and therefore reap the benefits, changes will have to be made to make them more comfortable and confident in all aspects of gaming. Game developers need to understand the background, cultural values, and beliefs of target learners, applying it in game design. They (developers) should adopt values, norms, artifacts, colors and symbols to convey positive connotations to avoid negative interpretation of the games (Blamire, 2010). Moreover, game designers have the potential to influence young women in positive ways. Creating games that are appealing to females could ultimately increase female interest in STEM careers.

Success in STEM careers has also been linked to spatial ability (Terrell, 2007; Cherney, 2008). While it has been found that video games can increase spatial cognition abilities, it has also been found that females show larger improvements than males (Feng, Spence, & Pratt, 2007). This study also showed that video game practice decreased gender difference in these spatial cognitive abilities. Cherney (2008) found that computer games increased spatial rotation ability in both males and females but with females gaining skill significantly more than males. These findings are important when we consider Arnold and Niederman's (2001) suggestion that we could decrease the gender gap in STEM occupations if we began intervening at an earlier educational stage. Gaming in the classroom could ultimately change the way in which teachers are approaching spatial cognition training in the classroom as well as provide early promotion and preparation for STEM occupations.

CONCLUSION

As is the case with the integration of any new approach in education, there is a need to develop a quality repository of gender-friendly and pedagogically sound games. Kiili and Lainema (2008) accurately identify that, the "development of a theoretical foundation for game-based learning is crucial because, if educational games are developed without an appropriate pedagogical basis, the investments may be considered wasted (p. 470). This paper argues that part of that theoretical foundation must include an understanding of the gender differences in gaming and how those differences must be acknowledged when implementing educational gaming in teaching and learning.

References

Arnold, D., & Niederman, F. (2001). The global IT work force: introduction. *Communications of the ACM,* 44(7), 30–33.

Beasley, B., & Collins Standley, T. (2002). Shirts vs. skins: Clothing as an indicator of gender role stereotyping in video games. *Mass Communication & Society,* 5, 279–293.

Blamire, R. (2010). *Digital games for learning: Conclusions and recommendations from the IMAGINE project.* European Schoolnet.

Cherney, I. D., Bersted, K., & Smetter, J. (2014). Training Spatial Skills in Men and Women 1, 2. *Perceptual & Motor Skills,* 119(1), 82–99.

Childress, M. D., & Braswell, R. (2006). Using massively multiplayer online role-playing games for online learning. *Distance Education,* 27, 187–196.

Dickey, M. D. (2007). Game design and learning: A conjectural analysis of how massively multiple online role-playing games (MMPORGs) foster intrinsic motivation. *Education Technology Research,* 55, 253–273.

DiSalvo B. J. and A. Bruckman (2009). Questioning video games' influence on CS interest. *Proceedings of FDG '09. Proceedings of the 4th International Conference on Foundations of Digital Games.* ACM. ISBN: 978-1-60558-437-9.

Haninger, K., & Thompson, K. M. (2002). Content and ratings of teen-rated video games. *American Medical Association*, *291*, 856–865.

Ivory, J. D. (2006). Still a Man's Game: Gender representation in online reviews of video games. *Mass Communication & Society*, *9*, 103–114.

Johnson, L., Levine, A., Smith, R., & Stone, S. (2010). *The 2010 Horizon Report*. New Media Consortium. 6101 West Courtyard Drive Building One Suite 100, Austin, TX 78730.

Kenny, R., & Gunter, G. (2011). Factors affecting adoption of video games in the classroom. *Journal of Interactive Learning Research*, *22*(2), 259–276.

Kinzie, M. B., & Joseph, D. R. D. (2008). Gender differences in game activity preferences of middles school children: Implications for educational game design. *Education Technology Research Development*, *56*, 643–663.

McClarty, K. L., Orr, A. P., Frey, P. M., Dolan, B. P., Vassileva, V., & McVay, A. (2012). A literature review of gaming in education (Research Report). Iowa City, IA: Pearson. Available: http://www.pearsonassessments.com/hai/Images/tmrs/Lit_Review_of_Gaming_in_Education.pdf.

Niedermeyer, H. P., Arnold, W., Schwub, D., Busch, R., Wiest, I., & Sedlmeier, R. (2001). Shift of the distribution of age in patients with otosclerosis. *Acta oto-laryngologica*, *121*(2), 197–199.

Royle, K. (2008). Game-based learning: A different perspective. *Innovate: Journal of Online Education*, *4*, 1–8.

Sáinz, M., & Eccles, J. (2012). Self-concept of computer and math ability: Gender implications across time and within ICT studies. *Journal of Vocational Behavior*, *80*(2), 486–499.

Spence, I., & Feng, J. (2010). Video games and spatial cognition. *Review of General Psychology*, *14*(2), 92.

Tan, J. L., Goh, D. H. L., Ang, R. P., & Huan, V. S. (2013). Participatory evaluation of an educational game for social skills acquisition. *Computers & Education*, *64*, 70–80.

CHAPTER 7

■■■

A Reflection on Video Games in Society

Jesse Brasco, Ed.D.

INTRODUCTION

The video game industry is a very large sector of the American economy today, and it continues to grow. For instance, as of 2013, 58% of American households play computer or video games. The industry is valued at over $25 billion, and directly or indirectly employs more than 120,000 American citizens. Additionally, 52% of parents say video games are a positive part of their child's life. These statistics reflect the importance of video games in American society today, and show that they have more to offer the American population than just entertainment value. Games also help to encourage social development, as 65% of gamers played in person with other gamers in 2011. The educational and social aspects of games are not to be taken lightly. According to Michael D. Gallagher, president and CEO, Entertainment Software Association:

> "No other sector has experienced the same explosive growth as the computer and video game industry. Our creative publishers and talented workforce continue to accelerate advancement and pioneer new products that push boundaries and unlock entertainment experiences. These innovations in turn drive enhanced player connectivity, fuel demand for products, and encourage the progression of an expanding and diversified consumer base."

As video games continue to become a greater part of the American culture over time, it is important to understand the depth of the impact that video games have on the population. http://www.theesa.com/facts/pdfs/esa_ef_2013.pdf

CRITICAL THINKING AND ADAPTING

One of the most important aspects of learning is the ability to critically think and adapt. While the tagline "a minute to learn, a lifetime to master" belongs to the board game Othello, this trait is true of many video games as well. Video games that are not mastered in a short period of time require learning and adaptability from the players, as they will not improve at the games without developing and learning. For instance, consider the popular Multiplayer Online Battle Arena (MOBA) game, League of Legends (LoL). LoL consists of two five player teams, and the goal is to destroy the opposing team's base. There are three "lanes" to approach the opposing base, and each lane is protected by three towers, and waves of weak monsters called "minions" that spawn at fixed intervals. Each player in the game controls a single character, a "champion," that is substantially stronger than individual minions but weaker than the towers guarding the lanes. Different champions have different attributes and abilities for the players to utilize. Additionally, they earn experience and gold over time as they kill enemy minions and champions, which will allow them to purchase items and become strong enough to eventually pressure enemy towers. In between the three lanes, there are a variety of neutral monsters that can be slain by either team. These neutral monsters spawn at fixed times and respawn at fixed intervals, and serve as secondary objectives for each team. This brief amount of information is enough for an individual to begin playing League of Legends, but one will not master the game after only a few hours of game play. All players go through long periods of learning in LoL, and indeed, even seasoned veterans learn new facets about the game in order to improve.

A player in League of Legends will face dozens of decisions per minute, and it is impossible for a beginner player to make optimal decisions at this pace. For instance, when a champion has low health, it is often the correct decision to return to base to heal, purchase new items, and return to lane. However, a novice player may stay in lane too long, and get killed by an enemy champion. This gives the enemy gold and experience, as well as making the player miss more experience and gold than he would have by simply leaving lane and returning later. Decisions also happen on a smaller scale frequently throughout the game. If a player lands a killing blow on a minion, thus earning gold from that minion, but is weakened severely in the process, he may lose more gold in the long term if he is unable to continue to obtain future gold without dying to enemy champions. In this case, the seemingly "correct" decision to earn gold can prove incorrect if it denies greater gold gain in the future of the game. Finally, there are decisions made in LoL that happen on a much larger scale.

For example, players may work together to kill some of the important neutral monsters on the map, granting gold, experience, and sometimes other buffs as well. However, if the enemy team is able to destroy multiple towers in this time, the team that killed the neutral monster may actually fall further behind in gold and experience, relatively speaking, as well as losing the important map control that towers provide. Alternatively, if the enemy team suspects that players are working on killing a difficult neutral monster, the enemy team can attack after the team is weakened by the monster, and begin the team fight at a significant health advantage. Therefore, decision making in LoL can be very intricate, and only through learning over time and thinking critically and analytically can a player improve his decision making.

These examples from League of Legends also show the need for adaptability in decision making. The case constructions offered previously could all yield positive results in different circumstances, if the enemy team is unable to react properly. Decisions in LoL are not made in a vacuum—they depend on what has happened in the game up to that point. If a player's team has played poorly for the first fifteen minutes of a game, that team will have less gold and experience than the opposing team. In this case, the opposing team will be more likely to successfully punish aggressive decision making. Players need to adapt to what happens in the early portion of each game, as this greatly influences what happens later on in the game. They develop this adaptability through practice and trial and error, but the best players also learn outside of playing the game. Many professional players "stream" their matches, which allow the general player base to observe how professionals develop and react to various scenarios. Also, players can read about League of Legends to learn more about it. There are websites that offer guides for playing individual champions, statistics on how frequently certain champions win in tournament play or "ranked" games, detailed analysis about various facets of the game, and much more. Therefore, players in LoL are not simply learners: they are most certainly engaged learners. Players who engage and immerse themselves in learning games are more likely to apply this engagement to their studies as well.

ENGAGED LEARNING

James Paul Gee, author of the book *What Video Games Have to Teach Us About Learning and Literacy*, notes three benefits of a more active and engaged learning as "experiencing the world in new ways, forming new affiliations, and preparation for future learning." Gee goes further to say that critical learning includes these factors, as well as "think[ing] about the domain at a 'meta' level as a complex system of interrelated parts."(citation) All of these benefits are seen in the aforementioned example with League of Legends, and will translate over to learning outside of the game as well.

League is experienced in new ways as the player continues with the game over a period of time. Initially, many events in the game may be confusing, but the player learns and adapts as previous experiences help to forecast future actions and results. League forms new affiliations through the nature of the aforementioned "case constructions," which are scenarios and understandings developed as a player continues with the game. Finally, League of Legends prepares players for future learning, as techniques used to learn in LoL can be applied in other facets of the game, and outside of it as well. While each individual match is dynamic and has independent events, players build off of their knowledge from previous play in order to improve. Naturally, preparation for future learning is important to learning outside of video games as well, as the educational system seeks to prepare students for future learning and future application of their studies.

TRUE CONTENT

Video games can also offer learning in the form of true content, which means that players can learn actual information about the real world. While approaches to learning are valuable, so is true content. For instance, the popular real-time strategy game (RTS) Age of Empires II: Age of Kings contains a campaign mode which includes battles with historical figures, such as William Wallace, Joan of Arc, Saladin, Barbarossa, and Genghis Khan. Another example is Assassin's Creed II, which has a setting in Renaissance Italy for players to discover and explore while on their adventure. Assassin's Creed II offers a database for players to access during the game, to further learn about the historical context if they are interested in pursuing further knowledge. These are just two instances of games where true educational content is prominently featured.

In reality, many more games have some minor educational ideas or allusions strewn throughout the game. If these allusions are interesting, the players may seek to quickly learn a little more about them in their spare time. While this is not the most efficient way for a person to learn about a subject, people will retain more knowledge when they are genuinely interested in the topic. For example, there are several groups of large enemy monsters in the game Guild Wars: The Eye of the North known as Jotun. The name Jotun alludes to the Jotuun of Norse mythology, which were spirits with incredible strength, paralleling the power and size of the Guild Wars Jotun. While many gamers would normally show no interest in Norse mythology, they are more likely to show interest upon learning that Jotun is not just a gibberish word on behalf of the Guild Wars design team.

VIDEO GAMES AND STEM CURRICULA

The fields of science, technology, engineering, and mathematics (STEM) are very important in today's world. However, STEM learning is still not optimally integrated in U.S. classrooms, and video games can help close that gap.[1] Video games are helpful to this end because of the transferability of skills such as critical thinking, adapting, engaged learning, as previously discussed. In addition, most successful video games tend to force a player to utilize higher order thinking rather than simple memorization.[2] This is important because higher order thinking has applications to STEM courses. For instance, consider the study of mathematics. While some basic memorization (such as multiplication tables) is required, the purpose of studying math is not to ultimately memorize every theorem and problem ever posed. The purpose is to gain some real understanding of why certain facts hold true, and to learn how to use them to solve more complex problems. Achieving these goals requires higher order thinking from students, and this is a skill that can be developed and honed through video game play. Like mathematics, video games require some core memorization, but that is only the initial step to success.

PHYSICAL COORDINATION

Studies have shown that physical coordination is improved by video game play as well. For instance, Spence and Feng showed that, when compared with non-gamers, gamers have superior spatial cognition for both basic and more complex tasks, and that this learning "generalizes far beyond the training activities in the game," (http://individual.utoronto.ca/jingfeng1107/SpenceFeng_VideoGameReview_RGP.pdf). Similarly, action video games have been shown to improve eyesight, as compared with people who have not played action video games (http://www.ncbi.nlm.nih.gov/pmc/articles/PMC2819084/). These results are not surprising, as many different genres of video games require high levels of dexterity to succeed. One popular example is the RTS game Starcraft II: Wings of Liberty (SC2), which measures a player's actions per minute (APM) in each round of the game. Players with high APM are at a significant advantage in games like SC2, as these players are able to micromanage more actions in a finite game time, and this provides a competitive edge over opponents. However, APM is not a be-all, end-all measure of dexterity in video games. For example, Counter-Strike: Source is an example of a first-person shooter (FPS) game. This genre of gaming does not require the rapid inputs needed for multitasking like in most RTS games, and therefore, the dexterity needed is more defined by precision, aim, and reaction time. Finally, a new wave of video games has recently started to utilize motion technology. Nintendo's Wii, Microsoft's Xbox Kinect, and Sony's PlayStation Move all incorporate motion technology into their respective video game experiences. Games played with these motion technologies certainly require and improve physical coordination, as gamers are using their entire bodies for video game inputs rather than just using their fingers. Therefore, while players need different skill sets for different genres of video games, their coordination can be improved through practice and improvement at any genre.

SOCIAL ASPECT OF GAMING

The social aspect of video games is sometimes controversial, but it can be at least as important for the industry in the long run as learning from video games. While gamers may stereotypically be considered to be playing in isolation from others, 76% of gaming teens were found to be playing games with other people at least some of the time. (http://www.pewinternet.org/Press-Releases/2008/Major-new-study-shatters-stereotypes-about-teens-and-video-games.aspx) This shows that gamers are not only learning and abiding by the rules of the games they play, but they are also working together to achieve goals and play efficiently while coordinating actions with other players. When interactions with other players are a regular part of the video gaming experience, gamers are evaluated by other players as well as the game itself.

To understand this, first consider a game that is exclusively a single-player experience, such as RollerCoaster Tycoon. In this game, players design theme parks, highlighted by the potential to design custom roller coasters. Players can play parks with different opening scenarios and end goals, and the players are ultimately evaluated on park attendance, park profitability, and park rating. Park rating combines factors such as customer satisfaction, park safety, cleanliness, etc. All of these measures are completely objective as evaluated by the game's algorithms, so it is up to the player to make decisions to try to balance these factors and build the best theme park.

According to David Edery and Ethan Mollick, authors of *Changing the Game—How Video Games Are Transforming the Future of Business*, "cooperation is not a 'necessary evil' in the context of a game—it is the best part of the experience." Indeed the experience of single player games such as RollerCoaster Tycoon greatly contrasts with that of multiplayer games where players need to work together to achieve goals. While these games will usually offer some objective measures of success and failure, consideration from teammates is oftentimes more important. For instance, suppose that three gamers are sitting in the same room playing RollerCoaster Tycoon. At the end of a campaign, the game may tell the players that they had 100 visitors fewer than their expectations, and that the park rating was 40 points below the goal. However, this is not the kind of constructive feedback necessary to improve. Perhaps one player noticed that they did not hire enough security guards, and the vandalism in the park scared away potential guests. Another player may think that they invested too much money in small rides such as the merry-go-round and go-karts, while not investing enough money in big-ticket roller coasters. Therefore, evaluation from other players can be critical to learning and improvement in games, as it offers explanations and insight that games themselves usually cannot offer. This strongly parallels education, where there is a continued emphasis on group projects and assignments, brainstorming, etc. Just as students need to work together to best succeed on these projects and ultimately in their classes, so too do gamers benefit from teamwork in both the short-term and long-term.

While gaming encourages positive social behavior, sometimes there is negative behavior from various players. These negative behaviors can lead to similar behaviors in the real world. One example of negative behavior that some gamers display is "ragequitting." Ragequitting is best defined as a player leaving a game due to anger over his performance or the performance of others. This ruins the game for the other players, as one team is frustrated as they play with one fewer player, and the other team takes less excitement from their victory knowing it was not truly earned in a fair contest. Ultimately, players are able to ragequit in many online games because of the lack of consequences, and protection behind their Internet anonymity. Most games take measures to punish ragequitters, and one notable example is the "Leaverbuster" system implemented by Riot Games, creators of League of Legends.

Riot's Leaverbuster detects people who quit in the middle of the matches. It is an automated system, and is not concerned with the nature of the leave (ragequit, thunderstorm knocking out power, laptop battery dying, etc.). While this may seem unfair, as some players may leave for reasons beyond their control, the system punishes based on the frequency of leaving games relative to total games played (http://na.leagueoflegends.com/board/showthread .php?t=468889). Players who leave games due to extenuating circumstances do so scarcely, and will not be punished. By contrast, people who have a tendency to quit due to poor control of their emotions will leave games often and will ultimately be banned for their behavior. Therefore, based on this principle that leavers with genuine reasons leave games rarely, while ragequitters will leave games often, Riot was able to implement an automated system to successfully punish ragequitters and weaken the toxic component of the League of Legends player base.

However, the negative social component of gaming is not limited to repeated leaving of games and ragequitting. Many players will stay for the duration of a game, but commit offenses such as verbal abuse of others players and playing in a way that will intentionally hurt his chances of winning. While in the most extreme cases these behaviors are quite obvious to the human eye, it is very difficult for an automated system to properly recognize and punish them. Riot Games offers an innovative approach to dealing with player behavior in game, by outsourcing much of this work to their player base through a system called "The Tribunal." The system starts with players in game who "report" what they believe to be offending players. If a player receives enough reports over time, his case goes to the Tribunal. Here, ordinary LoL players can read the chat logs of each game the offending player was reported in, and ultimately vote to pardon or punish the players based on these chat logs. Players who vote in the majority receive a small reward of "influence points" (IP), which can be used in LoL to buy new champions or "runes," which make characters stronger in game. IP is also earned in greater quantity by playing the game over time.

Riot has released statistics reflecting the success of Tribunal. As of December 21st, 2011, 1.4% of the player base has been punished by the Tribunal, and 50% of those never reoffend (http:// na.leagueoflegends.com/news/tribunal-records-16-million-votes). These statistics show that the negative part of the LoL community are a small part of the player base, and furthermore, that they are capable of improving their behavior. The latter point is vitally important—it shows that people with bad behavior are often not inherently bad people, and when presented with the proper consequences and threat of future consequences, they can improve and behave like better citizens of a community. The real world application here is evident: from poor students to criminals, it is not always correct to take the easy route and simply give up on people.

CONCLUSION

Video games offer far more to their players than hours of entertainment, and it is important for educators to understand this. Many skills are learned through video game play, such as critical thinking, engaged learning, and positive social behavior. These skills could prove vital to students succeeding in their education, if they apply them to schoolwork with the same passion that many apply them to video games. It is important to distinguish between "educational" games and "regular" video games as well, because these types of games have different offerings for students. The offering from educational games is clear—lots of true content, offered to the student in what game designers hope is an appealing manner in terms of graphics and player interaction. Two examples of educational games are Where in the World Is Carmen Sandiego? and Number Munchers. In Carmen Sandiego, the player travels the world, using information and clues from different geographical regions to hunt down an international criminal and her henchmen. In Number Munchers, the player controls a character that must navigate a grid and "eat" numbers that fit certain criteria (i.e. primes, multiples of 4, etc.) while avoiding numbers that do not fit the criteria, and also avoiding enemies that appear periodically. These games are very simple from a game design perspective, and would be clearly categorized differently due to their strictly educational nature. The value of these games to educators is clear, as they offer true content to students in a manner that generates interest and activity.

By contrast, the value added from regular video games to education is harder to determine because of motivation. Even if gamers learn applicable skills, they are more motivated to use them in games than they are to apply them to education. The motivation in video games is intrinsic: players want to succeed at the game, enjoy themselves in the process, and are therefore willing to apply themselves. If they do not enjoy a game, then they simply put it down and find other uses for their free time. By contrast, education is mandatory through high school, so students will be forced to "go through the motions" even if they are not enjoying aspects of their education. This lack of motivation can be a problem, and educators need to find ways to encourage students to apply themselves and transfer these skills.

Notes

1. Robert Ormsby, Robin Daniel & Marka Ormsby (2011): Preparing for the Future with Games for Learning: Using Video Games and Simulations to Engage Students in Science, Technology, Engineering, and Math, *Astropolitics: The International Journal of Space Politics & Policy*, 9:2–3, 150–164

2. Paraskeva, Fotini, Sofia Mysirlaki, et al. "Multiplayer online games as educational tools: Facing new challenges in learning." *Computers & Education*. 54. (2010): 498–505. Web. 18 Jul. 2012.

CHAPTER 8

■■■

A Reflection on Video Games Economy

Edwin Tjoe, Ed.D.

Massively multiplayer online games (MMOs) are a popular genre of gaming, with World of Warcraft (WoW) being the most famous example. There are others of course like Second Life, Eve, Counter Strike Global Offensive, DOTA, and Hearthstone. Gamers in this genre tend to be highly involved in these games, and therefore are likely to learn greatly from their experiences here.

These days, virtual goods are sold for real money. Digital game players eagerly pay for avatars, power-ups, skins, weapons, armor, ammo, and other game items. But behind every virtual sale, there is a virtual economy, simple or complex. MMOs tend to have an in-game currency, with a fluctuating value based on circumstances within the game. While it may not truly be an MMO, the economy of Guild Wars serves as a great example of a dynamic in-game economy, with currency and valuable commodities that function as currency at higher levels of play. This example is representative of how much a player can inadvertently learn about economics from devoting time and effort to certain types of video games.

In Guild Wars, gold ("g") is the most basic form of currency. 1000g is referred to as platinum ("plat" or "k," abbreviating one thousand). Players can carry up to 100k on an individual character, and can store up to 1000k in a vault box that is shared across characters on a player's account. This drives the need in Guild Wars for commodities to serve as currency. Players can only offer 100k at a time in cash in a trade, so if the desired items exceed that in value, players need additional "currency" to balance out the value of the trade. Also, if players trade frequently and already have the maximum gold amount in their storage and on their characters, then they can no longer receive currency when selling or trading items. There are two primary commodities that Guild Wars players use for this purpose. The first is the item Globs of Ectoplasm (more commonly "ectos" or "e"). Ectos drop very rarely from difficult monsters, and are required to build popular high end armor. This limits the supply and drives the demand, and these factors allow for ectos to function as a secondary currency to complement gold. Similarly, Zaishen Keys (zkeys) are earned through player vs. player (PvP) combat rewards, and are used to unlock a chest with random items, as well as earning points for a player in a title track. The fact that zkeys are exclusively a PvP reward bottlenecks the supply, while the title track and potential rare item drops drive the demand.

Ectos tend to fluctuate greatly in value, while zkeys are more stable in their price. These prices are driven by economic principles; in particular, changes to the supply side of commodities affects the stability of the prices. Ectos sometimes are worth as little as 4k, while at other times they have been worth as much as 12k. Most ectos are accumulated by players "farming" in the player versus environment (PvE) aspect of Guild Wars. Farming is repeating the same select task or tasks in order to gain rewards over a period of time. Guild Wars is frequently patched, meaning that the game designers will update the effects of skills in an attempt to better balance the game. Therefore, if a skill combination is discovered that makes farming easier, many players will utilize this combination to farm ectos. This increases the supply of ectos, and simultaneously drives down their value. On the other hand, if Guild Wars designers see this and "nerf" (weaken) the strong combination, then it once again becomes harder to farm ectos, decreasing the supply, and increasing their value again. By contrast, the value of zkeys is rather stable at 5k, with little fluctuation. Zkeys are earned as rewards over time for PvP players, with those who win more often earning rewards at a greater rate than those who lose more often. PvP rewards are less susceptible to impact from balance changes, because, holding the number of PvP players to be constant, there will still be the same number of winners and losers, and therefore the same rewards will be earned for the same amount of time played. Theoretically, the value of zkeys would decrease if many more people started playing PvP in Guild Wars, or it could increase if people were discouraged from playing PvP. However, such supply side shocks have not happened, and the price of zkeys has held stable much more than the price of ectos. Therefore, while Guild Wars is an expansive game with much more to it than the commodities dominating its marketplace, gamers who play Guild Wars for a long period of time inevitably familiarize themselves with important economic concepts in order to succeed, and those who learn quickest find success in this regard.

REAL WORLD CURRENCY IN GAMES

In addition to economies within games using fictional currency and commodities, there is also real world money flowing to and from players, outside of that needed to purchase the game and pay subscription fees. For instance, World of Warcraft players buy and sell in-game items via websites such as eBay, and even sometimes buy and sell entire accounts. Some accounts have sold for nearly $11,000, despite it being a violation of the Terms of Service (ToS) and End User License Agreement (EULA) to participate in such activities (http://www.dickhoutman.nl/mediatheek/files/harambam_aupers_houtman_2011.pdf). While this is an extreme example, it demonstrates that there is in fact a real market for WoW characters and gear. World of Warcraft is made by the company Blizzard Entertainment, the same company that later made Diablo 3 (D3). Blizzard was well aware of the money being exchanged for WoW, and took steps in D3 to make it easier for players to participate in this marketplace, both through in-game currency and real world currency.

Diablo 3 has an "auction house" (AH) where players can bid on, buy, and sell items using gold, the in-game currency. All transactions in the AH have a 15% transaction fee that leaves the in-game economy. For example, suppose that a player sells an item on the AH for 10,000 gold. The buyer pays 10,000 gold, the AH takes its cut of 1,500 gold, and the seller receives 8,500 gold for the item. This transaction fee serves to limit inflation, by decreasing the money supply in Diablo 3. However, it does not lead to deflation, because of the amount of farming done by players, which increases the money supply at a far greater rate than gold being lost through transaction fees.

Similarly, D3 has a real money auction house (RMAH) that functions similarly to the auction house, but with the use of real world money instead of in-game gold for transactions. For the RMAH, Blizzard charges a $1 transaction fee for each successful sale or auction. Additionally, the maximum price that any individual item can sell for is $250. The impact of the RMAH on the economy in Diablo 3 is harder to evaluate using economic principles, because the effect of the RMAH on gold is simply not comparable to real world economies. In the real world, money is earned in exchange for selling products or providing services over a period of time. In Diablo 3, the gold system is not unlike this example. Players earn gold by playing over time, and selling spare items in addition to the gold dropped by monsters. In order to buy items via the AH, a player must have put in enough time and effort to have a sufficient amount of money to buy high-quality gear. By contrast, using the RMAH supersedes the need to put time into the game to end up with desired items. There is no real world shortcut comparable to the RMAH, and there are several ways that the RMAH can impact D3's gold economy.

The first way would be the destruction of the gold economy, due to frequent use of the RMAH for any item needs. In this instance, real money replaces in-game gold for any player-to-player transaction in Diablo 3. This represents a sharp decrease in the demand for gold, because much of its value is obtained from its use in player-to-player transactions. However, this scenario is not how the RMAH has played out. The second way that the RMAH could affect gold would be having virtually no effect at all. Paul Tassi of Forbes.com notes that "it's usually professional types, with lots of money but no time to play, who spend [up to $250 per item] for gear" (http://www.forbes.com/sites/insertcoin/2012/06/13/why-diablo-3s-real-money-auction-house-should-not-be-your-summer-job-2/). This reflects that usage of the RMAH is infrequent relative to the large player base of Diablo 3, and that many players would prefer to spend D3's in-game gold to buy items in the AH. Therefore, the use of the RMAH has not had such a strong, negative impact on the demand for gold that would decrease gold's value significantly. By contrast, while it has seen and will continue to see use, the vast majority of the player base does not use the RMAH and gold still serves its purpose in the Diablo 3 economy.

IN THE END, WHAT IS IT ALL FOR?

Virtual economies have several obvious conclusions drawn out by their manufacturer. Bitcoins and other cryptocurrencies are the by-product of technology. The theoretical emphasis is based on behavioral economics, macroeconomics, and sociology of consumption. While there are not as many regulators in the digital space or cyber ether as there are in the U.S. financial market, it still hurts when someone tries to short-circuit the system. Should each player suddenly receive his massive in-game currency? No, the game would be ruined. If everyone has high performance, no one has high performance.

The unseen conclusion is in regards to respect or lack thereof. A growing percentage of users are buying items for a type of e-respect or elitist class they have in a virtual world. The virtual world is backwards when it comes to society in the real world. There are few penalties or efforts to stop bullying. The consistent factor in video game society is the rollercoaster of bullies with virtual personas. For example, there is this one fictional character named Smokeyburr, which used to convince people to do odd things online in exchange for virtual goods and real life currency. To the demographic of young users, the in-game economies show them that a better life can be purchased if you don't work for it.

CHAPTER 9

■■■

The Postmodality Era: How "Online Learning" Is Becoming "Learning"

Thomas B. Cavanagh

Jennifer is a 20-year-old sophomore at a large state university. She lives in a dorm, works as a resident assistant, belongs to a sorority, works part time at a local hotel, and dances ballet. By all external measures, she is the typical "traditional" college student. Yet, within the past year, she has not only taken "traditional" face-to-face courses, but has also taken courses in what many might consider "nontraditional" modalities: both fully online and blended formats (blended learning mixes both online and face-to-face elements). And she is not alone.[1]

Jennifer is representative of a trend in higher education, where the growing ubiquity of online learning is eliminating the lines between what was once considered traditional and nontraditional. Nontraditional students—typically adult learners and other working adults—have always required flexibility. Before online learning, nontraditional students took night classes, weekend seminars, and correspondence courses. They had no choice. Their family and work commitments prevented them from participating in traditional weekday courses during daylight hours. The advent of online learning has provided these students with another option for accessing higher education.

Now we find ourselves in an era where even the traditional 18- to 24-year-old college student increasingly requires nontraditional flexibility. Ironically, many of these students leverage the convenience of online courses to more deeply engage in the on-campus experience. Like Jennifer, they may be involved in sororities or fraternities, play intramural or intercollegiate athletics, are involved in clubs or other affinity groups, or even work part time. Where it is offered widely at an institution, online learning affords these traditional students much greater scheduling flexibility and enables much deeper on-campus participation.

INTRODUCTION

According to the National Center for Education Statistics, between 2000 and 2008, the percentage of undergraduate students taking at least one online class grew from 8 to 20 percent.[2] The Sloan Consortium states that approximately 5.6 million students enrolled in at least one online course during fall 2009, and nearly thirty percent of all higher education students now take at least one course online.[3] Clearly, the percentage of students taking one or more courses online is trending upwards, reflecting an increased reliance on the flexibility they afford.

Juxtapose these online learning growth trends with the following statistics: of the 17.6 million undergraduates currently enrolled in American higher education, only 15 percent attend four-year institutions *and* live on campus. Thirty-seven percent are enrolled part time and 32 percent work full time. Only 36 percent of students who are enrolled in four-year institutions actually graduate in four years.[4]

What these statistics indicate is a blurring boundary between the traditional and nontraditional. Even classically traditional students at classically traditional institutions, such as Jennifer, increasingly require nontraditional flexibility to meet their educational goals. Online learning has become the catalyst for this change and it is forever altering the landscape of higher education. Classifying a student as "main campus" or "extended campus" or "distance" becomes meaningless in an environment where students take whatever courses they need in whatever location or modality best suits their requirements at the time. These students are unconcerned with categorical labels—they are concerned with getting the courses they need in the formats that fit their lifestyles, whether they are a working adult or an undergraduate who travels frequently as part of the volleyball team. The Sloan Foundation has dubbed this concept "localness," meaning that student access to education is always local to them, even if they do so through online learning. Students may take courses at an institution's main campus, regional or extended campus, completely online, or in a blended format. Institutions can support "localness" by constructing programs that are flexible and that deliver courses in multiple modalities.

Most traditional, non-profit institutions with large commuter, non-residential and part-time student populations are well-known and trusted within their localities. When online learning burst into the academic consciousness in the mid-90s there was a rush by many of these institutions to downplay their locality, and to emphasize their role in meeting the needs of all kinds of geography-independent and global student populations. However, many of these same institutions eventually came to realize that many of their local and in some cases *even their residential student populations were as interested in enrolling in online learning courses as were students living afar.* The institutions are known in their local regions; that's not the issue. What is not always known is that they are offering a "quality" online or blended product.[5] [emphasis added]

Some research indicates that even in end-of-course evaluations, students do not consider modality an important factor in their course-taking experiences. According to Dziuban and Moskal,[6] "When students respond to the end-of-course evaluation instruments for online, blended, and face-to-face courses . . . they do not differentiate the instructional idiosyncrasies found in the three modalities."[7] Students are able to translate specific end-of-course evaluation questions to apply to any of the three modalities without any problem. The modality is not a factor. Further, the same study indicates that course mode is not an effective predictor of success or withdrawal within a course. "Historically, students who have done well in courses do well in any mode; a course is a course."[8] To these students, *a course is a course;* modality makes no difference.

The postmodality blurring of boundaries between traditional and nontraditional is being hastened by the intersecting dynamics of these student preferences for flexibility and convenience with the desire for efficiency by system and state policy leaders. The University System of Maryland now requires undergraduates to complete twelve credits in alternative-learning modes, which include online learning. Texas has proposed a similar rule with a 10 percent threshold. The Minnesota State Colleges and Universities system is advocating that 25 percent of all student credits be earned online by 2015.[9] When top-down systemic mandates such as these align with the bottom-up preferences of students to have maximum flexibility in their course-selection practices, a powerful force for change across all of higher education is created. Online learning has catalyzed these forces into a movement that university administrators and faculty members are trying to address in a variety of ways, depending upon the institutional mission and available resources. This chapter will highlight several examples, from several different types of schools.

UNIVERSITY OF CENTRAL FLORIDA

If there is a "ground zero" for this postmodality phenomenon, it may be the University of Central Florida in Orlando. When UCF began its online learning enterprise in the mid-1990s, it quickly discovered that 75 percent of online students were already on campus or lived nearby. That gave rise to the university's blended learning initiative, which mixes both face-to-face and online elements. UCF has grown rapidly, with enrollment expanding from 21,000 in 1991 to 58,600 in fall 2011, and it now ranks as the nation's second-largest university. Constructing physical classrooms quickly enough to keep pace with this growth has been a challenge, exacerbated in recent years by reduced state funding. By some estimates, the university is 40 percent short of classroom space. Offering online learning has become a key strategy for fulfilling UCF's institutional mission of educational access. As more and more students choose to attend UCF, the institution has expanded the ways that they can access courses and services.

Students at UCF, such as Jennifer, make little distinction between face-to-face, online, and blended courses when registering for a particular semester. As illustrated in Table 9.1, UCF students mix and match modalities in a variety of ways. Of particular note is that during fall 2010, almost 2,700 students took face-to-face, online, and blended courses *at the same time*. This is the definition of student behavior in a postmodality era. These students are not "online" or "distance" or "main campus"—they are simply students. In fact, UCF's online learning unit is intentionally called the Center for *Distributed* learning, eschewing the more commonplace "distance" for "distributed" in recognition of its students' "localness" and course-taking preferences.

TABLE 9.1. UCF Student Head Count by Modality Combinations (Fall 2010)

Total UCF Students	56,129
Students in Face-to-Face (F2F)	49,510
Web OR Blended	23,741
F2F + Web	12,157
F2F + Blended	8,827
F2F + Web OR Blended	18,288
F2F + Web + Blended	2,696
Online Exclusive (excluding video-lecture capture)	4,109 Summer 2011: 6,972 (Online exclusive students always increase during the summer semesters.)

UCF's students don't even draw much distinction between "main campus" face-to-face classes and "regional campus" face-to-face classes. The university maintains a network of ten regional campuses located throughout central Florida, from Ocala to Daytona Beach to Palm Bay. Students will not only register for courses in various modalities but will also register for courses at various locations, depending upon what they need and the times at which they need it (Figure 9.1).

As indicated in Figure 9.1, during fall 2010, 478 students took courses on the main campus, at one or more of the regional campuses, and online. Additionally, 764 students took courses on the main campus, at the Rosen campus (which is a separate residential campus located near Orlando's attractions area and is not part of the regional campus system), and online. These students are unconcerned with labels of "main," "regional," or "distance." They are highly mobile, often changing their location/modality mix from term to term. In tracking these numbers over several years, researchers discovered one undeniably clear trend: growth in online learning continues to far outpace all other university

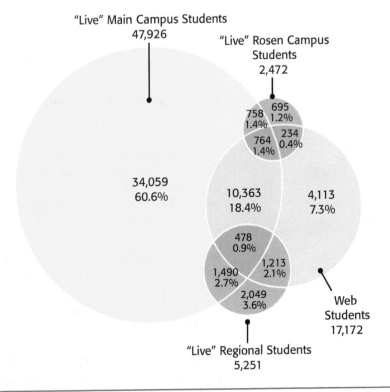

FIGURE 9.1. UCF Head Count by "Location" (Fall 2010)

Note: Students in "blended" courses are not included in the "web students" category.

growth. During the 2010–2011 academic year, overall online-student credit-hour production increased 32.2 percent, while classroom-based student credit-hour production increased 4.1 percent. Online learning now represents 30.2 percent of UCF's total student credit-hour production. While UCF offers nearly sixty exclusively online programs, the vast majority of these online credits are produced by students in traditional (not online) programs. Of the top-ten programs (graduate and undergraduate) for students taking online courses,

- only three completely online undergraduate programs are represented and none are in the top three, and
- only five completely online graduate degrees are represented and only one is in the top three.

What this indicates is that students from all majors, both graduate and undergraduate, traditional and online, all across the university, are integrating online courses into their studies, leveraging the flexibility offered by technology to meet both their educational goals and lifestyle needs, whether they are a traditional student in a dorm on campus or an adult learner with a mortgage forty minutes away by interstate highway.

EMBRY-RIDDLE AERONAUTICAL UNIVERSITY

A very different sort of institution from UCF is Embry-Riddle Aeronautical University (ERAU). Yet ERAU finds itself with a student population just as illustrative of a postmodality mind-set. Founded only twenty-two years after the Wright brothers' first flight, ERAU is a private, nonprofit university best known for its emphasis on education and research related to aviation and aerospace. The university is comprised of three distinct campuses: a residential campus in Daytona Beach, Florida, with approximately 5,100 students; a residential campus in Prescott, Arizona, with approximately 1,700 students; and Embry-Riddle Worldwide, global teaching centers and online offerings with approximately 27,260 students. The university's total unduplicated head count is 34,532 (fall 2009–summer 2010).

Where ERAU finds its students most exhibiting postmodality course-taking behavior is within its Worldwide campus. Headquartered in Daytona Beach, Florida, ERAU's Worldwide campus consists of both its online operation (Worldwide Online) and approximately 150 teaching locations throughout the United States, Canada, Europe, and the Middle East (many of which are affiliated with U.S. military bases). Distance learning at ERAU began in the 1970s with correspondence courses designed to support the highly mobile military student. That distance-learning operation has since evolved into a significant online initiative, with thirty-seven different completely online programs, from undergraduate certificates of completion to associate's, bachelor's, and master's degrees. The university also recently launched an online/low-residency Ph.D. in Aviation.

On its website, Embry-Riddle Worldwide specifically advertises that it offers "five ways to learn." These five modalities are as follows:

- Classroom Learning, which is traditional face-to-face instruction in a synchronous, physical location
- EagleVision Classroom, which is a synchronous web-video conferencing platform that connects multiple physical classrooms into a single live, real-time classroom
- EagleVision Home, which is a synchronous web-video conferencing platform that connects individual users for live online learning
- Online Learning, which is completely online, asynchronous instruction facilitated through a learning management system
- Blended Program, which combines elements of Classroom and Online Learning

Here is how the university describes its approach to serving its postmodality student:

> At Embry-Riddle Aeronautical University–Worldwide, our goal is to give you exactly the education you need, exactly the way you need it. That's why, in addition to offering the industry's most sought after degrees and programs, we offer you more ways to take courses and complete those programs. Each of our learning modalities, while distinct in its delivery and operation, provides the same high-quality information, instruction, and opportunities for interaction with faculty and fellow students. Simply pick the one that fits your learning and lifestyle best, and embark on the road to educational success.[10]

This is "localness" writ on a large, global scale. ERAU's students are especially mobile, literally traveling the world as pilots, military service personnel, and other aviation-related professionals.

While the Worldwide campus students might primarily be considered "nontraditional," their course-taking behavior mimics that of the more traditional students at UCF. As described in Table 9.2,

TABLE 9.2. ERAU Worldwide Campus Course Registrations by Delivery Modality

	2009–10	2010–11	% Growth
Blended Program	1,140	1,763	54.65
Classroom Learning	42,747	38,577	–9.76
EagleVision Classroom	4,219	5,625	33.33
EagleVision Home	3,080	5,870	90.58
EagleVision/Blended Program	917	1,389	51.47
Online Learning	37,606	39,478	4.98
Total	**89,709**	**92,702**	**3.34**

ERAU's Worldwide campus students are not only creating their own mix of modalities, but they are doing so at a growing rate. The registrations listed in Table 9.2 represent duplicated head count, meaning that a single student taking more than one course is likely represented in more than one category. Of particular note in Table 9.2 is the year-to-year growth in the Blended Program and the EagleVision modalities, contrasted with the decline in Classroom Learning registrations.

This growth (and decline) indicates a shift away from the "traditional" forms of instruction to technology-enabled modalities, enabling the kind of flexibility ERAU's mobile students need. As the university continues to expand both overseas and domestically, this type of postmodality flexibility has become a key strategy for achieving institutional goals.

UNIVERSITY OF WISCONSIN–MILWAUKEE

The University of Wisconsin–Milwaukee (UWM) is similar to UCF in that it is a relatively large state university. With almost 31,000 students, UWM sits in an urban location, which complicates its ability to grow physically. Online and blended learning have proved to be key strategies for the university to serve its students. UWM Online was the recipient of an Alfred P. Sloan foundation Localness Blended Learning grant (as was UCF) and has leveraged that funding to expand its blended-learning initiative.

When examining UWM student course selections, we again see evidence of postmodality behaviors (Table 9.3). Of UWM's 7,017 students taking at least one fully online course (fall 2011), 5,654 of them are also taking face-to-face courses. Of the 1,783 students who are taking at least one blended course, 1,725 of

TABLE 9.3.   University of Wisconsin–Milwaukee Student Head Count by Modality

	Fall 2010	Fall 2011
Number of students taking at least one fully online course	6,181	7,017
Number of students taking exclusively fully online courses	1,299	1,363
Number of students taking at least one blended course	1,918	1,783
Number of students taking exclusively blended courses	74	58
Number of students (unduplicated) taking a blended OR online course	7,707	8,329
Number of students taking a combination of face-to-face AND fully online courses	4,881	5,654
Number of students taking a combination of face-to-face AND blended courses	1,844	1,725

them are also taking traditional face-to-face courses. When comparing these numbers to previous terms, as at UCF and ERAU, we see the amount of course-taking variety continuing to grow.

UWM Online's website describes its localness philosophy thusly:

> UWM offers the opportunity for you to take both online and on-campus courses and programs. It's your option. Some students like entirely online while others choose the combination of both online and in-person courses. Either will provide a quality, student-centered experience. For most students looking to save time and for students who prefer a more flexible learning and study environment, online classes and programs are often a preferred option.[11]

Similar to UCF and ERAU, UWM has structured its online support infrastructure in a manner conducive to student choice. The university has positioned itself to meet the needs of students who are increasingly unconcerned with the labels of modality and location.

RIO SALADO COLLEGE

Part of Arizona's Maricopa Community College system, Rio Salado College was founded specifically to be innovative and to meet the needs of the nontraditional student. Founded in 1978 as a "college without walls," the institution has grown into a well-known practitioner of online learning, leveraging technology to serve students both local and distant.

When examining the course-taking behavior of Rio Salado students (Table 9.4), it is interesting to observe that a college now

TABLE 9.4. Unduplicated Head Count of Rio Salado Students Enrolled by Modality (Academic Year 2011)

Modality	Credit Students	Noncredit Students	Total
Blended (Hybrid)	51	2	53
In Person	14,463	286	14,749
Independent Study	122	0	122
Internet	40,481	436	40,917
Mixed Media	176	0	176
Print-Based	1,002	13	1,015
Multiple Modalities	2,002	29	2,031
Total	**58,297**	**766**	**59,063**

known primarily as an online institution sees 25 percent of its students taking courses in traditional classrooms in one of the college's fifteen locations in and around Phoenix and Tempe. It is also noteworthy that more than 2,000 Rio Salado students are concurrently taking courses in multiple modalities, a figure not too different from UCF's 2,700 students (each institution's total student head count is comparable).

What these figures indicate in the context of a postmodality discussion is that where UCF's traditional students are leveraging technology to achieve nontraditional flexibility, Rio Salado's non-traditional students are doing the same to choose more traditional course options for supplementing their online coursework. Post-modality behavior works both ways—originating from either the traditional or nontraditional student populations. This phenomenon is consistent with the institution's stated mission:[12]

Rio Salado College transforms the learning experience through
- choice, access, and flexibility;
- customized, high-quality learning design; and
- personalized service and organizational responsiveness.

"Choice, access, and flexibility" are at the core of localness and are the driving forces behind postmodality behavior.

K–12 PERSPECTIVE

If the alignment of student preferences and state-level initiatives (enabled by technology) has created a higher education ecosystem supportive of postmodality course-taking behavior, then the future growth of that environment may actually lie outside of higher education. Postmodality course-taking behaviors are occurring at a rapidly growing pace in K–12 schools all across the country. Among the statistics compiled by the international association for K–12 online learning,[13] the following are particularly relevant to this discussion:

- Supplemental or full-time online-learning opportunities are available statewide to at least some K–12 students in forty-eight of the fifty states, plus Washington, DC.
- Twenty-seven states, as well as Washington, DC, have state-wide full-time online schools.
- 75 percent of school districts had one or more students enrolled in an online- or blended-learning course.
- 72 percent of school districts with distance-education programs planned to expand online offerings in the coming year.
- 82 percent of high school administrators interviewed in the United States had at least one student enrolled in a fully online course and 38 percent had at least one student enrolled in a blended or hybrid course.
- iNACOL estimates a total of 1,500,000 K–12 students were enrolled in online-learning courses in 2009.
- In 2010, over 4 million K–12 students participated in a formal online-learning program. This includes 217,000 students in cyber charter schools. Online-learning enrollments are growing by 46 percent a year, and the growth rate is accelerating.

In addition to the local preferences and desires of students and schools/districts to have online course offerings, statewide, systemic forces are also acting upon the K–12 ecosystem. States such as Michigan, Alabama, and Florida now require all high school students to take at least one online course in order to graduate. Idaho recently approved a plan to become the first state to require two credits to be completed online for high school graduation. These states are actually mandating postmodality course-taking behaviors, compelling secondary students to take online courses in addition to their traditional, face-to-face high school classes. Based upon the growth of K–12 online learning (46 percent a year, as cited above) in an environment where these state requirements did not yet exist, it can only be assumed that the growth of online learning in this sector will now grow even more quickly.

Florida has not only established a requirement for high school students to complete at least one online course to graduate, it has also mandated that each of its sixty-seven K–12 school districts provide virtual-learning options to its students. Further, it is now possible for a student in Florida to complete his or her entire kindergarten-through-high-school experience completely online at state expense as a fully funded public school option. In practice, however, students are mixing and matching various modalities. "Most students who participate in virtual education do so to supplement their work in traditional schools. Last year, more than 115,000 students across the state took at least one course with the Florida Virtual School."[14]

As these students arrive on our postsecondary campuses, they will already be accustomed from their high school experiences to taking a concurrent mixture of face-to-face, online, and blended courses. They will expect (perhaps even demand) that same flexibility and choice from their colleges and universities.

CONCLUSION

During a panel of presidents at the 2011 EDUCAUSE Annual Meeting, James J. Linksz, president of Bucks County Community College in Pennsylvania, described how his institution's students move back and forth between face-to-face and online modalities. He estimated that approximately 20 percent of his college's student credit hours are generated online and that about double that number of students have taken one or more online courses. This type of behavior has become commonplace at both community colleges and universities, at institutions serving both traditional and nontraditional students alike.

Demand for online and blended courses continues to grow at a rapid pace. Faculty and administrators who have not already done so need to recognize postmodality student preferences and behaviors on their own campuses and respond accordingly with a supportive infrastructure. Institutions will need to expand campus information systems to make it easier for students to select and register for online and blended offerings. Academic support services, including advising and library assistance, will need to be reconfigured to address online, asynchronous learners. On-campus classrooms will potentially need more multimedia and network capability to help bridge the online and on-ground environments for students moving seamlessly between the two. Campus technology infrastructure may need to be expanded to accommodate greater numbers of students conducting online coursework from on-campus facilities and using on-campus bandwidth. Finally, faculty and course-development services will need to be expanded to prepare and support faculty who will also be moving back and forth between modalities just as their students do. It is not uncommon for a single faculty member at UCF to concurrently teach face-to-face, online, and blended courses, mirroring the course-taking behaviors of his or her students.

For students like Jennifer, and her younger peers currently in middle and high school, online learning is no longer a novelty. It is simply a regular part of their education. They are increasingly unconcerned with the distinctions between face-to-face and online learning, instead choosing individual courses that meet their particular needs at any given time, regardless of modality. This postmodality behavior, enabled by instructional technology, has become their normal routine. Going forward, meeting the needs of these students with institutional ecosystems that support, encourage, and enable them to succeed will become key components of college and university strategic plans.

Notes

1. M. Parry, "Tomorrow's College," *The Chronicle of Higher Education* (October 31, 2010), retrieved from http://chronicle.com/article/Tomorrows-College/125120/.

2. A. W. Radford, "Learning at a Distance: Undergraduate Enrollment in Distance Education Courses and Degree Programs," U.S. Department of Education National Center for Education Statistics (2011), retrieved from http://nces.ed.gov/pubs2012/2012154.pdf.

3. I. E. Allen and J. Seaman, "Class Differences: Online Education in the United States, 2010," Babson Survey Research Group and The Sloan Consortium (2010), retrieved from http://sloanconsortium .org/publications/survey/pdf/class_differences.pdf.

4. R. Hess, quoting NCES in blog, "The Changing Face of Higher Education," *Education Week* (October 7, 2011), retrieved from http://blogs.edweek.org/edweek/rick_hess_straight_up/2011/10/the_changing_face_of_higher_education.html.

5. A. F. Mayadas and A. G. Picciano, "Blended Learning and Localness: The Means and the End," *Journal of Asynchronous Learning Networks* 11, no. 1 (2007): 3–7, retrieved from http://www.eric .ed.gov/PDFS/EJ842682.pdf.

6. C. Dziuban and P. Moskal, "A Course is a Course is a Course: Factor Invariance in Student Evaluation of Online, Blended and Face-to-Face Learning Environments," *Internet and Higher Education* 14, no. 4 (2011): 236–241, http://dx.doi.org/doi:10.1016/j.iheduc.2011.05.003.

7. Ibid., 239.

8. Ibid., 240.

9. M. Parry, "Tomorrow's College," *The Chronicle of Higher Education* (October 31, 2010), retrieved from http://chronicle.com/article/Tomorrows-College/125120/.

10. Embry-Riddle Aeronautical University Worldwide, "Five Ways to Learn" (2011), retrieved from http://worldwide.erau.edu/why-worldwide/five-ways-to-learn/index.html.

11. UWM Online, "Frequently Asked Questions about Online Learning" (2011), retrieved from http://www4.uwm.edu/future_students/online/faq.cfm.

12. Rio Salado, "College Culture" (2011), retrieved from http://www.riosalado.edu/about/research-planning/culture/Pages/default.aspx.

13. iNACOl, "Fast Facts about Online Learning" (2011), retrieved from http://www. inacol.org/press/docs/nacol_fast_facts.pdf.

14. L. Postal, "Is Florida's Virtual-Learning Push Visionary—Or 'Blizzard of Hype'?," *Orlando Sentinel,* September 11, 2011, 1A & 6A.

CHAPTER 10

■■■

Feature Masking in Computer Game Promotes Visual Imagery

Glenn Gordon Smith, Ph.D.
University of South Florida

Jim Morey, Ph.D.
Wesleyan College

Edwin Tjoe, Ed.D.
Stony Brook University

ABSTRACT

Can learning of mental imagery skills for visualizing shapes be accelerated with feature masking? Chemistry, physics, fine arts, military tactics, and laparoscopic surgery often depend on mentally visualizing shapes in their absence. Does working with 'spatial feature-masks' (skeletal shapes, missing key identifying portions) encourage people to use visualization strategies? This experimental study tested that hypothesis using an online computer game involving rotating and stamping a 3D cube on a 2D pattern. According to a chi-squared test, people who trained with 3D feature-masks reported using significantly more visual imagery strategies on a related visualization posttest. Spatial feature-masks provide a new building block for instructional designers to address educational outcomes involving visual imagery of shapes.

INTRODUCTION

Consider visual imagery of shapes as an instructional design challenge. If the educational goal is visual imagery of shapes, what is the instructional activity? Mathematics, chemistry, engineering, astronomy, and a host of other fields all depend on the effective use of spatial skills and visual imagery of shapes for their effective practice (Battista, 1990; DesCoteaux, Donnon, Fortin, & Allen, 2001; DesCoteaux & Leclere, 1995; Humphreys, Lubinski, & Yao, 1993; Mathewson, 1999; McGee, 1978; Pallrand & Seeber, 1984; Pearson & Ferguson, 1989; Piburn, Reynolds, Leedy, McAuliffe, Birk, & Johnson, 2002; Pribyl &

Bodner, 1987; Smith, 1964). Yet learners often try easier, but less effective, *analytical* strategies. Such strategies include: 1) "key feature" reasoning (looking for small distinctive features, as opposed to the whole shape); and 2) logical deduction. These strategies are effective for some problems. But, surprisingly, there are many spatial tasks where these analytical strategies are both slower and less accurate than strategies using visual imagery of the whole shape (Lohman, 1979; Schultz, 1991; Tapley & Bryden, 1977; Zimowski & Wothke, 1986). There is a real instructional need for activities that push students to choose and use visual imagery strategies in their learning. Inspired by blindfold chess, arthroscopic surgery, and field-stripping of rifles, the authors investigated whether "feature masking," concealing identifying marks of three-dimensional virtual shapes, would help students use visual imagery strategies.

The term "feature masking," to the knowledge of the authors, is new to education and spatial skills research. It has been used in research on face recognition in chimpanzees (Parr, Winslow, Hopkins, & deWaal, 2000) and generically in Geographic Information Systems. Feature masking can be conceived of as the glass half-empty or as half-full, as subtracting or adding visual information, either as feature masking, i.e., removal of visual information, or as scaffolding, i.e., providing more visual information than would be available in the eventual visual imagery task.

This study hypothesized that learners who trained with 3D imagery "feature masks" would use more strategies based on visual imagery and holistic spatial reasoning (visualizing the whole shape). Working with 3D feature-masks may help people: a) memorize the shape and then visualize the memorized object and b) cultivate a more patient mind-set for "spatial planning," as opposed to an impulsive "click-first and explore" mind-set.

Investigating pedagogies for teaching and learning complex spatial skills is very important because: a) Spatial skills are vital to a variety of educational and vocational fields such as mathematics, the sciences, fine arts, and engineering (Battista, 1990; Humphreys, Lubinski, & Yao, 1993; McGee, 1978; Pallrand & Seeber, 1984; Pearson & Ferguson, 1989; Pribyl & Bodner, 1987; Smith, 1964); and b) Women often do less well in spatial tasks (Scali, Brownlow, & Hicks, 2000). This is a potential blocking point for entering the sciences and engineering.

The current study explored, as potentially valuable to computer-based training, the use of spatial feature masking to promote visual imagery strategies.

LITERATURE SYNTHESIS

This literature search comprises two major perspectives: 1) *educational computing and spatial skills*; and 2) *a cognitive science approach to spatial skills*. The first perspective, "*educational computing and spatial skills*," is further broken down into two areas: 1) computer environments specifically designed to develop spatial skills (for example Microworlds and virtual reality); and 2) computer games which de-facto develop spatial skills.

Educational Computing and Spatial Skills

Computer Environments Designed to Developing Spatial Skills

Within the microworlds educational community, there have been both de-facto and premeditated attempts to improve spatial skills. Clements and Burns (1999) observed that children programming a LOGO robot to draw simple figures on large sheets of paper used their bodies to visualize and model what the robot would draw. In a process of "spatial weaning" (Smith, 1998) or "spatial curtailment" (Clements & Burns, 1999), children's gestures and bodily modeling of shapes tailed off over time and presumably were internalized into visualized mental models of shapes. In terms of premeditated attempts, some educators (Baker & Belland, 1986) have developed activities and advocated for the use of microworlds, such as ExperLOGO, for improving "visuo-spatial aptitude," but have not conducted empirical studies to test validity. However, McClurg (1992) demonstrated that third and fourth graders training for 40 minutes a week for 16 weeks with microworld activities, involving rotation of objects, improved significantly more on a figure classification test, than children training with other microworld activities. Curiously these significant differences were not found on mental rotation tests, perhaps because the relatively more atomic mental rotation is less susceptible to training.

Other computer environments, besides microworlds, have been used to improve spatial skills. Virtual reality can remediate the spatial orientation of disabled children with limited mobility. For example, children with "cerebral palsy, arthritis and other motoric disorders," used virtual reality to learn the layouts of large buildings, a task otherwise extremely difficult given the children's limited mobility (Foreman, Wilson, & Stanton, 1997). Similarly, blind people acquired cognitive maps of unknown architectural spaces by interacting with a multi-sensory virtual environment featuring audio and force feedback (Lahav & Mioduser, 2004).

Computer Games Which De-facto Develop Spatial Skills

Computer games and video games deserve their own category. While not designed to develop spatial skills, but rather as commercial entertainment products, they do de-facto develop spatial skills.

The research on computer games and spatial skills dates mostly from the late 1980s and early 1990s, the early classical age of computer games which saw the emergence of two-dimensional games such as Tetris, Pacman, Pong, and slightly later, 3D first-person perspective maze games, such as Wolfenstein and its progeny.

This research is usually cast in a common psychometric taxonomy of three spatial abilities: spatial orientation (SO), mental rotation (MR), and spatial visualization (SV). SO is the ability to imagine how large-scale scenes (landscapes, cityscapes, country-side, ocean scenes, etc.) appear after a change in viewpoint. MR is the ability to mentally visualize a smaller object rotated into another orientation, while SV, the ability to solve multi-step problems with configurations of shapes, is a conceptual "catch all" for more complex multi-step spatial skills (Smith, 1998).

Playing Tetris improves MR and SV skills (Okagaki & Frensch, 1994), but improvements tail off after a period of extended play. Improving a particular spatial skill with a specific computer game is usually a "one-shot deal," with limitations. As discussed in Smith (2005), this improvement requires: a) not having played that particular computer before (benefit not accrued), b) a certain familiarity with computer games (able to avoid a high learning curve or extraneous cognitive load (Sweller, 1994) while learning the game), and c) structural elements of the computer game directly exercise that spatial skill (Tetris involves interactively and mentally rotating shapes). In one study, Targ and Battlezone improved women's SV (Gagnon, 1985), but not men's. Gagnon theorized the men had already accrued the benefit from extensive earlier play. In another study, Zaxxon improved both men and women's SV (Dorval & Pepin, 1986). Obviously, the current crop of computer games is much more sophisticated in terms of graphics, range of structural designs, and scale of virtual worlds, and might warrant new studies; however this line of research has largely gone out of vogue.

Visual Imagery of Shapes for Various Disciplines

Educators at many levels acknowledge the importance of spatial skills and visual imagery in academic excellence. For example, the National Counsel of Teachers of Mathematics (NCTM) (http://standards.nctm.org/document/chapter7/geom.htm) suggests, in their geometry standards, that high school students should be able to "use visualization, spatial reasoning, and geometric modeling to solve problems" and "apply transformations . . . to analyze mathematical situations."

At the university level, visualization is no longer a question of standards, but is often absolutely vital for mastery of key concepts. In the biological sciences, diagrams and pictures carry a disproportionate amount of the meaning, particularly for concepts involving microscopic structures and abstract processes like photosynthesis and meiosis (Fletcher & Sanders, 2002). To understand these diagrams, students must use *spatial perception* to translate diagrams from the two-dimensional page to a 3D mental image—often dynamically animating a mental model. Although these spatial skills involving mental images are important to science, they are under-represented in the K12 curriculum (Mathewson, 1999), in all likelihood forcing university students to learn them long past the age of maximal neural plasticity (Munakata, Casey, & Diamond, 2004). Geology students must visualize the earth and its forces in both space and time (Libarkin & Brick, 2002). This involves both mental rotation and spatial visualization (Piburn et al., 2002). In college astronomy, regardless of the sophistication of scientific causal beliefs, spatial ability is positively correlated with problem-solving performance (Rudman, 2002).

Many disciplines have spatial skills embedded in the content, but do not explicitly acknowledge them as spatial skills, nor single them out for special instruction. However in other disciplines, instructors acknowledge that the spatial skills, part of their content, are fundamentally different from content in other modalities, such as verbal. They sometimes make an organized effort to help students develop these content-related spatial skills with software. Mathematics illustrates this point.

In the mid 1980s to 1990s, coinciding with the emergence of dynamic geometry software, such as Geometric Supposer, Cabri Geometre, GPTutor, and Geometer's Sketchpad, which can improve spatial skills (McCoy, 1991; Scholfield, Eurich-Fulcer, & Britt, 1994; Schumann & Green, 1994; Schwartz, Yerushalmy, & Wilson, 1993), a movement emphasizing visualization in mathematics was born. Mathematicians used the word "visualization" to mean visual mental imagery. They advocated the use of dynamic geometry software to scaffold students' visualization. The movement was most stimulated by a seminal volume, "Visualization in teaching and learning mathematics," edited by Zimmermann and Cunningham (1991). One chapter (Eisenberg & Dreyfus, 1991) discusses how students are reluctant to "visualize in mathematics," instead preferring a prescribed step-by-step algorithmic approach which is cognitively less demanding. This is consistent with psychology research literature which says an effort of will is needed to conjure up the visual mental imagery required for holistic spatial thinking, such as mental rotation (Hasher & Zacks, 1979). Logical/deductive approaches to many spatial problems are less effortful, but paradoxically slower (Lohman, 1979; Schultz, 1991; Tapley & Bryden, 1977; Zimowski & Wothke, 1986) and often less accurate (Cochran & Wheatley, 1989; Mumaw & Pellegrino, 1984; Schultz, 1991). The visualization movement in mathematics perseveres with vitality. For instance, at the latest installment (2004) of the "International Conference on Mathematics Education," held, like the Olympics, every four years, there was a lively "Spatial Visualization Group" making numerous presentations and hosting lively debate.

Visual imagery and spatial skills are also vital to some professional fields. For example, with the three-dimensional complexity and dynamism of the human body, success in medical practice, particularly surgery, requires spatial skills (DesCoteaux & Leclere, 1995; Schueneman, Pickleman, Hesslein, & Freeark, 1984). Laparoscopic (also known as arthroscopic surgery) particularly requires spatial skills and the ability to create and sustain a complex, dynamic mental model and visual imagery of the organs operated on (Tendick et al., 2000).

Laparoscopic or arthroscopic surgery, inserting a miniature video camera through a tiny incision, is minimally invasive allowing for a faster recovery time than conventional surgery with its broad slices through living tissue. However the laparoscopic constraint of a small entry point through the "fulcrum" hole in the abdominal wall "limits the range of motion," providing less visual/tactile information, requiring the surgeon to plan more and to create and maintain dynamic mental imagery of instruments and internal organs (Tendick et al., 2000). Particularly spatially challenging is obtaining a good view of the operation site with an angled laparoscope (objective lens at an angle to the axis of the laparoscope) (Tendick et al., 2000). Of key interest to the current study is how "less is more." Less range of motion causes more spatial planning. Less visual information causes more visual imagery of shapes; but the glass is also half-full. The small remaining amount of visual and tactile information effectively stimulates creation of a more complex mental model, spurring the laparoscopic surgeon on to heights of vivid visual and kinesthetic imagery.

Different Strategies for Spatial Problems

When solving spatial problems, one can choose from many different strategies. Yet what appears to be a myriad of strategies boils down to a small number. In solving questions from standardized tests of spatial abilities (mental rotation, spatial orientation, and spatial visualization), there are three basic strategies: a) mentally moving an object such as might be done with one's hand; b) mentally moving one's self relative to a larger terrain (imagining viewing a terrain or cityscape from a different position or orientation); and c) analyzing in terms of key features (noting presence and/or position of a key feature in one object and then checking for the presence/position of that key feature in another object) (Schultz, 1991).

The cognitive styles literature provides an interesting taxonomy, spatial visualizers versus object visualizers, recently validated by neurological and psychometric evidence (Chabris et al., 2006; Kozhevnikov, Kosslyn, & Shepard, 2005). Object visualizers, common in the arts and humanities, visualize whole shapes including the colors and other aspects of the visual appearance not necessary for spatial tasks. Spatial visualizers, common among scientists, mathematicians, and videogame players, visualize the shape of objects, and analyze objects in terms of their shape, leaving out visual details unnecessary for those spatial operations. The two styles of visualizers correspond to the distinction between two neurological pathways in the human brain, the ventral and dorsal systems, known in layman's terms respectively as the "what stream" and the "where stream," which people use to process *what* objects look like versus *where* objects and their spatially relevant features are (Ungerleider & Haxby, 1994). Object visualizers perform better on tests of visual recognition, while spatial visualizers perform better on spatial tests (Chabris et al., 2006). On spatial problems, object visualizers may use more logical approaches incorporating non-spatial visual characteristics of objects, while spatial visualizers use strategies making use of the spatial characteristics of objects.

For solving surface development problems (a type of spatial visualization problem involving flattened patterns that can be hypothetically folded up into three-dimensional shapes), Kyllonen, Lohman, and Snow (1984) reported two strategies: 1) "systematic mental construction using holistic (either symbolic or analog) representation and comparison" (whole object represented at once) and 2) "analytic strategy, features encoded, transformed and compared sequentially" (key parts of object represented sequentially, also known as "key-feature strategy"). For educational purposes, Kyllonen, Lohman, and Snow's dichotomy is further simplified into 1) visual/spatial versus 2) logical/analytic strategies. That is, strategies where people 1) visualize whole shapes versus 2) focus on parts of shapes, use logic and symbols, or use some combination thereof.

Discussion about visual imagery of shapes can become impossibly complicated and esoteric. There is little agreement on terminology. The two basic approaches cited above go by many names: 1) whole shape, holistic, visual imagery of shapes, visualization and parallel, etc. versus 2) non-visual, logical, deductive, analytic, semantic and sequential, etc. More problematic is that some academics stubbornly argue that visual imagery of shapes does not exist at all, i.e., that human brains are incapable of representing information in a spatial format, that all thinking is ultimately reducible to descriptive, logical, and symbolic assertions (Pylyshyn, 1973, 1999, 2000, 2001; Schwitzgebel, 2002; Slezak, 1994). They maintain this position despite contrary scientific evidence from multiple methodologies—psychometric factor analysis, timing/latency studies (Kosslyn, 1980, 1994; Kosslyn, Ball, & Reiser, 1978; Kosslyn, Behrmann, & Jeannerod, 1995; Kosslyn, Pinker, Smith & Shwartz, 1979; Shepard & Cooper, 1982), concurrent and retrospective subject reports and some brain imaging studies (Denis & Kosslyn, 1999; Kosslyn et al., 1979; Kosslyn et al., 1995). They discount visual mental imagery against the mainstream of scientific opinion and even in denial of their own subjective experience of visual imagery. The scientific mainstream asserts that humans definitely use visual imagery in their cognition. The current authors also hold this view.

Visual imagery of shapes and logical strategies diverge in several important ways. First, visual imagery strategies are harder, requiring an effort of will (Hasher & Zacks, 1979). However, if a person makes the mental effort to conjure up visual imagery to do mental rotation and other similar 'holistic' spatial strategies on spatial problems, the results are usually more accurate (Cochran & Wheatley, 1989; Mumaw & Pellegrino, 1984; Schultz, 1991) and faster (Lohman, 1979; Schultz, 1991; Tapley & Bryden, 1977; Zimowski & Wothke, 1986). Although, it may seem counterintuitive, analytical or logical strategies are often more automated (Lohman, 1979). They require no special effort of will, but paradoxically are slower (Lohman, 1979). Because they are largely automated, not requiring a special effort, students often gravitate toward the easier analytical strategies. However, as mentioned, visual strategies (visual imagery strategies) are faster and markedly better for certain classes of spatial problems.

Various educational studies confirm the advantage of visual imagery strategies. For example in a study of multiple-choice geometric analogy problems, Bethell-Fox, Lohman, and Snow (1984) found two strategies, constructive matching (up-front visual encoding in memory of shapes) versus process of elimination of answers (without premeditated preparation). The stronger participants used constructive matching, the weaker subjects used elimination, particularly on difficult items.

Allen and Hogeland (1978) suggest another strategy is to use some external object (a drawing, folded-up paper, or even a computer model) to represent shapes. In effect this means "off-loading" some memory for visualization, using tools as an "extended memory" (Newell & Simon, 1972). However the other spatial strategies discussed thus far are cognitive strategies, using only eye and brain. Does the use of external props constitute a spatial strategy? The line between the brain, body, and tools is thin and blurry. When performing holistic mental rotation, many people, almost unconsciously, rotate their thumb and forefinger as if miming screwing on the lid of a jar (Just & Carpenter, 1985). As people do mental rotation, motor, as well as visual, areas of their brains activate (Richter et al., 2000; Vingerhoets et al., 2001). While acknowledging the ambiguity, it is convenient to say that spatial strategies do not include the premeditated use of external props. However this blurry line between eye and brain, hand and tool suggests natural ways to develop spatial strategies.

Promoting Visual Outcomes

We return to the instructional design challenge mentioned earlier: "If the educational goal is visual imagery of shapes, what is the instructional activity?"

There have been organized efforts to improve students' spatial skills set in academic context. Lord (1985, 1987) improved college students' spatial skills, by having them visualize sections through three-dimensional objects and then making cuts through the objects to test their predictions (Lord, 1985, 1987). Piburn et al. (2002) designed and tested educational modules for visualizing typography, using interactive three-dimensional geologic blocks, to develop spatial skills for introductory college geology. There was some evidence that this improved students' visualization and geospatial skills.

Since visual imagery strategies often work better than less demanding logical/analytical strategies (Cochran & Wheatley, 1989; Mumaw & Pellegrino, 1984; Schultz, 1991), it is important to find ways to: 1) get students to choose visual imagery strategies; and 2) help students strengthen those visual imagery strategies. Time pressure on simple mental rotation tasks may encourage people to use a spatial/holistic approach. However, on more complicated tasks, time pressure may actually intimidate people. There is a strong need to provide a non-intimidating way to encourage people to use holistic spatial strategies. At the time of this writing, the authors found no research literature on instructional design efforts that specifically encourage people to choose visual imagery strategies.

Therefore the current investigators looked outside of instructional design to other walks of life for ideas. Specifically, the authors noticed, across a number of academic, vocation and recreational areas, a relationship between: a) the level of sensory support or extended memory (Newell & Simon, 1972); and b) the level of expertise of in building and maintaining visual imagery or mental models—the less the expertise in visual imagery of shapes, the greater the reliance on external models and sensory support; the greater the expertise in visual imagery of shapes, the less reliance on external support.

In crystallography and chemistry, students first learn about important symmetry operations within the structure of complex molecules, by working with hand-held models (in combination with diagrams in their textbook). Later as students develop more skill, they can visualize the structure of molecules by just looking at diagrams. Experts in chemistry and crystallography can visualize complex structures without external support. However when experts encounter a new molecule with unfamiliar structure (or one that is much more complicated than what they are used to), they often make use of computer models to first understand the molecule and then to visualize the structure. Once this new molecule is incorporated into their collection of visual imagery, they no longer need external support (based on Smith, 2002, unpublished interviews with chemists and crystallographers, conducted by the current first author).

In the military, soldiers often field-strip and reassemble their rifles blindfolded. The motivation is that they may be required to do similar manipulations under harsh night-time combat conditions. Such blindfold training also presumably helps soldiers build a mental model of the mechanical workings of the rifle. Blindfold field-stripping of a rifle promotes mentally visualizing the parts of a rifle. Tactile sensory information is provided, but not visual. The soldier substitutes a mental model for visual feedback. Blindfold field-stripping is logically an intermediary step between: a) assembling a rifle with eyes open, and b) field stripping a rifle entirely in one's mind's eye (with neither visual or tactile external sensory support).

The phenomenon of "blindfold" chess provides another interesting example. Chess experts first spend countless hours visualizing chess combinations over the board before attempting to visualize an entire chess position "blindfolded." A chess board could be conceived of as scaffolding for visualizing entire chess positions. As players decide on a move, they often imagine the position several moves in advance. They do not have to represent, with visual imagery, all the pieces of the position, only those pieces which would be moved from their current positions. Blindfold chess means having to represent the entire chess position in one's head.

Based on these and other examples from a variety of fields, the relationship between visual imagery skill and sensory support seems to be: less skill, more support; more skill, less sensory support. Presumably as students develop skill, they start "spatially weaning" themselves off the sensory support (Smith, 1998, 2005). Based on these ideas, the research questions for the following article are: Is it possible to deliberately use this "weaning" process as part of instructional design? If you take away some sensory support by feature masking, will it encourage people to use visual imagery strategies? Is it possible to promote visual imagery by masking identifying features of objects? The *main research question* is: 1) Will feature masking (masking identifying features of shapes) encourage students to choose visual imagery strategies? However, since people can only choose to do something if they are able to, a second research question is implied: 2) Will feature masking facilitate students' ability to perform visual imagery strategies?

METHOD

Materials

To investigate some of these ideas, the investigators modified a simple computer game, to create two modalities: a) full sensory ("control group") and b) feature masking of identifying features of shapes ("feature masking"). The investigators customized an online Java-based interactive mathematical game called CopyCat, based on group theory (developed by Dr. Jim Morey) (see Figure 10.1a). CopyCat involves 'stamping' a cube to replicate a pattern of colored square tiles. Using the up, down, left and right buttons, the player can rotate the cube on the left until the upper face of the cube matches a pattern on a tile. At that point, the player clicks on that tile. If there is a match, the patterned face is dropped in the appropriate position on the pattern and the colors of that tile brighten to indicate a match. In Figure 10.1a, the upper face of

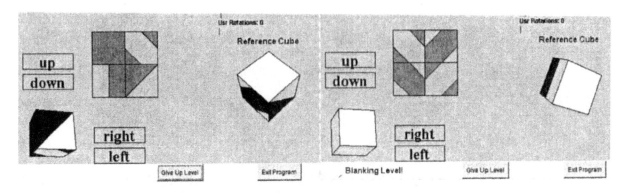

FIGURE 10.1. The CopyCat Game in Normal and in Blanking Modes.

the cube matches the pattern on the lower right tile and could be deposited there by clicking on the lower right tile.

For a pretest, treatment, posttest experimental design, the investigators constructed three tasks based on the CopyCat computer game. The first six levels of the CopyCat game constituted the pretest. Both groups encountered exactly the same initial six levels under exactly the same conditions. For the treatment phase, the investigators created a modified version of the game, with some "blanking levels" (see Figure 10.1b). The cube turned white on all six sides as soon as a participant rotated it, thereby masking some key visual feedback when doing a sequence of rotations. Yet, as they rotated it, the white cube provided some visual support (scaffolding). They could see that the cube was rotating and visually keeping track of how many rotations and what directions (up, down, left, or right) they were rotating it, but they had to keep track of the positioning of the colored faces via visual imagery or by planning the sequence of rotations beforehand. Only when the player clicked on the target tile would the cube replay the sequence of rotations with full visual feedback showing the patterns on the cube as it rotated. The idea was that the player would have to plan, imagine, and keep track of the cube as it was rotated. The replaying of the sequence of rotations provided feedback. This blanking condition constituted the feature masking of key portions of shapes to promote visual imagery. During the treatment, the next 12 levels, half the participants played the game in its original form, half with occasional "blanking levels." The participants scores and various other information was written back to a database on a server so that the investigators had ready access to all data.

The posttest (see Figure 10.2) comprised 12 multiple-choices items. Participants were shown a static image of the cube and path it was to roll along. They are asked to determine which face

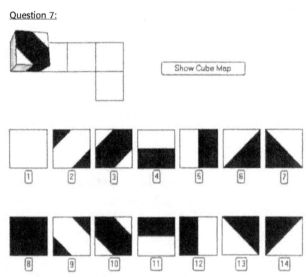

FIGURE 10.2. The Multiple Choice Posttest.

of the cube, in what orientation, would appear on top of the cube after rolling along that path. They then picked from a set of 14 possible alternatives (see Figure 10.2). If participants could not remember the cube, they also had the option to use a static "cube map," showing all faces of the cube. The score on the posttest was computed as follows: A person received full score on a multiple choice item by predicting both the correct face of the cube that would be on top, as well as its rotational orientation. If they picked the correct face, but the wrong orientation, they received half credit.

Following the posttest, participants were asked to report the strategies they used on the posttest. These self-reported strategies were later categorized, by the investigators, as either "visualization strategies" or "non-visual strategies." Examples of participants' visualization strategies used were: "*I tried to visualize the cube in my mind and tried to rotate the cube*" and "*Mental pictures used to figure this out.*" Examples of participants' non-visual strategies include: "*The Process of elimination*" and "*mostly guess work.*"

Participants

Seventy-four college undergraduate students participated in the experiment for extra credit in a sophomore-level course, "Technological Trends in Society." In order to boost motivation in the experiment, the top five scoring males and females received twice the extra credit. A total of 39 males and 35 females participated. In the control group (no blanking levels) there were 20 males and 16 females. In the feature masking condition, (blanking), there were 19 males, and 19 females.

Procedure

The experiment comprised two sessions, separated by a week. At the start of the first session, the experimenters explained to the participants, the goal and nature of the game. Each participant was then given a painted wooden cube corresponding to the cube in the CopyCat game, which they could use while they played the game during the first session. The wooden cube helped the participants to learn the cube and to visualize its rotations. The participants were instructed to play the game as well as they could. The object of the game was to solve levels with the minimum number of rotations and in the least amount of time. The first six levels of the game during the first session comprised the pretest. During this pretest, both groups encountered exactly the same computer game levels.

After the pretest (the first six levels), the experiences of the two treatment groups diverged sharply. The feature masking group was alerted: "You have reached a special challenging level!" The feature masking group then solved two blanking levels, designed to make them plan and visualize apriori the rotations on the cube.

At the conclusion of the first session, as the participants left the computer laboratory, all participants were given a sheet of paper with a URL and password for six levels of the CopyCat game to be played in the intervening week before the next experimental session. During that intervening week, the control group solved six normal levels, the feature masking group solved three normal and three blanking levels. Since data from the CopyCat game was written back to a database, the experimenters were able to verify whether participants actually completed this intervening exercise, eliminating their data from the final mix if they did not.

After one week, participants returned for session two of the experiment. Both groups worked on eight levels of the game. For the control group, all levels were normal. For the feature masking group, half the levels were blanking.

In order to avoid contamination, the experimental sessions were arranged so that the treatment groups were entirely separate. In other words, in an experimental session with the control group, only control group participants would be in the computer lab at that time. Similarly, feature masking group participants never mixed with participants from the control group.

After completing the eight levels of the game, all participants were instructed to rest for five minutes. They then took the multiple choice posttest described above. Following the posttest, they were asked to describe (type into a text box) the strategies they used on the posttest.

RESULTS

On the pretest (the first six levels in the first session with identical conditions for both groups), there were no significant differences between the two groups. In terms of number of levels completed, the control group on average finished 4.4 of the six levels, while the feature masking group finished 3.9. However, an ANOVA indicated this difference was not statistically significant. The average number of rotations per level (rounded to three significant digits) was 18.9 for both groups. The average elapsed times per levels were 186 seconds for the control group, 172 seconds for the feature masking group.

On the multiple-choice posttest, the feature masking group had higher scores, but this difference was not statistically significant. On the posttest, the feature masking group had an average score of 4.34, while for the control group it was 4.14. According to an ANOVA test, this was not significant.

Main Research Questions, Choice of Strategies

However, on the main research question, choice of visual versus non-visual strategies, there was an important significant difference. According to a chi-square analysis performed on the self-reported posttest strategies, the feature masking group reported using significantly more "visualization strategies" than did the control group, $\chi^2 (2, 74) = 5.84$, $p = 0.016$.

Moreover, across both groups, those who reported "visualization strategies" had significantly higher scores on the posttest. The participants who reported visualization strategies averaged 4.59 on the posttest, while participants who used non-visual strategies averaged 3.45. According to an ANOVA test, this was significant at the 0.05 level, $F(1, 72) = 4$, $p = 0.049$. A similar result was obtained with a simpler measure on the multiple choice items, i.e., the number of items correct on the posttest. Those reporting using visualization strategies averaged 4.59 items correct, while those reporting non-visualization strategies averaged 3.45 items correct. This was significant at the 0.05 level $F(1, 72) = 4.53$, $p = 0.037$.

DISCUSSION

The main research question, "will feature masking encourage students to choose visual imagery strategies," received a "Yes." The significant results on the chi-squared test of self-reported post-test strategies strongly indicated that those who worked with feature masking reported using significantly more visualization and visual imagery strategies. Moreover, the use of visual imagery and visualization appears to have been important for the experimental task (multiple choice items, determining which cube face was up, after rolling along a prescribed path). Across the groups, those who reported using visualization strategies scored significantly higher on the posttest.

Some academicians have called into question the value of self-reported data. Others have defended the validity of self-reporting and demonstrated some level of validity by using the strategies reported by people as software algorithms which successfully performed the task (Erickson & Simon, 1993; van Someren, Barnard, & Sandberg, 1994). That in the current study, participants reporting visual strategies did better on the posttest, lends validity to the self-reporting.

These major significant results ("feature masking" or partial sensory support group reported more visual strategies, those who reported visual strategies scored higher on the posttest) have two major implications: a) feature masking to promote visual imagery is a viable research topic deserving further study, b) feature masking to promote visual imagery is potentially useful for instructional design involving visuo-spatial outcomes.

Feature Masking to Promote Visual Imagery as Research Agenda

Those using the feature masking reported more visualization strategies. Those reporting visualization strategies scored significantly higher on the posttest. The significant results point out the value of feature masking to promote visual imagery. The limitations of the study point out the directions for further research. The study was designed to quickly investigate the construct of feature masking, with minimal extraneous variables.

What specifically were the limitations? a) The experimental task lacked an authentic context. Participants in the experiment took part, for extrinsic motivation, because they received extra credit in a course. However the tasks themselves—(a) rolling a virtual cube and stamping with it; and b) determining the upper face of a cube after hypothetical rolls)—were unfamiliar to students and, except for a superficial similarity to computer games, lacked any real power for intrinsic motivation. b) Because of time constraints, participants were forced into the more difficult feature masking condition without choice. Educationally, it is perhaps more sound to let people grapple with a new challenge when they feel ready. c) The training task was vulnerable to non-visual opportunistic strategies. Examples are finding solutions by trial and error, and then mechanically repeating such sequences of rolls to stamp the cube on other tiles. d) Participants did not have enough time to fully develop the visual imagery skills specific to the CopyCat game. Because of practical limitations, each person's participation comprised three interventions over one week. It can take chess-players years to learn to effectively visualize combinations three moves deep. According to crystallography experts, it takes several weeks for students to initially visualize the simplest symmetry operations, months, if not years, to visualize transformations on more complex molecules (Smith, 2002, unpublished interviews of crystallography experts by the current author). And in the current study, the experimenters' experiences were that picking up visualization skills, even on the CopyCat game, requires regular practice over an extended period of time.

It is nothing short of remarkable that significant results were achieved within the limitations of the study. Future studies on feature masking to promote visual imagery should address the limitations: a) Provide an authentic context by setting the study in an authentic academic or recreational setting such as chemistry, anatomy, chess, etc.; b) allow participants to choose more challenging visual imagery feature masking conditions when they feel they are ready; and c) design experimental tasks so that they are not vulnerable to opportunistic non-visual strategies; and d) extend studies to span regular activities over months.

Potential of Spatial Feature Masking for Instructional Design

The results of the current study have some implication for situations where educators would like their students to use visual imagery strategies. Feature-masks for visual imagery could be used in simulations and virtual worlds to promote the use of visual strategies, for instructional design situations where the desired learning outcome is for students to use a mental model involving visual imagery. In theory, spatial feature masking would operate in a three step sequence: 1) Students interact with the objects with full sensory information. 2) Students interact with spatial feature masks, i.e., a simulation with partial sensory information. Some spatially relevant visual information would be removed from the model, but some orienting visual information would remain to support the visual imagery. The amount of sensory information would be intermediary between full sensory information and the amount of information in the ultimate, desired target visual imagery outcome. Furthermore, the spatial feature-masks would be set in the context of a goal-oriented task with accountability. 3) Step three is the full learning outcome where students use a mental model built on visual imagery, without feature-masks/partial visual support, but set in a task with accountability.

At each step of the feature masking process, there is an intriguing relationship between external and internal visual representations. The more complete the external representation, the less complete the internal representation. The less complete the external, the more complete the internal. Some partial external information scaffolds the internal model. This three step model can be applied to a number of academic fields with mental model outcomes, chemistry, geology, biology, engineering, architecture, health care, etc. In medical school and for surgery, students need to learn to work with the complex three-dimensional geometry of organs within the human body. In fact, the spatial skills of surgeons are stronger than those of other practicing medical doctors (Schueneman et al., 1984). For medical students learning the visual imagery and mental model skills for surgery, it might be helpful to develop sophisticated simulations of human anatomy that make use of spatial feature-masks, through different levels of visual information. As step one, students dissect cadavers. Obviously this is a full-sensory experience. For step two, students could work with a rather sophisticated simulation of three-dimensional anatomy which masks some spatially relevant visual information, while providing some orienting visual information as support. Medical students would work with this feature masking model on a goal-oriented task with accountability. The exact specifications for such a feature masking task would be difficult to delineate without some trial and error by designers working with content experts and students. However one possibility for a step two simulation model might be a simulation using "wire frame" models of organs and with no color information. As a goal oriented task, students might have to find and "retract" the liver.

Step three could be actual surgery, perhaps arthroscopic surgery which requires extensive spatial planning and an accurate and dynamically updated mental model of the anatomy involved in the surgery. A similar three-step progression could potentially work for the learning of visuo-spatial mental models in a variety of other fields such as: crystallography, chemistry, biology engineering, architecture, etc.

Such simulations using feature-masks to promote visual imagery could easily be cast in the form of computer games, drawing on the motivational qualities of interactive electronic recreational media. Indeed, the spatial feature masking model of progressively less key visual information could provide for levels of increasing difficultly, a design structure common in computer and video games.

CONCLUSION

The current study tested the hypothesis that "spatial feature masking" could encourage students to employ visual or visual imagery strategies in visuo-spatial problems. Spatial feature masking was defined as skeletal shapes, missing key identifying information, but with some remaining orienting shape information as support for visual imagery. The major results of the study were that participants who used the spatial feature-masks reported employing significantly more visual or visual imagery strategies on the posttest than did their non-feature-mask using counterparts. Moreover, across both groups, those who reported using visual or visual imagery strategies performed better on the posttest. These results strongly suggest that: 1) visual and visual imagery strategies were important for success on the posttest; and 2) spatial feature-masks are effective for encouraging people to use visual imagery strategies. Since the task in the current study was purely experimental, with no meaningful context for the participants, the authors suggest extending the use of spatial feature-masks into real-world, work, recreational, military and educational contexts. Spatial feature-masks can be useful both as a research construct for investigating spatial abilities as well as a tool for instructional designers and educators in disciplines with visuo-spatial outcomes.

References

Allen, M. J., & Hogeland, R. (1978). Spatial problem-solving strategies as functions of sex. *Perceptual and Motor Skills, 47*(3), 348–350.

Baker, P. R., & Belland, J. C. (1986). *Developing spatial skills with ExperLOGO on the Macintosh.* Paper presented at the meeting of the Great Lakes Conference of the Educational Compute Consortium of Ohio, Cleveland, OH.

Battista, M. T. (1990). Spatial visualization and gender differences in high school geometry. *Journal of Research in Mathematics Education, 21*(11), 47–60.

Bethell-Fox, C. E., Lohman, D. F., & Snow, R. E. (1984). Adaptive reasoning: Componential and eye movement analysis of geometric analogy performance. *Intelligence, 8,* 205–238.

Chabris, C. F., Jerde, T. E., Woolley, A. W., Gerbasi, M. E., Schuldt, J. P., Bennett, S. L., Hackman, J. R., & Kosslyn, S. M. (2006). Spatial and object visualization cognitive styles: Validation studies in 3800 individuals, paper submitted to *Applied Cognitive Psychology*.

Clements, D. H., & Burns, B. A., (1999, April). *Students' development of strategies for turn and angle measurement*. Paper presented at the meeting of the American Educational Research Association, Montreal, Canada.

Cochran, K. F., & Wheatley, G. H. (1989). Ability and sex-related differences in cognitive strategies on spatial tasks. *The Journal of General Psychology, 116*(11), 43–55.

Denis, M., & Kosslyn, S. M. (1999). Scanning visual images: a window to the mind. *Cahier de Psychologe Cognitive/Current Psychology of Cognition, 18*, 409–465.

DesCoteaux, J-C., Donnon, T., Fortin, A., & Allen, S. (2001, April). *The effect of mental practice as a learning strategy for the development of laparoscopic suturing skills*. Paper presented at the annual meeting of the American Educational Research Association.

DesCoteaux, J-C., & Leclere, H. (1995). Learning surgical technical skills. *Canadian Journal of Surgery, 38*, 33–38.

Dorval, M., & Pepin, M. (1986, April). *Effect of playing a video game on adults' and adolescents' spatial visualization*. Paper presented at the annual meeting of the American Educational Research Association, San Francisco, CA.

Eisenberg, T., & Dreyfus, T. (1991). On the reluctance to visualize in mathematics. In W. Zimmermann & S. Cunningham (Eds.), *Visualization in teaching and learning* (pp. 25–38), MAA Notes 19, USA: Mathematical Association of America.

Erickson, K. A., & Simon, H. A. (1993). *Protocol analysis: Verbal reports as data* (Rev. ed.). Cambridge, MA: The MIT Press.

Fletcher, J., & Sanders, M. (2002). Developing spatial skills to improve students' understanding of 3-D diagrams. *Proceedings of ED-MEDIA 2002: World Conference on Educational Multimedia, Hypermedia & Telecommunications, USA, 3*, 1819–1824.

Foreman, N., Wilson, P., & Stanton, D. (1997). VR and spatial awareness in disabled children. *Communications of the ACM, 40*(8), 76–82.

Gagnon, D. (1985, Winter). Videogames and spatial skills: An Exploratory Study. *Educational Computing and Teaching Journal, 33*(4), 263–275.

Hasher, L., & Zacks, R. T. (1979). Automatic and effortful processes in memory. *Journal of Experimental Psychology: General, 3*, 356–388.

Humphreys, L. G., Lubinski, D., & Yao, G. (1993). Utility of predicting group membership and the role of spatial visualization in becoming an engineer, physical scientist, or artist. *Journal of Applied Psychology, 78*(2), 250–261.

Just, M. A., & Carpenter, P. A. (1985). Cognitive coordinate systems: Accounts of mental rotation and individual differences in spatial ability. *Psychological Review, 92*(2), 137–172.

Kosslyn, S. M. (1980). *Image and mind.* Cambridge, MA: Harvard University Press.

Kosslyn, S. M. (1994). *Image and brain: The resolution of the imagery debate.* Cambridge, MA: MIT Press.

Kosslyn, S., Ball, T., & Reiser, B. (1978). Visual images preserve metric spatial information: Evidence from studies of image scanning. *Journal of Experimental Psychology. Human Perception and Performance, 4,* 47–60.

Kosslyn, S. M., Behrmann, M., & Jeannerod, M. (1995). The cognitive neuroscience of mental imagery, *Neurophsychologia, 33,* 1335–1344.

Kosslyn, S. M., Pinker, S., Smith, G., & Shwartz, S. (1979). On the demystification of mental imagery. *Behavior & Brain Sciences, 2*(4), 535–581.

Kozhevnikov, M., Kosslyn, S., & Shepard, J. (2005). Spatial versus object visualizers: A new characterization of visual cognitive style. *Memory & Cognition, 33,* 710–726.

Kyllonen, P. C., Lohman, D. F., & Snow, R. E. (1984). Effects of aptitudes, strategy training, and task facets on spatial task performance. *Journal of Educational Psychology, 78*(1), 130–145.

Lahav, O., & Mioduser, D. (2004). Exploration of unknown spaces by people who are blind using a multi-sensory virtual environment. *Journal of Special Education Technology, 19*(3), 15–23.

Libarkin, J. C., & Brick, C. (2002). Research methodologies in science education: Visualization and the geosciences. *Journal of Geoscience Education, 50*(4), 449–455.

Lohman, D. F. (1979). *Spatial ability: Individual differences in speed and level* (Technical Report No. 9). Stanford, CA: Aptitude Research Project, School of Education, Stanford University.

Lord, T. (1985). Enhancing the visuo-spatial aptitude of students. *Journal of Research in Science Teaching, 22*(5), 395–405.

Lord, T. (1987). A look at spatial abilities in undergraduate women science majors. *Journal of Research in Science Teaching, 24*(8), 757–767.

Mathewson, J. H. (1999). Visual-spatial thinking: An aspect of science overlooked by educators. *Science Education, 83*(1), 33–51.

McClurg, P. A. (1992). Investigating the development of spatial cognition in problem-solving microworlds. *Journal of Computing in Childhood Education, 3*(2), 111–126.

McCoy, L. P. (1991). The effect of geometry tool software on high school geometry achievement. *Journal of Computers in Mathematics and Science Teaching, 10*(3), 51–57.

McGee, M. G. (1978). Human spatial abilities: Psychometric studies and environmental, genetic, hormonal, and neurological influences. *Psychological Review, 86,* 889–918.

Mumaw, R. J., & Pellegrino, J. W. (1984). Individual differences in complex spatial processing. *Journal of Educational Psychology, 76*(5), 920–939.

Munakata, Y., Casey, B. J., & Diamond, A. (2004). Developmental cognitive neuroscience: Progress and potential. *TRENDS in Cognitive Sciences, 8*(3), 122–128.

Newell, A., & Simon, H. A. (1972). *Human problem solving*. Engle-wood Cliffs, NJ: Prentice Hall, Inc.

Okagaki, L., & Frensch, P. A. (1994). Effects of video game playing on measures of spatial performance: Gender effects in late adolescence. *Journal of Applied Developmental Psychology, 15*(1), 33–58.

Pallrand, G. J., & Seeber, F. (1984). Spatial ability and achievement in introductory physics. *Journal of Research in Science Teaching, 21,* 507–516.

Parr, L. A., Winslow, J. T., Hopkins, W. D., & de Waal, F. B. (2000). Recognizing facial cues: Individual discrimination by chimpanzees (Pan troglodytes) and rhesus monkeys (Macaca mulatta). *Journal of Comparative Psychology, 114*(1), 47–60.

Pearson, J. L., & Ferguson, L. R. (1989). Gender differences in patterns of spatial ability, environmental cognition, and math and English achievement in late adolescence. *Adolescence, 24,* 421–431.

Piburn, M. D., Reynolds, S. J., Leedy, D. E., McAuliffe, C. M., Birk, J. P., & Johnson, J. K. (2002, April). *The hidden earth: Visualization of geologic features and their subsurface geometry*. Paper presented at the annual meeting of the National Association for Research in Science Teaching, New Orleans, LA.

Pribyl, J. R., & Bodner, G. M. (1987). Spatial ability and its role in organic chemistry: A study of four organic courses. *Journal of Research in Science Teaching, 24,* 229–240.

Pylyshyn, Z. W. (1973). What the mind's eye tells the mind's brain: A critique of mental imagery. *Psychological Bulletin, 80,* 1–25.

Pylyshyn, Z. W. (1999). Is vision continuous with cognition? The case for cognitive impenetrability of visual perception. *Behavioral and Brain Sciences, 22*(3), 341–423.

Pylyshyn, Z. W. (2000). Situating vision in the world. *Trends in Cognitive Sciences, 4*(5), 197–207.

Pylyshyn, Z. W. (2001). Visual indexes, preconceptual objects, and situated vision. *Cognition, 80*(1/2), 127–158.

Richter, W., Somorjai, R., Summers, R., Jarmasz, M., Menon, R. S., Gati, J. S., Georgopoulos, A. P., Tegeler, C., Ugurbil, K., & Kim S-G. (2000). Motor activity during mental rotation studied by time-resolved single-trial fMRI. *Journal of Cognitive Neuroscience, 12*(2), 310–320.

Rudman, D. S. (2002, April). *Solving astronomy problems can be limited by intuited knowledge, spatial ability, or both*. Paper presented at the Annual Meeting of the American Educational Research Association.

Scali, M., Brownlow, S., & Hicks, J. (2000). Gender differences in spatial task performance as a function of speed or accuracy orientation. *Sex Roles, 43*(5/6), 359–376.

Scholfield, J. W., Eurich-Fulcer, R., & Britt, C. L. (1994). Teachers, computer tutors, and teaching: The artificially intelligent tutor as an agent for classroom change. *American Educational Research Journal, 31*(3), 579–607.

Schueneman, A. L., Pickleman, J., Hesslein, R., & Freeark, R. J. (1984). Neuropsychological predictors of operative skill among general surgery residents. *Surgery, 96,* 288–293.

Schultz, K. (1991). The contribution of solution strategy to spatial performance. *Canadian Journal of Psychology, 45*(4), 474–491.

Schumann, H., & Green, D. (1994). *Discovering geometry with a computer*. Lund, Sweden: Chartwell-Bratt (Studentlitteratur).

Schwartz, J. L., Yerushalmy, M., & Wilson, B. (1993). *The geometric supposer: What is it a case of?* Hillsdale, NJ: Lawrence Erlbaum Associates.

Schwitzgebel, E. (2002). How well do we know our own conscious experience? The case of visual imagery. *Journal of Consciousness Studies, 9,* 35–53.

Shepard, R. N., & Cooper, L. A. (1982). *Mental images and their transformations*. Cambridge, MA: The MIT Press.

Slezak, P. (1994). Mental imagery and pictorial representation. In N. H. Narajanan & S. Chandrasekaran (Eds.), *Reasoning with diagrammatic representations*. Palo Alto, CA: AAAI Press, Stanford University.

Smith, G. G. (1998). *Computers, computers games, active control and spatial visualization, strategy*. Unpublished Ph.D. dissertation, Arizona State University, Tempe, AZ.

Smith, G. G. (2002). *Unpublished interviews with chemists and crystallographers*. Unpublished raw data.

Smith, G. G. (2005, April). How do computer games affect your children? *Eurasian Journal of Educational Research*.

Smith, I. M. (1964). *Spatial ability: Its educational and social significance*. San Diego, CA: Robert R. Knapp.

Sweller, J. (1994). Cognitive load theory, learning difficulty, and instructional design. *Learning and Instruction, 4*(5), 295–312.

Tapley, S. M., & Bryden, M. P. (1977). An investigation of sex differences in spatial ability: Mental rotation of three-dimensional objects. *Canadian Journal of Psychology, 31,* 122–130.

Tendick, F., Downes, M., Goktekin, T., Cavusoglu, M. C., Feygin, D., Wu, X., Eyal, R., Hegarty, M., & Way, L. W. (2000). A virtual environment test bed for training laparoscopic surgical skills. *Presence, 9*(3), 236–255.

Ungerleider, L. G., & Haxby, J. V. (1994). 'What' and 'where' in the human brain. *Current Opinion in Neurobiology, 4,* 157–165.

van Someren, M. W., Barnard, Y. F., & Sandberg, J. A. C. (1994). *The think aloud method: A practical guide to modeling cognitive processes*. London: Academic Press.

Vingerhoets, G., Santens, P., Van Laere, K., Lahorte, P., Dierckx, R. A., & De Reuck, J. (2001). Regional brain activity during different paradigms of mental rotation in healthy volunteers: A positron emission tomography study. *NeuroImage, 13,* 381–391.

Zimmermann, W., & Cunningham, S. (Eds.). (1991). *Visualization in teaching and learning mathematics.* MAA Notes 19, USA: Mathematical Association of America.

Zimowski, M. F., & Wothke, W. (1986, September). *The measurement of human variation in spatial visualizing ability: A process oriented perspective* (Technical Report 1986–1). Johnson O'Connor Research Foundation, Human Engineering Laboratory.

CHAPTER 11

■■■

The Direction of Online Courses

Marcella Mandracchia, Ed.D.

Online distance learning has been revolutionizing the landscape of higher education ever since its inception in the 1990s. Online learning has been credited with many of the positive transformations in higher education, from pushing administrations to embrace technology across campus, revitalizing instructional pedagogy on part of the faculty, and most importantly, offering a pathway to progress to students who would have been otherwise excluded from college. The proportion of undergraduate and graduate students taking at least one online course has reached an all-time high of 33.5% to a new total of 7.1 million (Allen & Seaman, 2014). This explosion in online course enrollment is driven by the learners' increasing desire for flexibility in scheduling, location, and access to content resources (Bichsel, 2013). With 80% of institutions offering courses online, Internet-based learning is poised to replace the traditional face-to-face approach as the primary method to deliver education. However, online learning is not without its shortcomings. There are concerns about the quality of online education and that online learning depersonalizes education (Bowen et al., 2013). Despite its problems, online learning will continue to shape the development of college education in the United States (Allen & Seaman, 2014) and worldwide (Valentine, 2002).

DEFINING ONLINE EDUCATION

Online distance education is a large umbrella that encompasses many different learning environments. The configurations of online courses can vary by time and location (Teaster & Blieszner, 1999; Romiszowski, 2004). Students may work through the content at their own pace (flex-time) at various physical locations (distributed), or they may have to attend a live video instruction (real-time), or be present at the same place to work on an assignment (same place). The mode of delivery (Jack & Curt, 2001) differs based on the amount of content delivered online. Web-facilitated courses have up to 29% of the content online, in these cases, the Internet is used to access a course management system to obtain and submit assignments. Blended or hybrid courses have a substantial portion of the content delivered online (30 to 79%), and they typically include discussion forums with reduced number of face-to-face meetings (Allen & Seaman, 2014). Then there are courses in which 80% or more of the content is online and they usually do not have in-person instructions. It must be stressed that online courses are fluid in their operations. A single course can be delivered in real-time or flex-time, or can involve in-class components at the beginning of the course and cease face-to-face meetings towards the end. Online courses are not bound by the elements of time, location and mode of delivery, instead, they utilize them interchangeably.

THE POSITIVE AND NEGATIVE ASPECTS OF THE VIRTUAL CLASSROOM

The success of online education rests on its ability to satisfy the desires of its key stakeholders: the students, instructors and educational institutions. For students, online courses create an access to higher education that they would not have otherwise. However, students may not possess the necessary critical thinking skills to be successful in this new learning environment. The asynchronous nature of online courses requires students to be able to process a large volume of information without direct and immediate feedback from the instructor. Thus students have to be more independent, motivated and committed to learning (Huynh et al., 2003) than those studying in traditional settings. While some students may feel empowered by the control they have over how and when they learn, some may perceive online courses to lack structure and support. These negative experiences are causes for a high incidence of withdrawal and incomplete grades in online courses compared to the classrooms. Therefore, it becomes necessary for students to learn time management, assertiveness, initiative, self-motivation, and written communication in order to foster a positive virtual class environment. The skill set required to be successful in online learning is difficult to acquire, and not all students are suited to this type of learning, and not all subjects are best taught via this medium (Valentine, 2002).

Online education can be equally challenging to the instructors. Teaching online courses requires a certain level of technical sophistication and a willingness to adapt to this new learning environment. Very often the instructor is also the course content creator, which requires an extensive knowledge of software applications. The lack of training for instructors is a problem, but it pales in comparison to the instructor's attitude towards online education. An instructor who is resistant to change will not take advantage of the technology, and will not modify the curriculum to fit online learning. In the end, the quality of instruction will suffer.

A positive virtual classroom environment allows for flexibility in both class schedule and the teacher availability (El Mansour & Mupinga, 2007; Mahoney, 2009). The flexibility of the courses allows professors and students to correspond with each other when convenient rather than interacting simultaneously. It also eliminates the barriers of time and space. Gayton and McEwen (2007), as cited by Dixson (2010), "found [that] rapport and collaboration between students, thought provoking questions, and dynamic interaction among the top instructional processes identified by instructors and students" (p. 2). With interactive learning, instructors are provided with insights into the difficulties, misconceptions, verbal pitfalls, and conceptual problems that students may have (Nagel, Blignaut, & Cronje, 2009). Virtual classrooms also have the flexibility of instructional pace.

Also, the distance education program has allowed students to be fully engaged in some of the class activities. These class activities are based in collaborative/cooperative, group discussion, and other forms of student-student interactions (Dixson, 2010). Furthermore, students must be active rather than be passive by watching and listening to the professor. These online courses implore the use of audio, video, color, graphics, and animations in order to "stimulate student interest" (El Mansour & Mupinga 2007, p. 3).

Many course management platforms, such as Blackboard, do not need to install in any of the computers/laptops. Therefore, the students and professors will only need to have internet service in order to access the course. Because the courses can be done at any time, students do not need to feel confined to do the work at home or school. They are able to do the assignments from any place and at any time.

However, there are technology hiccups such as hardware malfunctions, security threats (such as Trojans and viruses), and problems with internet services and class management platforms along with the "sense of feeling lost in Cyberspace" (El Mansour & Mupinga, 2007, p. 1). In addition, the asynchronous communication is slow and does limit the amount of communication among the professor and students. Thus, there is a feeling that the professors do not get to know the students personally.

Furthermore, El Mansour and Mupinga (2007) cite the cost of online education can often be more expensive than traditional classroom education. Professors need to be professionally trained in order to effectively prepare online classes. Students need to have an orientation towards online learning so that they are familiarized with the course management platforms (El Mansour & Mupinga, 2007). In addition, "the teaching behaviors and strategies required for effective teaching online are not the same as those required for [face-to-face] teaching" (Loveland, 2007). The professors need to make sure that the organizational component of the course management platform is appropriate. Loveland (2007) states that the course materials need to be accessible from multiple locations, need to have consistent design of the course pages, and content modules with organized related materials. The professors must also use proofreaders for online lectures and other materials so that the students' perceptions of the instructor's effort are not affected (Loveland 2007). Thus, through appropriate actions, the professors are able to promote a virtual class environment that has quality work along with fostering positive student behaviors through collaborative activities.

HOW TO MAKE ONLINE CLASSES WORK

In order for online courses to work effectively, the following goals need to be followed:

- Goal 1) we will provide a sound professional development to both professors and students so that they can effectively use the course management platform.
- Goal 2) our professors will effectively use Internet services and course management platform.
- Goal 3) the use of the course management platform will promote collaborative/cooperative learning and group discussions among the students. Essentially, the students will be interacting with each other rather than mostly with the teacher.

- Goal 4) the professor will invoke a strong presence in these courses by being a facilitator with discussions in the discussion; however, they are not the main focus of the classroom.
- Goal 5) the professor will make their virtual classroom easy to navigate and make it presentable to the class.
- Goal 6) ultimately, the professor will promote a quality education and the needed qualities of self-motivation skills, time management, assertiveness, initiative, and well-written communication.
- Goal 7) finally, the students will be well introduced to online distance learning so that they are better prepared for their future educational and work related endeavors.

These seven goals allow for the students and teachers to learn to incorporate and use technology for their educational benefit. For accomplishing these goals, the students need to be "self-directed, motivated, organized, independent, and take responsibility for their own learning" (Mahoney, 2009). These students will be able to demonstrate creativity and innovation, communication and collaboration, conduct research and use information, think critically, solve problems, and make decisions, and use the technology effectively and productively (ISTE, 2011).

ONLINE COURSES STRATEGIES AND ACTIVITIES

The online courses strategies and activities are based on interactive and active learning. Typically, the professors educate the students through collaborative learning. They often move away from "recorded lectures, readings, homework and tests" (Dixson, 2010, p. 2). It incorporates group work, regular assignments, and solid feedback. The activities as proscribed by Dixson (2010) call for the use of "collaborative activities, group discussion, and other forms of student-student interaction" (p. 2). Even though Dixson (2010)'s call for interactivity and collaboration, there are online courses that are taught through audio recording. Furthermore, there are approaches, called Personalized System of Instruction, where independent study is emphasized through web modules. These strategies are useful in online courses because they build a quality education and also teach the students the following characteristics—self-motivation skills, time management, assertiveness, initiative, and well-written communication. These students will be able to focus on building knowledge and collaborate in order to promote understanding in their content fields

(Nagel, Blignaut, & Cronje, 2009). Thus, Nagel, Blignaut, and Cronje (2009) further illustrate that the immediate feedback from the peers and instructors contribute to learning and also social interaction. Furthermore, the peer interaction allows the students to not learn in isolation.

EVALUATION PLAN OF ONLINE COURSES

It is essential to assess online courses in order to see if they are meeting standards. Assessment of the Online Course should be both quantitative and qualitative. Students should be surveyed before the start of the semester on their thoughts about participating in an online course and about the qualities of self-motivation skills, time management, assertiveness, initiative, and well-written communication. At the end of the semester of the online course, they should be again surveyed on their perceptions of online courses and the qualities of self-motivation skills, time management, assertiveness, initiative, and well-written communication as well as the content, level of difficulty, and their perceived level of mastery of the concepts. Second, faculty members teaching the online course should be asked to judge its effectiveness in monitoring student achievement throughout the semester. Also, it is recommended to use two additional instruments that have been tested as reliable and valid—Rubric for Assessing Interactive Qualities in Distance Courses (RAIQDC) and Student Course Engagement Questionnaire (SCEQ) (Dixson, 2010). In addition, faculty members who have been teaching the chosen courses for several years should be asked to compare students' abilities with those in previous years who have not used online courses and also the students currently enrolled in the traditional version of the same classes. Finally, the final grades of students using the online courses should be compared with those from previous years and currently who are not in online courses.

PROFESSIONAL DEVELOPMENT FOR ONLINE COURSES

Professional development is the most important component of online courses. In order for the students to receive a quality education that prizes assertiveness, initiative, self-motivation, and time management skills, both the professors and students will receive professional development. El Mansour and Mupinga (2007) states both professors and students need to be trained in order to use the course management platform properly. The professors should receive training on both the course management platform and also strategies for teaching an online course. Therefore, the professors should be trained by a course management specialist and a well-known professor that has been teaching online classes for some time. The well-known professor that teaches online classes will speak to the professors about interactive and student centered activities that will promote group discussion and collaborative efforts.

The students should receive an orientation towards what qualities are needed in order to effectively be a part of an online course and also an introduction to the course management platform. In addition to the orientation, the students should receive video and written tutorials provided by course management platform and the technology director. These tutorials and troubleshoot/help guides will allow the students some guidance if they have additional problems or questions. There should also be a help desk that is headed by the technology team at the school, which should also have communications with the course management platform help desk.

Thus, it is essential to be adequately and actively prepared in the creation and maintenance of online courses. In this preparation, professors and students must be properly introduced in how an online course is managed. With a more student centered approach, students are to take part in discussions and activities that teach specific domain knowledge and also other skills. Those skills are self-motivation, time management, assertiveness, initiative, and effective written communication. These skills are extremely valuable for the students to possess and useful in future education and work related experience.

References

Allen, I. E., & Seaman, J. (2014). *Grade change: Tracking online education in the United States.* Wellesley, MA: Babson Survey Research Group.

Bichsel, J. (2013). *The state of e-learning in higher education: An eye toward growth and increased access.* Louisville, CO: Educause Center for Analysis and Research.

Bowen, W., Chingos, M., Lack, K., & Nygren, T. (2013). Online learning in higher education. *Education Next, 13*(2). Retrieved from http://educationnext.org/online-learning-in-higher-education

Dixson, M. D. (2010). Creating effective student engagement in online courses: What do students find engaging? *Journal of the Scholarship of Teaching and Learning, 10*(2), 1–13.

El Mansour, B., & Mupinga, D. M. (2007). Students' positive and negative experiences in hybrid and online classes. *College Student Journal, 41*(1), 1–10.

Frydenberg, J. (2007). Persistence in university continuing education online classes. *International Review of Research in Open and Distance Learning, 8*(3), 1–15.

ISTE. (2011). NETS for Students. Retrieved from http://www.iste.org/standards/nets-for-students.aspx

Jack, Z., & Curt, U. (2001). Why blended will win. *Training and Development, 55*(8), 54–60.

Loveland, K. A. (2007). Student evaluation of teaching (SET) in web-based classes: Preliminary findings and a call for further research. *The Journal of Educators Online, 4*(2), 1–18.

Mahoney, S. (2009). Mindset change: Influences on student buy-in to online classes. *The Quarterly Review of Distance Education, 10*(1), 75–83.

Nagel, D. (2009). Most college students to take classes online by 2014. Retrieved from http://campustechnology.com/articles/2009/10/28/most-college-students-to-take-classes-online-by-2014.aspx

Nagel, L., Blignaut, A. S., & Cronje, J. C. (2009). Read-only participants: a case for student communication in online classes. *Interactive Learning Environments, 17*(1), 37–51.

Romiszowski, A. (2004). How's the e-learning baby? Factors leading to success or failure of an educational technology innovation. *Educational Technology, 44*(1), 5–27.

Teaster, P., & Blieszner, R. (1999). Promises and pitfalls of the interactive television approach to teaching adult development and aging. *Educational Gerontology, 25*(8), 741–754.

Valentine, D. (2002). Distance learning: Promises, problems, and possibilities. *Online Journal of Distance Learning Administration, V*(3). Retrieved from http://www.westga.edu/~distance/ojdla/fall53/valentine53.html

CHAPTER 12

■ ■ ■

Gifted Students and Technology

Marcella Mandracchia, Ed.D

Jenny Yang, Ed.D

Gifted students are identified by individuals, such as teachers, administrators, and parents. These students are capable of high performance. Therefore, these students require differentiated educational programs and services that go beyond the regular school programs (Davis, Rimm, & Siegle 2011). The differentiation of educational programs can be done through the use of technology. Periathiruvadi and Rinn (2012) believe that this differentiation through the use of technology "serves as an educational and creative outlet for some of the best and brightest minds in the world" (p. 153). It becomes essential that these students become engaged with what is considered to be 'complex technological advancements'. It is important to have the students engaged in the 'complex technological advancements' by relating it to the modes of technology that they are using. For example, students should come into contact with mobile phones and computers. These modes of technology allow education to be interactive with their needs. In order to meet the needs of these students, there is a need for strong programming standards for the curriculum.

NATIONAL ASSOCIATION FOR GIFTED CHILDREN PROGRAMMING STANDARDS

According to the National Association for Gifted Children (NAGC) (2010), there are several different strands that must be met in order to educate a gifted child in the most appropriate manner. Those strands are as followed: (1) learning and development, (2) assessment, (3) curriculum planning and instruction, (4) programming, (5) learning environment, and (6) professional development.

Learning and Development with Technology

In terms of the strand of learning and development, it is important to note that technology must support the needs of the students through understanding the attitudes of the students towards technology, the use of computer-aided instruction using educational software, and understanding how technology influences the socio-emotional development of the students (Periathiruvadi & Rinn, 2012).

When discussing gifted students' attitudes towards technology, it is important to note that the student needs to understand why the technology is critical to their learning. Therefore, the student needs to see the relevancy. For example, Periathiruvadi and Rinn (2012) spoke of Kahveci's study (2010), which demonstrated that it was important for the students to feel that the technology use was relevant and regularly used. In this study, it became critical for the students to not feel discouraged by their performance with the technology. The constant use of the technology allowed students to feel more confident with their abilities. In addition to confidence, it allowed students to really take part in problem solving. This taps into the idea of the use of computer-aided instruction, which allows for students to improve their critical thinking skills and quality of their writing. Dixon, Cassady, Cross, and Williams (2005) concur with this notion that the students are able to take their time and expand their thoughts so they can become engaged in their tasks.

In terms of engagement, it also becomes critical to not only address the cognitive aspects of the students, but also the socio-emotional needs of the students. The socio-emotional needs of the students are not always readily addressed as it is not deemed to be the primary focus of education. However, the socio-emotional needs of the students are crucial to the overall development of those said students. It becomes ridiculous to ignore those needs because of the increasing use of e-mail, chats, blogs, and social media networking. For example, these previously mentioned forms of technology allow for a constant interaction. Because of the constant interaction, students can become affected negatively or positively. In the negative aspects, students could become stressed or bullied. However, there are positives, which can allow students to learn cooperative skills and decision-making skills. Therefore, the effect of technology on the socio-emotional needs of the students becomes dependent on how the technology is used and managed.

Assessment and Technology

NAGC (2010) have employed three forms of assessments for gifted students that have impacted gifted students' success. Those three forms of assessments are as followed: (1) assessments that identify gifted students, (2) ongoing assessments of gifted students' learning, and (3) assessments that evaluate gifted programs in order to help meet the strengths and weaknesses of the gifted students. Why is the use of technology so critical in assessing the needs of the gifted students? It is because the computer itself can generate a self-report. Because of the way it can allow instant scoring, it allows for students, instructors, and administrators to make adjustments as well as knowing what needs and strengths the students have. These computer-based assessments allow instructors to "analyze how much time their students took to complete their assessments, and whenever a student spent more time on a particular section, they could analyze the data and help the student to understand difficult concepts" (Periathiruvadi & Rinn, 2012, pgs. 158–159).

Curriculum and Instruction Planning

When looking at the results of assessments, there is a need for changes in the curriculum and instruction planning. When dealing with curriculum, it is important to differentiate instruction so that students are equipped with the 21st century skills, which are inquiry skills, problem-solving skills, critical thinking skills, self-regulating skills, and scaffolding for their own learning (Periathiruvadi & Rinn, 2012).

The 21st century skills are learning the core subjects of English and language arts, world language, arts, mathematics, economics, science, geography, history, and government and civics along with information, media, and technology skills (Bellanca & Brandt, 2010). While learning these skills, students also learn life and career skills such as flexibility, adaptability, productivity, leadership, responsibility, self-direction, and social skills. In addition, the students would learn about innovation and learning skills, such as creativity, critical thinking, problem solving, communication, and collaboration (Bellanca & Brandt, 2010). Additionally, the students would also learn 21st century themes, such as global awareness, financial, economic, business, and entrepreneurial literacy, civic literacy, health literacy, and environmental literacy. Also, 21st century skills also comprise the idea of metacognition, which is thinking about how you think (Bellanca & Brandt, 2010). These skills are all important so that the students become viable productive individuals in their future endeavors.

In order to build these crucial skills, the use of technology facilitates open-ended problem solving. For example, the use of graphic calculators and emulator programs allows for the solution of problems. Periathiruvadi and Rinn (2012) state that the "use of graphing calculators . . . allowed students to explore new concepts unfamiliar to them and helped them obtain a concrete understanding of math theories and problems" (p. 159). Another example is the use of an online plotting program, which allows students to be eager to share results together. The main purpose of this digital drawing tool is to express the math understanding of the students' in a visual format. Technology can also be used for scaffolding skills, which is the case with the use of digital cameras and palm-held computers. These crucial skills are also compounded by the need of proper training for the students. It becomes necessary for the students to know how to use these technologies in a productive, honest, and safe way. Therefore, there is a need to build digital citizenship. Thus, it becomes necessary to also follow the National Educational Technology Standards (NETS), which are outlined as followed:

1 Promotion of Creativity and Innovation
2 Promotion of Communication and Collaboration
3 Promotion of Critical Thinking, Problem Solving, and Decision Making
4 Promotion of Digital Citizenship.

In accordance to NETS, students should encounter ways to build their information technology and creative practices (ITCP). Some ways students may build these practices are as followed:

- Student writing using desktop or laptop computers
- Desktop publishing
- Online publishing of classroom projects
- Computer-based design tools
- Digital cameras and imaging projects
- Graphics and photo editing
- Computer animation and movie making
- Student-created podcasts and digital movies.

In addition to building those practices, students should build their media and digital literacy through the following ways:

- Webquests and other online research projects
- Classroom websites that involve students in design and maintenance
- Student-created web materials
- Web material used by students for critical reviews

- Online newspapers and news broadcasts
- Bookmarking and social bookmarking
- Digital dictionaries
- Multimedia timelines
- Information alerts.

The Importance of Creativity

The Information Age necessitates that people learn and work in communities or in a social atmosphere (West, 2009). In addition, collaboration is now valued as creative output rather than knowing how matters have been solved previously. Thus, researchers, such as Csikszentmihalyi (1990), have come to realize that creativity must be studied as a social event. Glaveanu (2011) concurs with Csikszentmihalyi (1990) that creativity is a social process that allows for enhancement of ideas. According to Glaveanu (2011), creativity takes place in between the creator and the social world. Every person and activity has the potential to be creative. Creativity belongs everywhere, including markets, streets, science labs, and theaters. Creativity is intertwined with traditions, rules, and constraints. Thus, creativity must be seen and discussed as a psycho-socio-cultural nature rather than individualistic. Therefore, there is a need to enhance creativity through collaborative methods. Examples of techniques that enhance creativity through collaborative methods are brainstorming and brainwriting. These collaborative techniques allow for ideas to be built upon each other, so that it becomes the notion of 'quantity generating quality'. Paulus and Nijstad (2003) state that it may be better to have an electronic version rather than face-to-face due to the nature of feeling less discomfort because of not seeing the group members directly. In addition, it also allows for more members to come together to generate the ideas. The stimulation of these activities allows for ideas that may not have been readily generated. Also, West (2009) states the diverse, but well-balanced group can avoid groupthink, which is when a dominant person offers an idea and the group prematurely accepts it, and improves group divergent thinking. In addition, group members must feel comfortable in expressing their dissenting opinions (West, 2009). West (2009) further elaborates that there needs to be a strong community, in which members feel valued, confident, and interdependent. This interdependence and strength in diversity improves group divergent thinking processes.

The divergent phase of the project allows for the generation of numerous, novel ideas. However, if the process shifts to a collaborative convergent thinking phase, the group must choose only the best idea out of the numerous, novel ideas (Paulus & Nijstad,

2003). Interactive groups are more successful on convergent thinking tasks than on divergent thinking tasks. Therefore, there is a need for more interactivity in the group innovation process. The diversity and interactivity of the group is important in group convergent thinking because it leads to superior ideas and improved decision-making based on critical evaluations. The independent judgment is important in keeping a group consensus before fully evaluating all ideas, which is considered to be 'premature closure'. In addition, it is also imperative that groups avoid premature consensus and conformity pressures when evaluating the ideas (Paulus & Nijstad, 2003). Participation from all group members is critical. The group must act as a unified whole. For example, if there are low levels of interpersonal trust categorized by a restrictive group climate, then there will not be a good exchange of ideas (West, 2009). Furthermore, if the group cannot exchange relevant ideas or withhold ideas because of fear of critical evaluation, group creativity will suffer. Therefore, it is most critical that group members share their unique information and that the information is taken into consideration (Paulus & Nijstad, 2003).

For creativity to be achieved, the overall organizational climate should be conducive to innovation. Amabile et al. (1996) present a model for how an organization influences its members' creativity. There are five components, which are as followed: (1) encouragement of creativity, (2) autonomy/freedom, (3) resources, (4) pressures (both positive and negative), and (5) organizational impediments. In terms of autonomy, it leads to a higher level of motivation for the group to solve problems. Thus, the climate must allow for the group members to feel safe to participate, be supportive of innovation, vision, and task orientation. West (2009) contends that the group members must have dynamic expertise (where they are sometimes a novice, or expert, but always growing in expertise). Therefore, the group members must push themselves to complete intrinsically interesting projects that are just beyond their level of expertise. There needs to be ten key conditions to enable group flow: (1) shared goal, (2) close and deep listening, (3) complete concentration, (4) being in control of the group's actions and environment, (5) blending of individual egos, (6) equal participation, (7) member's familiarity with each other, (8) constant communication, (9) elaboration of each other's ideas, and (10) frequent failure (and learning from failure) (West, 2009). West (2009) posits that there needs to be an "entrepreneurial network that allows members of the community to retrieve organizational knowledge from other experts, re-use and repurpose the information, and create new knowledge that is then shared with the network" (p. 322). In addition, the group members must raise questions, analyze the situation, model a new explanation, examine and implement the model, reflect on the process, and consolidate the new practice. In order for group creativity to really be productive, there must be a communal, group introspection and reflection in the area of psychological safety. The group members must also have contact with experts outside of the group in order to acquire new, critical information (Paulus & Nijstad, 2003).

These factors allow for the social aspect of creativity to be placed in the forefront rather than the individual. Creativity, as Glaveanu (2011) notes, does not reside in the object that was created but largely depends on a social agreement. There are societal discourses about creativity that can legitimatize who can be called creative. Therefore, it becomes recognized as more of a "we-paradigm." Thus, the social approach of creativity can be summed up as followed: (1) creativity's trademark feature of originality and value is dependent on 'subjective reception', (2) subjective reception is shaped by broader framework of 'cultural reception', (3) creative processes take place in a social mind, (4) creativity requires a social world, collaboration, and division of labor, and (5) the enhancement of creativity can and should exploit the networks of social relations (Glaveanu, 2011).

Creativity requires a social world (Csikszentmihalyi, 1990, 1997; Glaveanu, 2011). Csikszentmihalyi (1990, 1997)'s model positioning creative production at the confluence between the person and their characteristics, the field of experts and gatekeepers, and domain of the creation. Thus, all creativity is collaboration. Creativity requires collaboration of what is considered to be 'multiple actors'. Two such instances are group or team creativity (which is short term, common in an organizational setting) and creative long-term collaboration (i.e. Pierre & Marie Curie).

Furthermore, creativity requires a division of labor. There are more invisible and pervasive forms in which the social world is involved. For example, the notion of the art world is produced by a network of people in a cooperative activity. The creator is not seen as the isolated author but fundamentally relies on the division of labor in order to create. Creativity requires a social mind. Not only the knowledge we use to be creative is acquired through social means, but the mind itself is dialogical in nature and functions 'in terms of the other'. Group members should try to carry out functions of the creative cognitive systems (executive control, attention to input from the environment, representation of the problem, representation of the current solution plan, storage of knowledge, and retrieval of knowledge) instead of one-to-one correspondence. Therefore, Glaveanu (2011) suggests that is critical to have a diverse group in order for this effectiveness of idea generation to occur.

The Demands of 21st Century

The goal of schools is to prepare students for the workplace, citizenship, and economic success. In addition, it is important in order to stay competitive with other countries. Currently, the American students are scoring lower compared to their global counterparts in reading, mathematics, and science. Therefore, there is a critical need to make sure that our students are prepared for the future.

In order to make sure the students are ready for the future, teachers and educational officials need to be prepared by revising standards, assessments, instruction, professional development, teacher preparation, and technology programs. Also, teachers need to use the content as a way to teach these important skills. Educators implement the 21st century skills through using technology and connecting content through the curriculum. Technology and software has to be implemented with fidelity, so that the purpose matches the use. Therefore, when purchasing the technology and software, it needs to stay true to models and frameworks that are proscribed.

Programming and Technology

In terms of programming and technology, the gifted students need to be provided with many programming options, such as acceleration, enrichment, and individualized learning opportunities through the use of independent studies, mentorships, internships, and online courses (NAGC, 2010). It has been seen that students feel online enrichment programs foster higher order thinking skills and social skills. Even though fostering these skills is important, the main issue with programming is making sure that the students are engaged and challenged.

Learning Environment and Technology

The students' role has changed from a passive receiver to an active problem solver. Thus, students should be engaged in experiential learning, where they experience exactly what they are learning. Therefore, the teacher must guide the students' learning and become an active learner themselves. Thus, the teacher must "structure a learning environment to help students construct, transform, and extend knowledge," (Masouleh & Jooneghani, 2012, p. 8). Levitt (2001) states teachers believe that teaching and learning should be student-centered. Teachers must create a safe but challenging environment where the students' participation is encouraged and errors are allowed. Teachers are called to guide the students by asking questions, exploring options, suggesting alternatives, and encouraging students. The goal is to develop students' capacity for independent action and responsibility.

Similarly, Reeve (2006) states that those teachers can learn to be more autonomy supportive towards students, engage students when they offer high levels of both autonomy support and structure, and create an autonomy supportive motivating style for high quality teacher-student relationship. Students must be able to feel attuned, supported, receive gentle discipline, and feel as if the teacher can relate to them. Reeve (2006) claims those aforementioned characteristics create that high quality relationship of students and teachers. Even in the case of online courses, there needs to be a learning environment that is learner centered, encourages independence and innovation, offers various grouping options, and be flexible. Furthermore, there are social aspects of online classrooms as it calls for students to be more open to offer ideas and opinions as well as interact with like-minded peers from different parts of the global community.

Professional Development and Technology

Professional development should be integrated with other planning activities so that the people who are using the technology know how to use the technology before it is in the schools. If they do not know how to use the technology before it is implemented they will have problems and they will need additional help. The personnel in a school district that should participate in the professional development are everyone, such as administrators, teachers, clerical staff, and all those who will be using the technology. Periathiruvadi and Rinn (2012) state that training is the strongest predictor about attitude towards technology. The planning objectives in designing a professional development program for technology should be the integration of the professional development and the planning activities, assessing the needs of the district or school, designing a program that meets the needs of both the district and school, providing incentives for staff to participate, implementing the program, and evaluating and reviewing the program.

Some of the critical questions that need to be answered in a needs analysis are the types of specific applications, educational objectives, or individuals needed to be targeted. Also, it is important to realize if the technology hasn't had been properly introduced in professional development in the past. If it is the case, there is a need for a comprehensive analysis. There is a need for an in-depth examination of all existing applications and proposed computer applications including administrative and instructional. In addition, there is a need to evaluate the knowledge and ability of the staff that will use the technology.

CONCLUSION

Addressing the social and emotional needs using technology becomes critical. The cognitive aspects are critical for the long-term functioning of the students in a professional setting. However, how the students use the technology necessitates a lot of critical analysis. The technology must be used in a productive, honest, and safe way. Therefore, there needs to be a structure at every aspect of the integration of technology in a gifted classroom, which is similar to how it should be integrated into a mainstream or special education classroom. There needs to be a logical reason for the technology's incorporation. The technology itself must allow the students to use it so that they are being the active users of the technology. It must build many cognitive and socio-emotional skills. The teachers must be able to use the technology in a productive manner. Finally, it must satisfy the goal of making students ready to be 21st century professionals.

References

Amabile, T. M., Conti, R., Coon, H., Lazenby, J., & Herron, M. (1996). Assessing the work environment for creativity. *Academy of Management Journal, 39*(5), 1154–1185.

Bellanca, J., & Brandt, R. (2010). *21st Century skills: Rethinking how students learn*. Bloomington, IN: National Educational Service.

Csikszentmihalyi, M. (1990). *Creativity: a systems approach*. In G. Klein (Ed.) Creativity and Flow. Stockholm: Bromberg Verlag.

Csikszentmihalyi, M. (1997). Flow and education. *The North American Montessori Teachers' Association Journal, 22,* 2, 2–35.

Davis, G. A., Rimm, S. B., & Siegle, D. (2011). *Education of the gifted and talented* (6th ed.). Boston: Pearson.

Dixon, F., Cassady, J., Cross, T., & Williams, D. (2005). Effects of technology on critical thinking and essay writing among gifted adolescents. *Journal of Secondary Gifted Education, 16,* 180–189.

Glaveanu, V. (2011). How are we creative together? Comparing socio-cognitive and sociocultural answers. *Theory and Psychology, 21*(4), 473–492.

Levitt, K. E. (2001). An Analysis of elementary teachers' beliefs regarding teaching and learning of science. *Science Education, 86*(1), 1–22.

Masouleh, N. M. & Jooneghani, R. B. (2012). Paradigm shift: A shift in the role of teacher from a vessel filler to a facilitator! A Philosophical perspective. *International Journal of Academic Research*, 4(5), 5–9.

National Association for Gifted Children. (NAGC). (2010). *Pre-K– Grade 12 gifted programming standards*. Retrieved from http:// www.nagc.org/index.aspx?id=546

Paulus, P. B., & Nijstad, B. A. (2003). *Group Creativity: Innovation through collaboration*. England: Oxford University Press.

Periathiruvadi, S., & Rinn A. N. (2012). Technology in gifted education: A review of best practices and empirical research. *Journal of Research on Technology in Education*, 45(2), 153–169.

Reeve, J. (2006). Teachers as facilitators: What autonomy-supportive teachers do and why the students benefit. *The Elementary School Teacher*, 106(3), 225–236.

West, R. E. (2009). What is shared? A framework for studying communities of innovation. *Educational Technology, Research, & Development*, 57(3), 315–332.

CHAPTER 13

■■■

E-portfolio Today

Edwin Tjoe, Ed.D.

An ePortfolio (also known as an e-portfolio, digital portfolio, or online portfolio) is a collection of someone's work, i.e., artifacts, such as inputted text, electronic files, images, multimedia, blog entries, and hyperlinks, stored in one convenient place on the web. You, as the owner of the collection, determine who has access to your data, and how to share with other people. Many universities, colleges, and K–12 schools (to a lesser extent) nationally and worldwide use this e-portfolio as a way for students to submit their work to their professors. The student simply does the assigned work and then he/she puts the documents online in his/her e-portfolio for the professors to review, evaluate, and provide feedback. The advantage of using the e-portfolio is that it allows whoever views it to see all the work that a person did, including the history and supporting evidence. The professors can also post deadlines for when the work is due, and they can track when students submit the work. There are many uses for e-portfolios across many different industries, for similar applications, such as education, finance, recruiting, and other corporations where it can be used to track and manage training by the employees. This idea has been around since the early 1990s and since then, "forty percent of all types of campuses, whether large or small, public or private, research or liberal arts, or even community colleges, recently reported using student e-portfolios" (Rhodes, 2011). E-portfolios have influenced the way students around the world learn. This serves as a way of presenting information that is quickly becoming more and more popular ("History and Definitions," n.d.).

E-portfolios are mainly used by students. One example of an e-portfolio can be shown by a high school senior. The student first starts collecting information throughout the years of attending high school. After each assignment the student sends the documents completed to his or her portfolio. At the end of the year the student will have a handful of assignments that show how much they have grown over the years. Because the students have years' worth of work in front of them, they can reflect on the skills that they have obtained over time since the beginning. This is crucial because the student can see where he or she has progressed or still has weaknesses. This gives the students a sense of self motivation instead of the teacher just telling them about their progression. The students are gaining critical thinking and communication skills because they are reflecting and writing about their experiences. As quoted in "Making Learning Visible and Meaningful through Electronic Portfolios," Kathleen Blake Yancey said, "To reflect, as to learn (since reflection is similar to learning), we set a problem for ourselves. . . Along the way, we check and confirm, as we seek to reach goals that we have set for ourselves. Reflection becomes a habit, one that transforms" (p. 9). These students are also gaining technological skills because they are spending more time with computers and keeping up with the trend in digital technologies. In addition to giving students vital skills in college, e-portfolios can be used by students in high school to help them get prepared for college. Students can show colleges exactly what they accomplished in high school instead of just telling them, since they have an e-portfolio documenting their growth. College students can also benefit from having an e-portfolio because it can help them land the job they want. Job seekers can make themselves more noticeable to employers by having a collection of work that proves that they have the experience and skills to do the job (Lorenzo & Ittelson, 2005). "Employers . . . will want to see examples of how students apply their knowledge and use it to address complex, unscripted problems" (Rhodes, p. 12). Overall, students greatly benefit from creating their own e-portfolio.

Just like students, teachers can also use e-portfolios to document their skills and accomplishments (Lorenzo & Ittelson, 2005). This can help teachers who are looking to move to a higher level in their area of expertise, since e-portfolios are more advanced and more likely to impress employers. E-portfolios allow teachers to easily showcase all of their previous hard work and dedication. "Teacher e-portfolios are also used for a critical reflection and learning purposes; they make individual teaching practices public and therefore available for collective learning and knowledge sharing" (Lorenzo & Ittelson, p. 4). In the past, teachers could only share materials and ideas with other local teachers. With new technologies and advancements like e-portfolios, teachers can now share ideas with others all over the world. This is important because teachers who come up with effective lessons and innovative ideas can share them with others. This benefits teachers on the other side of the country who could use some extra help. An e-portfolio is also beneficial to teachers because it expands their knowledge and gives them more innovative teaching methods. This can also be beneficial to the student because it gives them a new way to learn in the classroom. If teachers did not get help, students wouldn't have new methods to use. Overall, e-portfolios can help teachers communicate better, give lessons to their students, and excel in their field.

Institutions, especially colleges, also use e-portfolios to help themselves succeed. For e-portfolios on this level, they collect "authentic work, data, and analysis that demonstrates institutional accountability and serves as a vehicle for institution-wide reflection, learning, and improvement" (Lorenzo & Ittelson, p. 5). By creating these portfolios they are examining their strengths and faults in order to better themselves. Since these portfolios are electronic, anyone in the world, including people who are interested in the institution, can see what the school can provide for them and how it has progressed. Two universities in particular that have used e-portfolios are Indiana University-Purdue University Indianapolis (IUPUI) and Portland State University (PSU). They use these portfolios as a self-study to make themselves better and have used them for reaccreditation. Anyone with access to the internet can see what is going on in the school. Based on the success of the e-portfolios from IUPUI and PSU, the Western Association of Schools and Colleges now suggests that all other institutions under their supervision also use this method for reaccreditation. This shows that the e-portfolio is being seen as something successful and will be used over time. A regional accrediting agency official said, as quoted in "An Overview of E-Portfolios":

> The vast majority of our evaluators find it useful and powerful to read an electronic report and be able to hyperlink and easily see documents. They can explore and dip in and out of web pages. It is all organized in a much more effective way than printed appendices in a paper report that you have to shuffle through to find things.

Institutions use student e-portfolios in their own e-portfolios to show how well the students have learned and how much they have accomplished. This can be a school's way of marketing themselves to the public. E-portfolios being used by institutions can make them more well-known and more successful (p. 6).

Although students, teachers, and institutions have successfully used e-portfolios, there are always still grey areas. For student portfolios there is an issue regarding whether information can be trusted. One of the first questions is whether or not an e-portfolio should be considered "official," since it is not evaluated by a professional. If a student is able to alter their e-portfolios, should it be considered official? There are also some general questions about how long a student should be able to access their portfolios and who actually owns these portfolios. There are issues with teachers' portfolios as well. Technically, teachers are not able to post student work because of privacy and copyright issues in place. If schools want teachers to create electronic portfolios, the school needs to provide information on how to use the technology. There are similar issues involved with institutional e-portfolios. A school that wants to show off their education by giving samples of faculty and student work needs their permission. Also, creating an institutional e-portfolio requires a lot of work because it's difficult to gather so much information. Even though there are still questions about e-portfolios, the software can still be very helpful (Lorenzo & Ittelson, 2005).

There are many benefits to using an e-portfolio. The first benefit is that they are easier to share and maintain than regular physical paper portfolios. If a student needs to make a change, it's much simpler to update something that's online (Jokinen, n.d.). "An e-portfolio provides flexibility, openness, and multiplicity compared to a traditional portfolio. E-portfolios can overcome time-space limitations; ease the collection, revision, and presentation of information; reduce budget and storage needs" (Kim, Wang & Lee). The software allows students to develop their own voices when they reflect and show evidence of being able to think and learn (Rhodes, 2011). "The samples available in the e-portfolio 'prove' a student's capabilities," (Kryder, 2011, p. 334). A teacher can easily assess a student's academic progress by reading the portfolio. This reduces the amount of tests students have to take and the amount of anxiety that students feel when having to study.

While there are many benefits to using e-portfolios, there are also some negatives. One is that there might not be enough technical knowledge. A student might be asked to create the portfolio, but might not be familiar with the software. Some schools have become more committed to e-portfolio systems so that everyone is more familiar with it (Kryder, 2011). Another negative about e-portfolios is that if you had a paper portfolio, you'd be able to explain it more to the person who is looking at it. With an e-portfolio, the person reading it has to figure it out themselves and the information might be misunderstood. Also, "students need an extended period of time over which to develop [e-portfolios], and they need opportunities and experiences through which they can develop good samples" (Worley, 2011, p. 332). An e-portfolio is not something that can be rushed. A lot of time would need to be devoted to it. Another negative about e-portfolios is that the information in them may be false. The writer of the portfolio may have had someone else write the assignments for them or they may just lie. Technology in general is not as dependable and can break down. This may cause problems for people and they may not be able to access the portfolios. One last possible negative about e-portfolios is that they "lack the reliability and validity of the standardized tests and therefore cannot be used to compare institutions, courses, programs, etc." (Rhodes, 2011, p. 10). E-portfolios might not be a reliable source of information about people because of what situation they were in while they were writing their essays. It is difficult to compare students that way. During the SAT, students are all together doing the same exact thing at the same time. There needs to be a set standard for what is expected of students using the e-portfolios. To provide this structure, the VALUE project was started (Rhodes, 2011).

The VALUE (Valid Assessment of Learning in Undergraduate Education) system was created by a group called Association of American Colleges and Universities (AAC&U). People from many different colleges joined together to create a system that "articulated their expectations for learning" (Rhodes, 2011, p. 8). They listed skills that students should have in order to show their learning. Necessary skills that should be shown in students' work include written and oral communication, problem solving, team work, and creative and critical thinking. "The VALUE rubrics are criterion-referenced, and all students can be judged against the criteria. Yet the primary usefulness of the rubrics lies in their ability to communicate faculty expectations for student performance to others and to engage with the students in gauging their progress during a single program or along an entire educational pathway" (Rhodes, 2011, p. 10). This makes e-portfolios more useful for observing student learning. There is also a challenge to those who are trying to view the results of the e-portfolio. There are steps being made to make sure that e-portfolio results are being communicated to people (Rhodes, 2011).

Several universities have used e-portfolios, as documented in "Making Learning Visible and Meaningful through Electronic Portfolios." One of those is Clemson University. They use e-portfolios to assess the students throughout their years at the school. The graduating class of 2010 started their e-portfolios in the beginning of their college careers and added to them each semester. These students successfully finished their portfolios and received positive feedback. Professors started to change their teaching methods and assignments because students were successful with their portfolios. Another college that used e-portfolios was Queensborough Community College. Four hundred fifty new freshman entering the school in 2010 and 23 faculty members came together to explore the different types of learning through e-portfolios. Students posted their essays on their portfolios and other students commented on the essays to help them. Overall, "faculty and student responses to the pilot were sufficiently positive to have QCC commit resources to offer the program to all students" (Rhodes, 2011, p. 10). Another school that used e-portfolios was the University of Michigan Medical School. Trainees in the school participated in a program to help students when they have patients in bad situations. Doctors wrote about their own past encounters and situations with their patients and created e-portfolios. Students read these so that they could be more prepared in similar situations. The portfolios focused on the way doctors and students at the medical school handle and analyze bad situations. The school has also developed positive reflective skills of medical students that attend the institution. A school that is known for using e-portfolios as a learning method is Spellman College. All students must create and pass their e-portfolio to graduate. The portfolio is not tied to one specific course and they have to include material in it, such as pictures, music, videos, etc., that describe their personalities. Overall, the purpose of the e-portfolios was sometimes difficult to understand for some students, but most students did well with the assignment (Rhodes, 2011).

A college that believes in the potential of e-portfolios is Emory University's Goizueta Business School. They feel that making e-portfolios is a useful tool for creating students' professional identities (Graves & Epstein, 2011). The portfolios that they create are not just typical e-portfolios that collect any assignment; these portfolios have a specific focus. The portfolios are "used as the foundation for a sequence of assignments designed to help students develop the self-awareness necessary to transition from a student into an emerging professional" (Graves & Epstein, 2011, p. 343). Students can use the e-portfolio to have a better idea of their strengths and weakness, which can in turn help them have a better idea of what they want to accomplish professionally. Students write a professional development plan that includes SWOT (Strengths, Weaknesses, Opportunities, Threats). Students examine their professional strengths and weaknesses and look at opportunities and threats that they may encounter in their field of choice. From this, they create a list of tasks that need to be done to reach their career goals. A career plan like this makes students more prepared and aware, which later gives them an advantage over their professional competition. By creating this portfolio, students are developing written and verbal communication skills. In today's world, employers find this very desirable. Overall, Emory University's Goizueta Business School feels that e-portfolios are a needed piece of a student's education to help them with their future profession (Graves & Epstein, 2011).

E-portfolios are helpful for students of younger ages as well. Faculty members at Conestoga Elementary School in Gillette, Wyoming developed a way for e-portfolios to be beneficial to students from kindergarten to third grade. During the early 1990s, while technology of computers was just being grasped by the public, this school came up with a portfolio system that was capable of recording "permanently the growth and development of children" (Campbell, 1996, p. 187). Beginning in their kindergarten year, teachers had students do tasks that the teacher felt would be a good example of how the student performed in that area. The teacher would then copy or record the task to a disk on the computer. This action would be repeated several times until the student was in the third grade. This type of e-portfolio was beneficial to the teachers because they were able to look back on previous years and see what the student's strengths and weaknesses were. This in turn helped the current teacher of that specific student. Teachers can also look at students' e-portfolios and see different ways to help the students. Third graders were able to look at the records too. The reason this became helpful was because students can see exactly how they are progressing. It can also improve a student's confidence because it shows the academic hardships that the student overcame throughout his or her earlier years. This portfolio system helped the school because the students' work showed how effective the school's learning plan was, instead of just telling (Campbell, 1996).

After this program was used, they realized there were some flaws. First, there was only one computer. This made it hard for the teachers to get to all of the students' portfolios frequently. The school didn't have enough funds to buy any more computers to use for the system. Second, the school saw that not enough people in the community, including parents, knew about how important the e-portfolio can be or what effect it can have. Another concern was security. The school was afraid that information could be seen by strangers, since there was only one computer. Despite these flaws, e-portfolios are still capable of having a positive effect on a young child's learning progression (Campbell, 1996). "This electronic portfolio version is a dynamic, student-centered process. Its purpose is to measure student learning and physical and social development. As students gain more ownership of their portfolios, the major change in how their achievement is measured will be in their developing a response to their own learning instead of choosing a response from a list of possible answers" (Campbell, 1996, p. 193).

E-portfolios also break the distance barriers and give opportunities to people all over the world to showcase their work. Since all the work is posted on the web, it is easy, for example, for a student in India or China to share his/her work with a university when applying for graduate admission. Another example is when people apply for internships or work overseas, and in general at a distant location where travel is not an option. I can argue the e-portfolios can have a similar impact on society (perhaps in smaller size) to the way YouTube videos go viral. Imagine being a music student, and you share your recordings with someone across the globe. Or even better, imagine using these recordings as an audition for *American Idol* or other similar shows.

It is important to think about students' input, ideas, and feelings about e-portfolios. As discussed in "Student Perceptions of ePortfolio Integration in Online Courses," there was a study done with students who were taking online classes. These classes typically have students interact through typing in discussion boards and don't have any actual verbal or physical communication. This could possibly be negative for a student because it doesn't give them a chance to actually interact socially and meet people. Also, wording can be misunderstood by others when you type something. In person, you use a tone of voice that communicates your feelings, but in text it can mislead others. By using an e-portfolio as part of an online class, students can learn more about each other's personalities. By looking at each other's e-portfolios, students can start to get a better idea about who the other person is. It can also encourage more interaction and friendships in the class. In this study, there were 43 students in two graduate courses in Spring and Fall 2009. They were required to make an e-portfolio and in the portfolio they had to design several web pages. This included a self-introduction, a resume, a learning philosophy, and a summary of goals and achievements. The students had to give each other an analysis of the others' e-portfolios and they received feedback from their teacher. Many of the students felt the use of e-portfolios "increased their desire to learn and students liked sharing their e-portfolio with their classmates." 52.5% of the students felt that having the e-portfolio put them in a more comfortable state regarding expectations. 75% of the students felt closer to their classmates than if they took a regular online class without an e-portfolio. As quoted in one of the studies, one of the students said,

The value of an e-portfolio is great to me and to my instructors . . . The instructors get to know me as a person, as a professional, and as a student. If I did not post an e-portfolio, how would the instructor know what I am about, my beliefs, philosophies? I like the opportunity to present myself to the instructions because I would be unknown to them otherwise. I think that the online school became more personal and real when I posted my portfolio. I felt more connected to the instructors and the graduate program.

Clearly, students have positive feelings about the e-portfolio because it helped them feel more involved in the class and more connected to the teacher and the classmates (Bolliger & Shepherd, 2010).

Overall, e-portfolios have shown a positive effect on students, employers, teachers, and institutions. They have all found a similar positive experience with this useful technology. While there are still minor complications related to e-portfolios, it is still an important part of our future. E-portfolios have the ability to help employers understand their employees before they even work in the field. Portfolios can help people express their personalities in ways we have never seen before. They can even help people learn about their own strengths and weaknesses. They can also teach important skills like technology, critical thinking, self-reflection, and communication. As technology in our lives increases, e-portfolios will become more and more important.

References

Bolliger, D. U., & Shepherd, C. E. (2010). Student perceptions of ePortfolio integration in online courses. *Distance Education*, *31*(3), 295–314. doi:10.1080/01587919.2010.513955

Campbell, J. (1996). Electronic portfolios: A five-year history. *Computers and Composition*, (13), 185–194. Retrieved from http://portfolios.biss.wikispaces.net/file/view/Epoftfolios-Afiveyrhistory-verydated.pdf

Graves, N., & Epstein, M. (2011). Eportfolio: A Tool for Constructing a Narrative Professional Identity. *Business Communication Quarterly*, *74*(3), 342–346. doi:10.1177/1080569911414555

History and definitions of e-portfolio system. (n.d.). Retrieved from http://www.ipangfu.net/EPS415/phase1/history-and-definitions-e-portfolio-system

Jokinen, T. (n.d.). About eportfolios - practise, history and different ways of using them. Retrieved from About E-Portfolios-Practise, History, and Different Ways of Using Them, http://www.elearnspace.org/Articles/eportfolios.htm

Kim, S. Y., Wang, E., & Lee , I. S. (n.d.). Incorporating learner modeling and design history in a design e-portfolio. Retrieved from http://www.apsce.net/ICCE2009/pdf/C6/proceedings920-924.pdf

Kryder, L. G. (2011). Eportfolios: Proving Competency and Building a Network. *Business Communication Quarterly*, *74*(3), 333–341. doi:10.1177/1080569911414556

Lorenzo, G., & Ittelson, J. (2005). An overview of e-portfolios. *Educause Learning Initiative*, Retrieved from http://net.educause.edu/ir/library/pdf/ELI3001.pdf

Rhodes, T. L. (2011). Making Learning Visible and Meaningful Through Electronic Portfolios. *Change*, *43*(1), 6–13. doi:10.1080/00091383.2011.538636

Worley, R. B. (2011). Eportfolios Examined: Tools for Exhibit and Evaluation. *Business Communication Quarterly*, *74*(3), 330–332. doi:10.1177/1080569911414558

CHAPTER 14

■■■

Enhancing Inquiry, Evidence-Based Reflection and Integrative Learning with Lifelong ePortfolio Process: The Implementation of Integrative ePortfolios at Stony Brook University

Nancy McCoy Wozniak
Learning Architect and ePortfolio Program Manager
Stony Brook University

ABSTRACT

Stony Brook University successfully piloted the use of eportfolios in the Fall 2010 Semester discovering that it facilitated the student's inquiry process. Integrative ePortfolios have been used successfully over the past three years in colleges and programs such as Writing and Rhetoric, Engineering, Business, Leadership and Service, and Technology Systems Management. As educators embrace learner-centered course delivery and curriculum design in which the student is an active participant in the instruction, the process of inquiry takes center stage. The learner-centered educator partners with the students encouraging them to continue their quest for discovery while building knowledge connections to the next levels of learning. The inquiry process is the foundation for high impact learning practices such as first-year experiences, learning communities, capstone projects, internships, and service learning that research has shown to increase student engagement and retention. Reflection plays a critical role in moving the learning to the next level of inquiry. In order to move to that level, the reflection must include evidence of learning. The main outcome for learner-centered instruction is to engage students in the inquiry process and integrate their learning in all areas of their lives. The inquiry process and integrative learning need to become a habit of thought and connection that ignites learning and the construction of knowledge throughout a lifetime. The Lifelong ePortfolio Process is becoming a recognized method to facilitate inquiry, evidence-based reflection, and integrative learning. This process helps the student to connect learning with knowledge and develop the habit of lifelong learning.

INTRODUCTION

From the moment Stony Brook students take their first steps on campus, they are encouraged to practice inquiry with evidenced-based reflection and integrate learning in their curricular and co-curricular experiences. Inquiry-based learning strategies that include questioning, investigating, communicating, and reflecting are included in the learning objective and outcomes of Stony Brook courses and programs. Faculty collaborate on building inquiry-based and integrative learning experiences into their curriculums. Integrative learning is an important goal for undergraduate education. The American Association of Colleges and Universities (AACU) and The Carnegie Foundation for the Advancement of Teaching (CF) describe integrative learning experiences occurring as learners address real-world problems, unscripted and sufficiently broad to require multiple areas of knowledge and multiple modes of inquiry, offering multiple solutions and benefiting from multiple perspectives. (AACU, CF, 2004) These learning experiences consider the whole student and foster lifelong learning skills that engage students in making their own learning connections between their courses, professional career goals, co-curricular activities, campus involvement, community service, job experiences, and personal interests. The undergraduate integrative learning eportfolios make the learning visible and facilitate their abilities to make these connections.

Whether course-required or not, every student at Stony Brook is encouraged to create an eportfolio account and own their eportfolios. The design of the eportfolios is their own and they are allowed to create multiple eportfolios. Students develop their own color schemes and banners. This enhances the ownership, relatedness, and sustainability of the eportfolio. ePortfolios are allowed to breath and grow with their learning maturity. Faculty encourage students to include self-directed artifacts (work and experiences) with those that are required for their course or program. These are showcase (hybrid learning) eportfolios which combine directed (required) and self-directed (non-required) artifacts that project evidence of the student's professional skills and abilities. A variety of eportfolios for different purposes are maintained by faculty, staff, and students, but showcase eportfolios are the foundation. The eportfolio owner can pull certain artifacts from their showcase eportfolio and design another eportfolio for a specific purpose. For instance, as students approach graduation, they work with the Career Center staff to build a career eportfolio with artifacts that focus on their job searches or admissions to graduate school. Another example is the use of a specific eportfolio created to demonstrate the learning outcomes in a particular course. In this instance, the faculty usually design course eportfolio templates. This collection and selection of artifacts between the showcase and topic specific eportfolios are illustrated in the Student-Owned Showcase ePortfolio diagram in Figure 14.1.

FIGURE 14.1. Student-Owned Showcase ePortfolio.

Source: Nancy Wozniak 2013

It is important to note that in order to support integrative learning practices, faculty are encouraged to direct students to post required course artifacts and reflections in one undergraduate showcase eportfolio.

Dr. Gary Halada, Undergraduate Program Director for Materials and Engineering, uses eportfolios in his courses and Nanotechnology Program. He sees the eportfolio process as a way to involve students in the ABET (Accreditation Board for Engineering and Technology) accreditation process. Involving the students in the accreditation process is key. Halada partners with his students on instruction and accreditation. He views eportfolios and student outcomes as a solid, practical way to "measure the immeasurable, such as an appreciation for the Field of Engineering and lifelong learning". Lifelong learning is a listed accreditation criteria for demonstrated student outcomes by ABET—(i) a recognition of the need for, and an ability to engage in lifelong learning. (ABET, 2012) Halada encourages his students to add artifacts from their other curricular and co-curricular activities, their accomplishments, and self-directed areas of campus and community involvement.

The following are examples of undergraduate student eportfolios with self-directed artifacts started in Halada's ESG 100—Introduction to Engineering course.

- Rebecca Nolan, Engineering Science
https://stonybrook.digication.com/rebecca_nolan
Since starting her eportfolio in her ESG 100 course, Rebecca has added her molecular biology research, community service, and her martial arts accomplishments.
- Angela Hortsman, Engineering Science and Applied Mathematics and Statistics
https://stonybrook.digication.com/angela_m_horstman
Angela continues to use her ESG 100 course eportfolio to document her work in her other Engineering Science courses with her campus and community involvement. She adds an inspirational reflection piece, Living With a Disability.
- Joseph Nowak, Engineering Science
https://stonybrook.digication.com/joseph_nowak
Joseph started his eportfolio as requirements for his Introduction to Engineering and Intermediate Composition courses. He has added his aircraft training certification and evidence of his growing experience with aircraft mechanics. Joseph reflects on his career goals and love for his profession, "After all these years and the countless number of projects I have worked on, I still love my job; and if you love what you do you will never feel like you have worked a day in your life."

WHAT IS AN EPORTFOLIO?

In an American Society for Engineering Education article, *Using Electronic Portfolios in a Large Engineering Program*, the authors offer a simple, concise definition. Notice how the portfolio process grows an "e".

A portfolio is a purposeful collection of artifacts to demonstrate effort, progress and achievement. Within an educational setting a portfolio can be prepared in the context of a course, a program, or an institution; the author of the portfolio can be the student, a faculty member, an administrator, or an organization (depart, program, etc.); and the purpose of the portfolio may be developmental, evaluative, and/or representative. With the ever increasing use and advancement of technology, the electronic portfolio (ePortfolio) is emerging as a viable option to the traditional paper portfolio. (Knott, Wolfe, Muffo, Mallikarjunan, Loganathan, Lohani, Paretti, Griffin, Adel, 2005)

The definition de-emphasizes the "e" in ePortfolio and presents the portfolio process. The lower case "e" can be disconcerting for educators, as it puts the focus on technology rather than the process of integrative learning. Looking at eportfolio definitions posted on many college and university websites, the process is termed as Collect, Select, Reflect, and Connect. Harshdeep Banwait, Mechanical Engineering major and Student ePortfolio Consultant with the Stony Brook Faculty Center, added Project at the end of the sequence—Collect, Select, Reflect, Connect, and Project. He uses his eportfolio to project to future employers his professional skills and abilities gained through his curricular and co-curricular activities and internships. Harshdeep's model eportfolio can be viewed at https://stonybrook.digication.com/harshdeep_banwait.

A Showcase (Integrative) ePortfolio at Stony Brook is a student-owned digital learning venue that promotes authentic learning by allowing students to organize knowledge, document learning evidence and connect the learning to their other courses, campus involvement, service, internships, jobs & personal interests. The eportfolio projects the student's professional skills and abilities. Throughout each semester the Student ePortfolio Consultants, an eportfolio peer support and review group employed by the Faculty Center, conduct focus groups with campus eportfolio owners and find that preparing for a career and establishing a professional online identity are the main benefits students find for creating and maintaining an eportfolio.

The eportfolio process (Collect, Select, Reflect, Connect, and Project) provides an organized digital thumbprint and timeline of knowing, doing, knowing how you know, and proceeding to the next level of inquiry. It allows the owner to synthesize learning, build knowledge, demonstrate learning connections, and project evidence of professional skills and abilities over a lifetime.

Stony Brook University first piloted eportfolio use in the Fall 2010 Semester with 33 faculty, 400 students in 40 courses and 3 programs. By the end of the Fall 2013 Semester, the program had grown to include 210 faculty, 3,050 students in 265 courses and 18 programs using eportfolios. The number of overall student eportfolio owners had grown to over 7,000 in our system with more than 9,500 created eportfolios. The Fall 2010 ePortfolio pilot was led by faculty in courses and programs that embraced student-centered learning and recognized the need for a change in teaching strategies and course delivery. The pilot faculty actively engaged their students in the teaching, learning and assessment process through learner-centered activities involving collaborative projects and peer-to-peer feedback with student-owned eportfolios. Stony Brook students began to collect, select, reflect, connect,

The ePortfolio Learning Process.

Source: Nancy Wozniak, Learning Architect, Stony Brook University

and project their learned skills and abilities in eportfolios. Many continued after completing their courses requiring eportfolios to add artifacts from their other courses and activities. These self-directed eportfolio activities demonstrated learning connections and a growing appreciation for lifelong learning.

The following eportfolio provide examples of self-directed activities added to student eportfolios:

- Dillon Winegar, Business
  https://stonybrook.digication.com/dillon_raymond_winegar
  Dillon adds his employment, campus involvement, and other course activities to his eportfolio that was created as a require-ment for his Leadership and Service internship. Dillon focuses on projecting his skills and achievements as he begins to build a professional online identity.
- Suxiao Li, Computer Science
  https://stonybrook.digication.com/suxiao_li_serena_li
  Suxiao was never required to start a course eportfolio. She is a model example of an independent eportfolio owner. Suxiao recognizes the value of maintaining an eportfolio for planning and documenting her academic career.
- Addie Browning, English and History
  https://stonybrook.digication.com/addie_browning
  Addie began her eportfolio as a requirement for a Leader-ship and Service Program. She uses her eportfolio to chart her

academic career and posts other campus involvements. Her eportfolio projects her love for photography and community.

- Jim Yee, Chemistry, Clinical Laboratory Sciences and Chemistry
https://stonybrook.digication.com/jim_yee
As a requirement for Technology Systems Management, Jim began his eportfolio and continues to use it to chart his academic career towards medical school.

- Daniel Ahmadizadeh, Business
https://stonybrook.digication.com/daniel_ahmadizadeh
Daniel organizes and integrates his curricular and co-curricular experiences throughout his eportfolio. He is a junior in the College of Business specializing in marketing and finance. He is the founder of the Stony Brook Quidditch team and current head manager of the Stony Brook Men's Basketball team. Dan is a member of Phi Delta Epsilon and works as a Resident Assistant and Student ePortfolio Consultant. He also is the Marketing Manager for Studio 360—Architecture and Design. Daniels diverse involvements, interests and leadership abilities are projected throughout his eportfolio.

Oftentimes, when the term eportfolio is mentioned, the tool or system takes center stage, causing the users to become frustrated and overwhelmed. There is no real value or benefit for the potential adopter when the tiny "e" is blown out of proportion. "It's another technology." "Who needs another technology?" "We have Blackboard." "It's Facebook." "I see no value in social networking activities in my classroom." "It's a website." "I already have my resume posted online." In a recent discussion, Dr. Cynthia Davidson, Emerging Technologies Coordinator and Senior Lecturer with the Writing and Rhetoric Program, pointed out, "Faculty often feel the tool is redundant because they think the technology used currently in their classroom fits their teaching purposes."

The Faculty Center, responsible for eportfolio implementation, made the mistake of focusing on the tool when they introduced eportfolios to the Stony Brook campus teaching community. They formed a faculty and staff committee to review eportfolio systems. They didn't start by introducing the purpose and learning processes facilitated by the use of eportfolios. Lifelong learning wasn't mentioned. Inquiry, evidenced-based reflection and integrative learning strategies were left off the committee's agenda and out of the discussions. The primary focus was the system. Consequently, it took time to counter the misconception of eportfolio as another Blackboard, Facebook, or website. So, an implementation committee was formed with the eportfolio faculty pilots that included elements of inquiry, evidence-based reflection, and integrative learning in their course designs. The Writing and Rhetoric Program was the pilot's hub. The faculty were practicing the portfolio process for learning and assessment of composition skills instituted by Dr. Peter Elbow, internationally acclaimed author and former director of Writing and Rhetoric at Stony Brook University. Supported by Dr. Eugene Hammond, director of Writing and Rhetoric (WRT), Cynthia Davidson took the lead with transitioning WRT from the use of paper portfolios to the use of Google Docs and eportfolios for peer-to-peer student learning and formative assessment during the term/exit assessment at the end of the course.

Helen Chen, researcher in the Department of Mechanical Engineering and the director of eportfolio initiatives in the Office of the Registrar at Stanford University, incorporates the eportfolio process in her learning approach, Folio Thinking. She points out that eportfolios are more than just a technology: they imply a process of planning, keeping track of, making sense of, and sharing evidence of learning and performance (Chen, 2012). Folio Thinking makes use of student-owned eportfolios for students to document their learning activities and experiences, and engage in reflective practices. The learning process centers on a self-coaching learning model which emphasizes learning through experience. Self-coaching involves giving students a set of ideas and a vocabulary to promote informal learning through experience by emphasizing awareness, observation, experimentation, and evaluation as the basic steps to gathering rich lessons from experience (Chen, 2001). Chen's research has shown that the students were likely to integrate and apply the knowledge gained from their learning activities and reflections captured over time in their owned eportfolios. ePortfolios were found to nurture and house Folio Thinking, emphasizing student-driven learning through experience.

WHAT IS INTEGRATIVE LEARNING?

Education experts often refer to integrative learning as a challenge and one of the most important goals of education. In the AACU Integrative Learning Value Rubric, it is defined as an understanding and a disposition that a student builds across the curriculum and co-curriculum, from making simple connections among ideas and experiences to synthesizing and transferring learning to new, complex situations within and beyond the campus (AACU, 2010). In a professional development workshop presentation, Roanoke College provides participants with an excellent working definition of integrative learning (Roanoke College, 2007).

> A system of learning that deliberately makes connections between classes, fields, and academic and co-curricular life, with the end goal being the development of students who encounter new challenges and new knowledge in a productive manner.

Dr. Melissa Peet, Academic Director for the Integrative Learning and MPortfolio Initiative at the University of Michigan, conducts research on how students integrate tacit (informal, nonstructured) and explicit (formal, structured) knowledge with learning to build leadership abilities and innovative skills. She inspires students to become agents of change and to realize they can change the world. Peet has developed a student-centered integrative learning pedagogy model known as the Integrative Knowledge Portfolio Process Model (IKPP). The purpose of IKPP is to facilitate learners in identifying, integrating, and synthesizing their emergent knowledge, skills and identities over time, across contexts and in relation to others (Peet, Lonn, Gurin, Boyer, Matney, Marra, Taylor, Daley, 2010). IKPP guides students with integrating, connecting, and synthesizing their learning experiences by identifying six dimensions of integrative knowledge and learning:

1 Identify, demonstrate and adapt knowledge gained within/across different contexts (i.e., the ability to recognize the tacit and explicit knowledge gained in specific learning experiences and the capacity to adapt that knowledge to new situations);

2 Adapt to differences in order to create solutions (i.e., the ability to identify and adapt to different people, situations, etc., while working with others to create positive change);

3 Understand and direct oneself as a learner (i.e., the ability to identify one's prior knowledge, recognize one's strengths and gaps as a learner, and know how one is motivated to learn);

4 Become a reflexive, accountable and relational learner (i.e., the ability to reflect on one's practices and clarify expectations within oneself while also seeking feedback from others);

5 Identify and discern one's own and others' perspectives (i.e., the ability to recognize the limitations of one's perspective and seek out and value the perspectives of others); and

6 Develop a professional digital identity (i.e., the ability to imagine how one will use current knowledge and skills in future roles and how one will create an intentional digital identity) (2010).

Integrative Learning ePortfolios are used to facilitate the integrative learning process as students connect and make meaning of the knowledge and skills gained from their life experiences. The IKPP Learning Model depicts conscious and unconscious learning as lifelong and life-wide experiences. In her research, Peet demonstrates that in order to truly integrate their learning, students must first learn how to identify and demonstrate the tacit knowledge (the unconscious and informal ways of knowing people develop from informal learning experiences) they've gained from previous experiences, and connect it to the explicit knowledge (the formal concepts, ideas and methods learned through formal education) they develop in their academic courses (2010).

Figure 14.2 illustrates the Integrative Knowledge Portfolio Process.

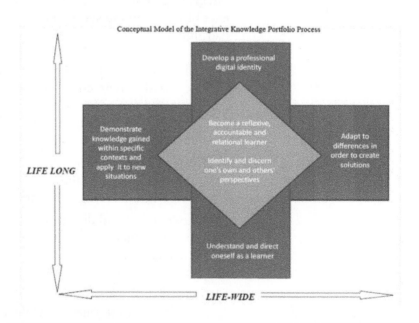

FIGURE 14.2. Integrative Knowledge Portfolio Process.

Peet's learning model is a working example of applied integrative learning with eportfolio use. Her Generative Knowledge Interviewing workshops are relevant to today's pedagogical practices and valued by learner-centered educators.

Integrative learning strategies at Stony Brook University involve the faculty and staff working as teams to engage students in making learning connections with their courses, professional career goals, co-curricular activities, campus involvement, community service, jobs and personal interests. Strategies include high impact first-year experiences, collaborative capstone projects, experiential learning and service activities, and multimodal media presentations and reflections such as digital stories and podcasts. Students also partner with faculty on the development of integrative learning experiences. Many of the model eportfolios featured in the Spotlight on ePortfolios website included student, self-directed integrative learning experiences encouraged by faculty and staff. The website can be viewed at https://stonybrook.digication .com/stony_brook_eportfolio_showcase.

WHAT IS LIFELONG LEARNING?

Darren Cambridge, Senior Consultant, Education Technology and Online Communities of Practice at American Institutes for Research, defines lifelong learning as an ongoing process of developing knowledge, skills, and strategies; putting capabilities and self-understanding into action; and, thereby, establishing an identity. (Cambridge, 2010) Success in life depends on having a sense of self, understanding who we are and knowing how we build knowledge and connect to our academic, professional, community and personal lives.

The AACU Foundations and Skills for Lifelong Learning Value Rubric categorize curiosity, initiative, independence, transfer and reflection as the key skills for lifelong learning and can be retrieved at http://www.aacu.org/value/rubrics/pdf/LifelongLearning.pdf (ACCU, 2010). Integrative Learning Value rubric, categorizes the objectives of the integrative learning process as:

1 **Connections to Experience**—Connects relevant experience and academic knowledge.

2 **Connections to Discipline**—Sees (makes) connections across disciplines, perspectives.

3 **Transfer**—Adapts and applies skills, abilities, theories, or methodologies gained in one situation to new situations.

4 Integrated Communication

5 Reflection and Self-Assessment—Demonstrates a developing sense of self as a learner, building on prior experiences to respond to new and challenging contexts (may be evident in self-assessment, reflective, or creative work) (2010).

Incorporating the integrative learning and lifelong learning objectives in course and program curriculums enhances successful learning outcomes for the students, program and institution and instill lifelong learning habits.

WHY ePORTFOLIO?

In the mid 1990s, Robert Barr and John Tagg wrote about a paradigm shift from teaching to learning taking place in education. In their article, *A New Paradigm for Undergraduate Education*, they clearly illustrated this shift from the teacher-centered Instruction Paradigm to the student-centered Learning Paradigm. The Instruction Paradigm is concerned with teaching productivity while the Learning Paradigm centers on learning productivity.

The main focus for the Learning Paradigm is to involve students in the teaching and learning process and produce learning outcomes more efficiently. With the shift, the controlled, competitive, individualistic instruction classroom becomes a collaborative, cooperative, supportive learning environment that fosters inquiry, reflection and higher order cognitive skills. In this rich learning environment, the integrative eportfolio process emerges as a method to produce, document and connect the learning. It is clear how the integrative eportfolio learning process (Collect, Select, Reflect, Connect and Project) enriches the mission and purposes of the Learning Paradigm (Barr & Tagg, 1995) to

- produce learning,
- elicit students discovery and construction of knowledge,
- create powerful learning environments,
- improve the quality of learning, and
- achieve success for a diverse population of students.

As educators embrace the learning goals, objectives and practices of the Learning Paradigm, eportfolio use will grow and play a major role in the teaching and learning culture.

The ePortfolio process helps us as lifelong learners to integrate learning experiences, build knowledge and make connections between our academic, professional, community, and personal lives. When we make these connections, we learn how we learn and we know how we know. The learning experiences are authentic. ePortfolio is the tool that helps us to connect and document the evidence of our expanding knowledge and to realize our diverse directions of learning throughout our lifetime.

The Stony Brook University students in Dr. Cathleen Rowley's Intermediate Composition class were asked if they knew about eportfolios. Most of the students had completed a paper portfolio for their writing classes in high school. The students came to the collective conclusion that portfolios are journals for reading and writing assignments compiled in Word documents and placed in a binder. They were asked where they kept their paper portfolios. Some said their teachers kept them and others had no idea where they had ended up. One student replied, "It's on my bookshelf in my bedroom at home. I never look at it. It's all yellow and dusty." They then were asked to define an eportfolio and another student replied,

"An eportfolio is a portfolio that doesn't gather dust."

How true. A paper portfolio sits on a shelf and gathers dust. An eportfolio is active and alive. It allows the owner to collect learning experiences and select evidence of gained professional skills and abilities over a lifetime. Examples of WRT eportfolios are listed below. Notice how the students are encouraged to add their other courses, co-curricular activities, job performances, community service involvements and personal interests. Other faculty requiring eportfolio use in their courses have the students continue with their eportfolios created in other courses. This collaboration between the faculty and programs supports integrative learning and the students maintain eportfolios that project their successful undergraduate experience. It should be noted that Cathleen Rowley maintains her own teaching eportfolio and uses it as an example when introducing the eportfolio requirement in her classes. Her students find purpose in eportfolio use after viewing hers and one commented, "if faculty don't use eportfolios for lifelong learning, why should we?" Rowley's eportfolio can be viewed at https://stonybrook.digication.com/cathleen_rowley.

These are examples of required WRT 102—Intermediate Composition eportfolios supporting integrative learning:

- Aaron Doucett, Marine and Atmospheric Sciences
  https://stonybrook.digication.com/aarondoucett
  Aaron has added other courses to his eportfolio. In his About Me section, he illustrates his multifaceted interests and strengths as he works toward building a career in meteorology.

- Ryan Earle Ong, Business
  https://stonybrook.digication.com/ryanearleong
  Ryan's required writing eportfolio expanded into an exemplary undergraduate eportfolio that demonstrates the important role eportfolio use plays in integrative learning strategies. Ryan uses multimedia to enhance his directed and self-directed eportfolio activities.
- Asaf Harari, Engineering Science and Business
  https://stonybrook.digication.com/asaf_harari
  Asaf started his eportfolio as requirements for his WRT 102 and ESG 100 courses. He brings out another dimension of himself as he adds his participation in a Stony Brook co-ed a cappella group. As an Engineering Science major, he explains how important it was for him to become involved with the Arts programs at Stony Brook.
- Linda Milano, Business
  https://stonybrook.digication.com/linda_n_milano1
  Linda is a Business major specializing in Marketing with a minor in Journalism. She plays the clarinet in the Spirit of Stony Brook Marching Band and is a teaching assistant in the Honors Business Program. Linda also is a Student ePortfolio Consultant and responsible for promoting eportfolio use in the College of Business. She uses her eportfolio to integrate her curricular and co-curricular activities and she synthesizes her learning experiences through evidenced-based reflection.
- Lisa Pesok, Engineering Science
  https://stonybrook.digication.com/pesok_lisa_writing_102_95
  Lisa was required to create an eportfolio in her WRT 102 and ESG 100 courses. She added the dynamics of her art in the eportfolio and connects them to her endeavors in Engineering Science.

An ePortfolio allows its creator to collect learning experiences and select evidence of gained professional skills and abilities over a lifetime. However, to stop there with the definition would imply that an eportfolio merely serves the same purpose as an electronic resume, scrapbook or journal.

WHAT IS THE RELATIONSHIP BETWEEN INQUIRY AND REFLECTION?

Inquiry is a continuous cycle of learning that involves questioning, investigating, analyzing, communicating, and reflecting on the knowledge gained. Reflecting on the evidence and conclusion produces more questions and the cycle of learning and discovery continues. Reflection connects the components of the inquiry cycle and serves as the catalyst to move to the next level of learning and discovery. Information is transformed to knowledge and fragmented pieces of knowledge are connected through reflection. ePortfolios help create an accessible online workspace for students and instructors to collaborate on inquiry-based projects and activities. The eportfolio also provides the students with an integrative learning space to question, investigate, analyze, communicate and reflect on their life experiences and connect the knowledge. This is an important reason for including reflection with artifacts posted in eportfolios.

In order for reflection to be the catalyst for binding knowledge and clearing pathways to higher levels of learning, it must be able to produce evidence of the learning. Dr. Trent Batson, Executive Director of the Association for Authentic, Experiential, and Evidence-Based Learning (AAEEBL), emphasized this point in his Campus Technology article, *Reviewers Unhappy with Portfolio "Stuff" Demand Evidence*. He refers to an eportfolio without demonstrated evidence-based learning examples and reflection as a collection of "stuff" (Batson, 2010),

> Simply collecting a lot of "stuff" and showing it on a Web page does not support any kind of claim other than that you've done the work and, presumably, the instructor has accepted your work. When students make a claim—for a grade on an assignment, a grade in a course, for a capstone requirement, for graduation, or for career purposes—they must also work within an evidence structure/process of some sort that is just as transparent as the scientific or legal process for using evidence.

Batson's article emphasizes the need for a structured process for posted artifacts, directed and self-directed, that provides evidence of learning and experience through inquiry and reflection. For program and institutional use the eportfolio process must take into consideration "the benefit of students, faculty (for review purposes), and reviewers and assessors, as well as for accreditation review, institutional curriculum review, institutional transformation, and for the improvement of learning." (2010).

When using eportfolios for learning and outcomes assessment it is essential to include inquiry and evidence-based reflection as structured components of the eportfolio process. Inquiry must be based on more than assumptions. Reflection must move beyond feelings. It is essential that students be given prompts to ignite inquiry and help them analyze and synthesize the learning

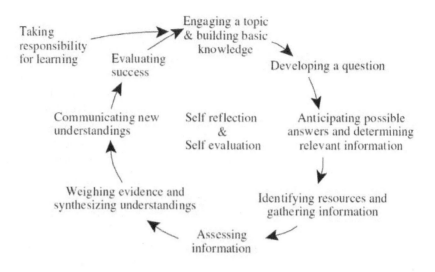

FIGURE 14.3. The Inquiry Process.

experience in their reflections. The prompts should be discipline-specific, yet offer a possibility for interdisciplinary connects, as well as connections to other facets of the student's life. Students must move beyond how much they liked the assignment to the point of producing and realizing the evidence, generation of new ideas, formation of opinions and changes in perspectives to confirm and document personal understanding of the learning experience and applied knowledge.

In their article, *Inquiry in Higher Education: Reflections and Directions on Course Design and Teaching Methods*, a McMaster University team of writing faculty used a diagram to illustrate the inquiry process used in their course. The article demonstrates their successful inquiry strategies using prompts and self-assessment assignments to help the students develop questions of inquiry and delve deep into the exploration and analysis of their chosen topics as they work collaboratively in small groups to come to a conclusion and present their findings. Reflection enhanced by a final self-assessment checklist brings about new questions prompting students to continue on to the next level of inquiry. The process is circular to represent the continuing nature of inquiry which ends in some answers, enhanced understanding, but always more questions (Justice, Rice, Warry, Inglis, Miller, Sammon, 2006).

The McMasters faculty identify the progressive components of their inquiry assignment by developing a good question, determining the information needed, assessing information effectively and efficiently, critically evaluating the information and its sources, synthesizing into a coherent whole, communicating the product and process of inquiry effectively, and evaluating success through the inquiry process (2006). Prompts are used at each stage. Self-assessment exercises launch and complete the inquiry projects.

When working with faculty and students on the design and maintenance of integrative eportfolios used to document learning, the Faculty Center staff emphasizes inquiry and reflection. Prompts related to these are encouraged. Stony Brook faculty and students are provided support materials during training sessions. The *What Makes It Model* document serves as a checklist for eportfolio design and posting artifacts with evidenced reflection. The document can be viewed at https://stonybrook.digication.com/stony_brook_eportfolio_showcase/What_Makes_it_Model1.

Included in the *What Makes It Model* document are prompts to guide students with inquiry and evidence-based reflection. The prompts can be modified for discipline specific use to help students produce evidence of their learning and acquired skills in their descriptions, summaries and reflections accompanying their artifacts:

1. What skills or abilities did you learn from this experience and how are you able to apply them to other courses and areas of involvement in your life (academic, career, service, campus, personal interests)?

2. What about this assignment was most useful to you? Can you see a relationship to what you've learned to your other courses or activities in your academic and professional careers?

3. How would you describe this assignment to your friends? How would you describe it to a future employer?

4. What areas and abilities in your life were strengthened by this assignment.

5. List the ways you have grown, professionally, as a result of this assignment.

6. What problems did you encounter and how did you solve them?

7. What risks did you take and what did you discover about yourself?

8 What personal strengths and abilities did you discover and demonstrate by doing this assignment?

9 If you had it to do all over again, would you? Why? What would you change?

10 How did this experience prepare you for your professional career and/or graduate school? How did it prepare you for life?

WRT faculty have long used prompts to help students compose reflective "cover memos" that explain how they have grown as writers during the course of the semester and how their writing inclusions provide evidence of learning outcomes delineated on a checklist in specific ways, the same checklist used to evaluate portfolio work by faculty assessors at the end of the semester. As previously mentioned, this portfolio practice for learning and assessment of composition skills began under the direction of Peter Elbow. Biology major Bryan Szeglin's WRT 102 eportfolio is a model example of the portfolio learning and assessment model—https://stonybrook.digication.com/bryanszeglin.

Another good example of the inquiry process and reflection guided with prompts is Cynthia Davidson's personal writing and emerging media courses that include digital stories and eportfolios. The guided inquiry is used to facilitate the composition process and, at the same time, integrative learning skills are enhanced by her use of peer support groups in brainstorm sessions. Integrative learning skills also are strengthened by the multimodal reflection experience of producing digital stories and the design of the eportfolio. Davidson provides prompts to guide the students through the process. These are examples of the guiding prompts:

- Start by thinking of a question or a statement that you would like to explore for your final project, something in which you have a personal stake: for example, how your life or career goals intersect with issues of new media and technology.
- Come to class prepared with an idea; post a one-page brainstorm in Discussion Board/Google Docs and take it from there.
- Look over your past writing for the digital story script. Look over all your mini-essays; you might find that one of your mini-essays could be transmuted into the perfect digital narrative.
- The final paper may be a retelling or expansion of the digital story, or it may be more tangential to it . . . it is up to you how you frame the relationship.

These creative integrative eportfolios created in Davidson's courses are model examples of inquiry-based learning and the use of multimodal reflection to strengthen integrative learning skills:

- Annie Bernberg, English and History
  https://stonybrook.digication.com/annie_bernberg/Writing_303_The_Personal_Essay222
  Annie's model eportfolio combines her writing talents with her extraordinary storytelling abilities. When you open Annie's eportfolio, you'll stay awhile and leave with a smile.
- Joseph Cavera, Environmental Studies
  https://stonybrook.digication.com/jcavera/Writing_302
  Joseph is an Environmental Studies major pursuing minors in Ecosystems and Human Impact and Writing. He uses his eportfolio to showcase his superb creative thinking and writing abilities.
- Vishwaja Muppa, Biology
  https://stonybrook.digication.com/vishwaja_muppa
  Vishwaja's digital story from her personal writing course is a creative, model example of digital storytelling. When asked the value of an eportfolio, Vishwaja replied with this thought-provoking answer, "An eportfolio allows me to leave a legacy so future generations can understand who I was." Vishwaja left a legacy with her eporttfolio. We now include a "What's Your Legacy?" exercise in our eportfolio training sessions.

Davidson maintains her own teaching eportfolio that serves as an example to her students. Her eportfolio can be viewed at https://stonybrook.digication.com/cdavidson.

INQUIRY AND EVIDENCE-BASED REFLECTION IN BIOMEDICAL SENIOR DESIGN EPORTFOLIOS

The Inquiry process with evidence-based reflection is crucial in Biomedical Engineering. Stony Brook Biomedical Engineering students are required to complete a senior design project that includes identifying the need, diagramming and analyzing the design, testing and developing a business plan and presentation to prospective venture capitalist. The students work in teams and are required to include weekly journals and individual reflections at the completion of the course. Dr. Jonathan Liu, Assistant Professor, Biomedical Engineering lays out his syllabus with inquiry prompts throughout the Senior Design course eportfolio template. The eportfolio template with inquiry and reflection prompts direct the students in a concise, organized manner. He encourages the students to enhance their artifacts with multimedia. When asked the benefits of using an eportfolio for their design projects, students remarked on how it organizes their thoughts and design progression. They also found the eportfolio provided a collaborative workspace that requires less face-to-face time.

Jonathan Liu created his course Biomedical Engineering Template to lead the students through the inquiry and design processes, https://stonybrook.digication.com/senior_biodesign_template2. He maintains his own eportfolio that serves as an example to his students, https://stonybrook.digication.com/liu. The Stony Brook Biomedical Engineering Senior Design ePortfolios have been viewed globally as model examples of eportfolios used to facilitate inquiry and invention:

- Non Electric Blood Pressure Assist Device
  https://stonybrook.digication.com/biodesign_group_5/need
  This model project eportfolio is a model example of critical and creative thinking, collaboration, and project management laid out on the digital pages of an eportfolio. The eportfolio has been viewed globally in training presentations on eportfolio use.
- Micro Fluidic Lab on a Chip
  https://stonybrook.digication.com/biodesign_group_7/need
  - Aman Sharma, member of the Lab on a Chip group, used his showcase and senior design eportfolios when applying to graduate school. He continues to use an eportfolio at the University of Toronto. He also maintain a blog at http://cebme.com.
  - Undergraduate ePortfolio—https://stonybrook.digication.com/aman_sharma
  - Graduate ePortfolio—https://stonybrook.digication.com/aman_sharma_mhsc

The Stony Brook eportfolio examples clearly demonstrate and organize the layers of inquiry the students employ with their projects. The integrative eportfolio process stimulates inquiry. Collect, Select, Reflect, Connect, Project, and What's Next would be a more accurate description of this process.

THE STUDENT'S PERSPECTIVE OF REFLECTION

In the semester eportfolio focus groups conducted by the Student ePortfolio Consultants, students comment favorably on including evidenced-based reflection in their eportfolios. Many have stated that reflection helps provide direction for course and career planning. One student commented on how reflection helps her to make sense of her academic pursuits and reevaluate her career goals.

Computer Science major, Ansue Jacob, spoke on the value of reflection in her eportfolio, "Reflecting on what you have done will inspire you to write more on what you have learned from your projects by making you think of things that you did not think of previously. " Ansue is a recent Stony Brook graduate and continues her eportfolio as a graduate student at Drexel University, https://stonybrook.digication.com/ansuejacob.

Eda Gimenez, Environmental Engineering major, wrote in her eportfolio an interesting explanation on the importance of reflection in life.

> You reflect to learn and connect the importance of everything you've done and learned. From studying your coursework to applying the learning to your career and other activities outside the classroom, reflecting allows you to develop and connect all areas of your life. Being conscious through reflection of all that is around you helps you realize your goals and direction in this world. Reflecting takes a broad concept like life and allows you to break it down in your own perspective with your own strengths so that you can succeed in life and be an agent of positive change in this world. —Eda Gimenez

Eda's showcase eportfolio can be viewed at https://stonybrook .digication.com/egimenez.

Marine Science major, Emily Madsen, didn't care for the eportfolio requirement in her Leadership and Service course. She considered reflection a tedious waste of time. Her opinion soon changed as she proofread her eportfolio for typographical errors.

My name is Emily Madsen and I have a rather public obsession for all things ocean-related.

> I had a very low opinion of the ePortfolio at the onset of this course. In high school, I always despised reflecting on my work—the material covered in my high school classes tended to be rather simple and any moderately extensive reflection, in my opinion, ended up being mostly busy work. However, I did see the value of having a digital chronology of my classes and decided to give it a go. As the material got increasingly difficult in my classes, I found the ePortfolio to be an incredibly useful organizational tool. At the end of the year, I found that looking over the work and reflections in my ePortfolio for typos and grammatical errors not only helped me remember what I enjoyed about the class, but also how the concepts were divided up—which helped me formulate a study schedule for my final exams. —Emily Madsen

Emily's eportfolio has been used globally as a model example of self-directed use for academic and career planning. She is creating her professional online identity through her creative approach to building her resume. Her eportfolio can be viewed at https://stonybrook.digication.com/emily_madsen

Others examples of building a professional online identity with eportfolios are listed below:

- Alicia Elliott, Engineering Science
  https://stonybrook.digication.com/aliciamelliott
  ePortfolio was never required in Alicia's course. She was inspired to start one after viewing Emily Madsen's eportfolio in the Stony Brook ePortfolio Campus Directory—https://stonybrook.digication.com/portfolio/directory.digi. Her self-directed eportfolio demonstrating her professional skills and abilities in various areas of her life are model examples of integrative learning.
- Michael Spikes, Technology Systems Management, Masters of Science
  https://stonybrook.digication.com/michael_a_spikes_eportfolio
  As a graduate student and professional in video and broadcast journalism, Michael uses his eportfolio to highlight and connect his past and present experiences in education and media production.
- Sarah Kardasz, Technology Systems Management, Masters of Science
  https://stonybrook.digication.com/sara_kardasz
  Sarah uses her eportfolio to document and integrate her graduate courses and work. She emphasizes her career, accomplishments, and professional development. Her goal is to secure a career in instructional design. Sarah's eportfolio gives evidence of her skills and abilities as an educator, and her instructional design talents.
- Chloe Bader—Stony Brook Graduate in Social Welfare and Graduate Student in New York University's Social Work Master's Program
  https://stonybrook.digication.com/chloe_bader
  Chloe uses her eportfolio to project her professional skills and abilities, achievements, community service, and awards. As she begins her graduate studies in Social Work at New York University she continues to build and project her professional identity with her eportfolio.

- Rachel Koeth, Bassoon Performance, Doctor of Musical Arts degree
  https://stonybrook.digication.com/rachel_koeth
  Rachel is pursuing her doctorial studies in Musical Arts and uses her eportfolio to document her performances and orchestra involvements. She teaches individual performance recitations and large lecture Introduction to the Musical Arts courses at Stony Brook. Rachel finds it important to develop her teaching philosophy and document her teaching experience in her eportfolio.
- Junaid Rajani, Biochemistry
  https://stonybrook.digication.com/junaidrajani
  Junaid's career goal is to be a periodontist. His undergraduate eportfolio showcases his leadership abilities and skills in his curricular and co-curricular activities. Junaid gives evidence of his abilities to help people through his work as a teaching assistant and eportfolio consultant. His passion for teaching and his natural abilities as an educator are accentuated in his eportfolio along with his natural abilities as an educator.

As Stony Brook students take ownership of learning how to learn and knowing how to know facilitated by the integrative eportfolio process, eportfolio use will continue to grow. ePortfolios provide digital workspaces for students to integrate their learning and develop habits of inquiry, evidenced-based reflection, and lifelong learning. Faculty and student focus group results have shown that eportfolios have been used successfully to stimulate and organize the inquiry process and help students integrate their learning. Published results will be available after the end of the 2012–13 Academic Year. As Stony Brook faculty continue to partner on high impact and integrative learning strategies, integrative eportfolios will play a leading role in multidisciplinary course and program design.

Inquiry and evidenced-based reflection are the foundations of teaching and learning at Stony Brook. The integrative eportfolio process (Collect, Select, Reflect, Connect, Project, and What's Next) helps to organize and move the cycle of inquiry. Students have discovered the academic and professional benefits of demonstrating their inquiry and evidenced-based reflective skills in their integrative, showcase eportfolios. The showcase eportfolio is their digital venue and workspace for highlighting and building evidence of their abilities to integrate learning experiences, identify, connect, synthesize and demonstrate the knowledge and skills they are gaining from all areas of life. Model examples of integrative, showcase eportfolios can be viewed at https://stonybrook.digication .com/stony_brook_eportfolio_showcase. ePortfolios will continue to grow at Stony Brook and become a dynamic part of the campus teaching and learning culture as students collect, select, reflect, connect, and project evidence of learning and continue on to discover what's next throughout a lifetime of learning.

Acknowledgements

A special thanks to Dr. Cynthia Davidson, Dr. Patricia Aceves and Dr. Lori Scarlatos for guiding me through the inquiry process with this article. My gratitude to Dr. Cynthia Davidson, Dr. Cathleen Rowley, Dr. Jonathan Liu and Dr. Gary Halada for their model, learner-centered eportfolio use that has inspired faculty at Stony Brook and other colleges and universities around the world. A heartfelt thank you and my gratitude to our agents of change, the Student ePortfolio Consultants Rachel Koeth, Harshdeep Banwait, Linda Milano, Emily Madsen, Junaid Rajani, Dillon Winegar, Alicia Elliott, Joeseph Carvera, Daniel Ahmadizadeh, Eda Gimenez, Ansue Jacob, Ahrum Kim, Paris Lingard, and Sourav Tamang., the driving force for self-directed inquiry, evidenced-reflection, and integrative learning with eportfolios at Stony Brook University. My enduring gratitude to Amanda Gales Sfiligoj, my daughter and partner in promoting diverse learning opportunities and respect for all students.

Note

1. **Nancy McCoy Wozniak** is the Learning Architect and ePortfolio Program Manager in the Faculty Center, Teaching Learning, and Technology at Stony Brook University. Her integrative showcase eportfolio can be viewed at https://stonybrook.digication.com/nancywozniak.

References

1. Association of American Colleges and Universities (AACU) and The Carnegie Foundation for the Advancement of Teaching (CF). (2004). *A statement on integrative learning*. In Association of American Colleges. Retrieved from https://www.aacu.org/integrative_learning/pdfs/ILP_Statement.pdf
2. Criteria for Accrediting Engineering Programs. ABET. In (2012). Criteria for Accrediting Engineering Programs 2012–2013. Retrieved from http://www.abet.org/DisplayTemplates/DocsHandbook.aspx?id=3149

3. Kott, T. Wolfe, M. C., Muffo, J. A., Mallikarjunan, K., Loganathan, G. K., Lohani, V. K., Paretti, M. C, Griffin, H., Adel G. T., Wildman, T. M. (2005, February). *Using electronic portfolios in a large engineering program.* American Society for Engineering Education Annual Conference & Exposition Assessing with technology, Atlanta, Ga. Retrieved from http://www.dlr.enge.vt.edu/project_documents/Using Electronic Portfolios in a Large Engineering Program.pdf

4. Chen, H. (2012, March). *Documenting learning with eportfolios: a framework for effective implementation.* Stony Brook ePortfolio Institute. Eportfolios: documenting a lifetime of learning, Stony Brook University. Retrieved from https://stonybrook.digication.com/eportfolio_institute_at_stony_brook_university

5. Testbed 6: Stanford learning lab's learning careers program. In H. Chen (2001), *Personal Learning Portfolios: Folio Thinking* (p. 18). The Wallenberg Global Learning Network Funding Program. Retrieved from http://dart.stanford.edu:8080/sparrow_2.0/pages/teams/FolioThinkingProposal.pdf

6. Association for American Colleges and Universities. (2004). AACU integrative learning value rubric. In *VALUE: Valid Assessment of Learning in Undergraduate Education.* Retrieved from http://www.aacu.org/value/rubrics/pdf/integrativelearning.pdf

7. Association for American Colleges and Universities. (2004). AACU foundations and skills for lifelong learning value rubric. In *VALUE: Valid Assessment of Learning in Undergraduate Education.* Retrieved from http://www.aacu.org/value/rubrics/pdf/LifelongLearning.pdf

8. Roanoke College. (2011). Integrative teaching and learning handout. Retrieved from https://stonybrook.digication.com/stony_brook_eportfolio_showcase/Roanoke_College_Definition

9. Cambridge, D. (2010). *Eportfolios for lifelong learning and assessment.* (1st ed., Vol. 1, preface). San Francisco, CA: Josey-Bass.

10. Peet, M., Lonn, S., Gurin, P., Boyer, K. P., Matney, M., Marra, M., Taylor, S. H., and Daley, A. (2011). Fostering integrative knowledge through eportfolios. *International Journal of ePortfolio, 1*(1), Retrieved from http://www.theijep.com ISSN 2157-622X

11. Barr, R. and Tagg, J. (1995, Nov./Dec.). From teaching to learning—a new paradigm for undergraduate education. *Change,* 13–25. Retrieved from http://www.ius.edu/ilte/pdf/BarrTagg.pdf

12. Batson, T. (2010, October 10). Reviewers unhappy with portfolio "stuff" demand evidence. *Campus Technology,* Retrieved from http://campustechnology.com/articles/2010/10/06/reviewers-unhappy-with-portfolio-stuff-demand-evidence.aspx

13. Justice, C., Rice, J., Warry W., Inglis, S., Miller, S,. Sammon, S. (2007). Inquiry in higher education: Reflections and directions on course design and teaching methods. *Innovative Higher Education, 31*(4), 201–214. doi: DOI 10.1007/s10755-006-9021-9

CHAPTER 15

■■■

Transforming Wikipedia into a Large Scale Multilingual Concept Network

Vivi Nastase
Corresponding author
HITS gGmbH, Heidelberg, Germany
vivi.nastase@h-its.org

Michael Strube
HITS gGmbH, Heidelberg, Germany
michael.strube@h-its.org

ABSTRACT

A knowledge base for real-world language processing applications should consist of a large base of facts and reasoning mechanisms that combine them to induce novel and more complex information. This paper describes an approach to deriving such a large scale and multilingual resource by exploiting several facets of the on-line encyclopedia Wikipedia. We show how we can build upon Wikipedia's existing network of categories and articles to automatically discover new relations and their instances. Working on top of this network allows for added information to influence the network and be propagated throughout it using inference mechanisms that connect different pieces of existing knowledge. We then exploit this gained information to discover new relations that refine some of those found in the previous step. The result is a network containing approximately 3.7 million concepts with lexicalizations in numerous languages and 49+ million relation instances. Intrinsic and extrinsic evaluations show that this is a high quality resource and beneficial to various NLP tasks.

INTRODUCTION

While the availability of large amounts of data has encouraged the development of successful statistical techniques for numerous natural language processing tasks, there is a concurrent quest for computer accessible knowledge. Knowledge allows a system to counter data sparsity (e.g. lexical semantic knowledge), as well as make connections between entities (e.g. BARACK OBAMA *president_of* UNITED STATES OF AMERICA).

Shortly after its launch in January 2001, the potential of Wikipedia as a large scale source of knowledge for Artificial Intelligence and Natural Language Processing in particular became apparent to researchers in the field. The appeal of Wikipedia is that it strikes a middle ground between accurate, manually created, limited-coverage resources such as WordNet [9], Cyc [18], general purpose (SUMO, [33]) or domain-specific ontologies (Gene Ontology,[1] UMLS[2]), dictionaries and thesauri, and automatic, wide-coverage, but still noisy knowledge mined from the web [38].

Unlike resources prepared by trained linguists, Wikipedia's structures have arisen through the collaboration of contributors and, with the exception of the category structure which was encouraged by the contribution guidelines, without prior planning. This may bring the quality of a resource based on such underspecified criteria into question, but its usefulness in a variety of Natural Language Processing (NLP) tasks has already been shown [22]. The category structure was not intended to be an ontology-like structure, but what has emerged is a *folksonomy*, mirroring the shared categorization preferences of the contributors. The collaborative aspect has also led to the implicit encoding of much information that when made explicit, reveals millions of new bite-sized pieces of knowledge.

Wikipedia contains a wealth of multi-faceted information: articles, links between articles, categories which group articles, infoboxes, a hierarchy that organizes the categories and articles into a large directed network, cross-language links, and more. These various types of information have been usually exploited independently from each other.

This paper presents WikiNet[3]—the result of jointly bootstrapping several information sources in Wikipedia to produce a large scale, multilingual and self-contained resource. The starting point is the category and article network. The most interesting feature of our approach is that it works completely automatically, in that it itself discovers relations in Wikipedia's category names for which it then finds numerous instances based on the category structure.

Building WikiNet involves three main steps. First, category names are deconstructed to retrieve the categorization criterion, which leads to the discovery of numerous binary relation instances. In the second step the relation instances discovered in the first step are refined based on information in the articles' infoboxes. In the last step the network obtained up to this point is formalized by merging nodes that refer to the same concept, and by adding lexicalizations for these concepts from redirect, disambiguation and cross-language links from Wikipedia versions in different languages. The resulting resource is a network consisting of 3 707 718 concepts and 49 931 266 relation instances (for 454 relations),[4] and covers multiple dimensions: multilinguality, world knowledge, lexical semantics, collocations, paraphrases, named entities. Because the processing does not rely on manual feedback, and both the relations and their instances in the network are automatically discovered in Wikipedia's categories and infoboxes, the algorithm can easily be applied to the latest Wikipedia versions to generate an updated resource.

Intrinsic evaluation of the knowledge extracted shows that combining different types of information leads to the derivation of accurate facts, not overtly expressed within articles or infoboxes, and as such not to be found by processing single aspects of Wikipedia. We contrast this approach with DBpedia [1] and YAGO [45]—the largest repositories of facts extracted from Wikipedia to date. We perform extrinsic evaluation through two tasks—semantic relatedness computation between pairs of terms, and metonymy resolution, i.e. finding the correct interpretation of terms which are not used in any of their literal senses (e.g. *White House* is often used to refer to the *President of the United States*). The extrinsic evaluation results show that the resource is of good quality—evidenced by high correlation results with manually assigned relatedness scores on disambiguated data—but it also has high ambiguity which cannot be solved for pairs of terms out of context. Applying WikiNet to the task of metonymy resolution shows consistent increase in precision and recall when using world knowledge to find the correct interpretation of potentially metonymic words, but due to the small size of the available data these increases are not statistically significant.

BUILDING WIKINET

The starting point for building WikiNet is the category and article network from one language version of Wikipedia. This network is modified step by step as more types of information from Wikipedia are taken into account. In the final step the nodes in the network are considered to represent concepts. Concepts and their lexicalizations are separated, and each concept—now represented through a language independent ID—has associated numerous lexicalizations in a variety of languages. An overview of the processing is shown in Algorithm 15.1, and each step is presented in more detail in the remainder of the section.

ALGORITHM 15.1. Algorithm for Building a Large Scale Multilingual Knowledge Network

Input:

W—the English Wikipedia dump

$\mathbb{R}$—a set of relational nouns

$\{W_x\}$—a set of additional Wikipedia dumps in different languages

Output:

WikiNet—a graph with nodes as concepts, and edges as relations between them

1: R_1 = DeconstructWikipediaCategories($W, \mathbb{R}$)

2: R_2 = PropagateInfoboxRelations(W, R_1)

3: **return** *WikiNet* = BuildConceptNetwork($R_2, W, \{W_x\}$)

The Wikipedia dump W is the file containing all English Wikipedia articles in XML format,[5] and $\mathbb{R}$ is a set of relational nouns extracted from an existing resource (NOMLEX,[6] Meyers et al. [23]) used for detecting one of four classes of relations in Wikipedia category names. The result of the category deconstruction process—R_1—is a set of relation instances, represented as tuples (x, r, y), where x, y are strings, some of which are Wikipedia article or category names, others are fragments of category names, and r is a relation, also derived from the category names. R_2, the result of infobox relation propagation, has the same structure as R_1, with the difference that some of the previously extracted relation instances are assigned new relations. *WikiNet*, derived from R_2 and additional information from W and $\{W_x\}$, is a graph. The nodes are concepts, which are identified through a unique numeric ID and have associated multiple lexicalizations in various languages. The edges are relation instances between concepts corresponding to the tuples in R_2, after mapping the arguments onto concepts and filtering out the tuples for which at least one argument could not be mapped onto a concept.

Each processing stage transforms the structure produced by the previous stage. The starting point is a Wikipedia dump, based on which we build a network whose nodes are the pages and categories and whose edges are the category–category and category–page links. The category deconstruction step (DeconstructWikipediaCategories) adds new nodes—substrings of category names—and (named) edges to the network, and it renames some of the existing edges. The infobox relation propagation step (PropagateInfoboxRelations) renames existing edges. After these two steps we build the actual network (BuildConceptNetwork), by collapsing together nodes (page/category nodes/category name substrings) that refer to the same entity, and by associating with each node numerous lexicalizations in multiple languages.

part of speech (POS):	The part of speech is the word class of a word—e.g. noun, verb, adjective, adverb, determiner, pronoun.
phrase:	Phrases are (grammatical) elements of clauses. There are five types of phrases: verb phrases, noun phrases, adjective phrases, adverbial phrases and prepositional phrases.
head word:	The head word defines the syntactic (and frequently also the semantic) properties of the phrase.
noun phrase (NP):	A noun phrase is a syntactic phrase whose head word is a noun.
constituent:	A constituent is a fragment of a larger grammatical construction that is itself a proper grammatical construction (word/phrase/clause). In this paper we refer to constituents of a noun phrase, and we only consider constituents which are noun phrases themselves.
dominant/head constituent:	A dominant constituent is the constituent of a phrase that has the same head word as the parent phrase.
relational noun:	Relational nouns are nouns that imply a relationship, e.g. *member, president*.
relation:	A relation—such as *is_a, president, caused_by*—describes a type of connection. In our case, we assume binary relations, that require two arguments.
relation instance:	A relation instance is a triple *(x, r, y)*, where *r* is a relation, and *x* and *y* are specified concepts.
concept:	In this paper we use the term *concept* to refer to what are called concepts (e.g. MATHEMATICS, SPACE SHUTTLE, etc.) as well as named entities (e.g. SPACE SHUTTLE ATLANTIS), because from an algorithmic point of view they are all treated the same. The resource however includes named entity information, thus allowing the two to be distinguished.
category:	By category we denote the Wikipedia category with all its implied structure (subsumed categories and pages).
category name:	When we need to differentiate between the category as a structure and its name, we refer to the name explicitly.

FIGURE 15.1. Glossary of Relevant Terminology.

In the following discussion we will make use of the terminology included in Figure 15.1.

Deconstructing Wikipedia Categories

To organize Wikipedia for easy access to pages, contributors are given guidelines for categorizing articles and naming new categories. A quick inspection reveals that categories[7] are noun phrases, many of which—e.g. ALBUMS BY ARTIST, PEOPLE FROM HEIDELBERG, MEMBERS OF THE EUROPEAN PARLIAMENT—do not correspond to the type of lexical concepts we would expect to encounter in texts and are not needed for processing a text automatically. Instead, they capture examples of human classification and relations that can be used as a source of information [27]. Complex categories combine multiple classification criteria—PEOPLE FROM HEIDELBERG contains pages about people who are from Heidelberg. From this

TABLE 15.1. Examples of Information Encoded in Category Names and the Knowledge We Extract

Category Name Type	Pattern	Relation Instances
explicit relation		
QUEEN (BAND) MEMBERS	X members members of X	FREDDY MERCURY *member_of* QUEEN (BAND) Brian May *member_of* QUEEN (BAND)...
MOVIES DIRECTED BY WOODY ALLEN	X [VBN IN] Y	ANNIE HALL *directed_by* WOODY ALLEN ANNIE HALL *is_a* MOVIE DECONSTRUCTING HARRY *directed_by* WOODY ALLEN DECONSTRUCTING HARRY *is_a* MOVIE
partly explicit relation		
VILLAGES IN BRANDENBURG	X [IN] Y	SIETHEN *located_in* BRANDENBURG SIETHEN *is_a* VILLAGE
implicit relation		
MIXED MARTIAL ARTS TELEVISION	X Y	MIXED MARTIAL ARTS *R* TELEVISION PROGRAMS TAPOUT (TV SERIES) *R* MIXED MARTIAL ARTS TAPOUT (TV SERIES) *is_a* TELEVISION PROGRAM
class attribute		
ALBUMS BY ARTIST	X by Y	ARTIST *attribute_ of* ALBUM MILES DAVIS *is_a* ARTIST BIG FUN *is_a* ALBUM

perspective, deconstruction of categories can be interpreted as separating each classification criterion captured in the category.

Analysis of category names reveals several types, based on the type of information they encode. We present them succinctly in Table 15.1, and then in more detail in the subsections to follow.

Explicit Relation Categories

These categories overtly express a relation that is common to all articles in a category. The relation can be expressed through a relational noun—e.g. member, president—or through a verb–preposition combination—e.g. caused by, founded in—corresponding to two types of explicit relation categories:

Relational nouns Relational nouns are nouns that indicate a relation. Their meaning is complete when their arguments are also present: e.g. *prime-minister*. Such nouns are present in category names and give clues about specific properties of the subsumed articles. Let us take for example the category MEMBERS OF THE EUROPEAN PARLIAMENT: All articles in this category describe some X_i, such that X_i *member_of* EUROPEAN PARLIAMENT.

Categories of this type can be identified if their name matches a pattern NP_1 NP_2 or NP_2 (of/of the) NP_1, where the head of the noun phrase NP_2 is a relational noun, such as member, president, prime-minister. To recognize explicit relations that involve a relational noun, we use a set R of singular and plural forms of relational nouns from NOMLEX [23] (699 word forms). *member* is an extreme example of a relational noun, in that it does not have meaning in the absence of both its arguments. *president*, on the other hand, is informative even when only one of its arguments is present—e.g. Barack Obama is a president. For this reason, the relations instances P_i *is_a* r_n are also added, where $r_n \in R$ is the relational noun that matches (part of) the category name.

Verb–preposition combinations In Wikipedia categories, verb past-participle and preposition combinations—such as *directed by, built in*—indicate a relation. The category AIRPLANE CRASHES CAUSED BY PILOT ERROR provides an example. All articles in this category describe airplane crashing events, *caused_by* pilot error. These categories match the part of speech pattern NP_1 VBN IN NP_2.[8] The relation consists of the verb–preposition combination in the category name. Recognizing this type of explicit relations relies on part of speech tags; to obtain them we use Stanford's POS tagger.[9]

Partly Explicit Relation Categories

Prepositions, although sometimes ambiguous, are strong indicators of semantic relations [17]. The preposition of, for example, may indicate a spatial (TREASURE TROVES OF EUROPE) or a temporal (TREASURE TROVES OF THE IRON AGE) relation, and the same is the case for the preposition in: VILLAGES IN BRANDENBURG encodes a spatial relation, CONFLICTS IN 2000 captures a temporal one.

Categories of this kind have the pattern NP_1 IN NP_2 (IN is the part of speech tag for (all) prepositions). Note that there is no overlap with explicit relation categories whose patterns are more restrictive (and will be attempted first). For partly explicit relation categories, we do not have the constraint that the noun phrase is headed by a relational noun, nor do we have a verb appearing in the category name.

To determine the relation R expressed in a category with the pattern NP_1 IN NP_2, we use the supercategories of NP_1 and $NP_2 - S_{NP1}$ and S_{NP2}:

- if S_{NP1} matches person or people, and S_{NP2} is organization or group, the relation assigned is *member_of*;
- if S_{NP2} matches location or geography, the relation assigned is *spatial*. Once a spatial relation is detected, specifications can

be made based on the connecting preposition (e.g. *located_in* for the preposition in, etc.). To facilitate the evaluation process, all spatial relations detected are named *spatial*, and their instances are labeled accordingly.

- if S_{NP2} matches time, the relation assigned is *temporal*.

Implicit Relation Categories

Some category names are complex noun compounds. These do capture relations, but do not give any (overt) indication of what the relation is: MIXED MARTIAL ARTS TELEVISION PROGRAMS has two noun phrase components—MIXED MARTIAL ARTS and TELEVISION PROGRAMS—and the relation between them, encoded in the category name, is *topic*. These categories have the pattern NP_1 NP_2.

For category names that are complex noun compounds, we use the parse tree to extract all embedded phrases (NP, PP, VP, ADJP, ADVP). An example is presented in Figure 15.2.

Each embedded phrase is considered to be a constituent C_j of the category name (C_1 = mixed martial arts, C_2 = television programs). Each C_j is dominated by another constituent C_j^h according to the syntactic structure of the category name (in our example, $C_2 = C_1^h$, i.e. C_2 dominates C_1). The constituent which corresponds to the phrase head is the dominant/head constituent of the category name and is denoted by C^h (C_2 is also C^h in the above example). We use only the noun phrase constituents of a category name, and denote the constituents accordingly as NP_j, NP^h.

Figure 15.3 shows examples of relations and some of their instances induced for this type of category. The process is shown in detail below.

1 add relation instances P_i *is_a* NP^h;

2 form pairs (NP_j, NP^h) for all NP_j for which $NP_j^h = NP^h$— form constituent pairs in which the first constituent is

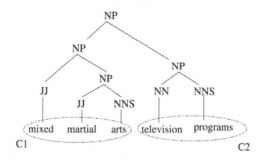

FIGURE 15.2. Example of Parse Tree for a Category Name.

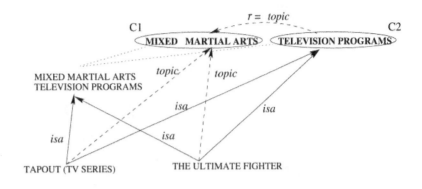

FIGURE 15.3. Example of Relations and Some of Their Instances Induced after Extracting Components of a Category Name.

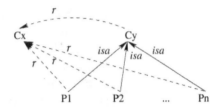

FIGURE 15.4. Propagating the Relation between Category Constituents to the Subsumed Pages.

dominated by the main dominant constituent. Determine the relation r that holds between ($\mathbf{NP}_j$, $\mathbf{NP}^h$) (detailed below);

3 add relation instances $\mathbf{P}_i$ r $\mathbf{NP}_j$.

Propagating the relation r from the category constituents to the pages follows the rule captured in Figure 15.4: *if* $\mathbf{P}_j$ *is_a* $\mathbf{NP}^h$ *and* $\mathbf{NP}^h$ r $\mathbf{NP}_x$ $\Rightarrow$ $\mathbf{P}_j$ r $\mathbf{NP}_x$.

Finding the relation between one pair ($\mathbf{NP}_x$, $\mathbf{NP}^h$) means automatically finding the relation between numerous ($\mathbf{P}_j$, $\mathbf{NP}_x$) pairs.

Class Attribute Categories

For categories with names that match the pattern [NP_1 by NP_2], we identify NP_1 as a class and NP_2 as an attribute. Categories with this pattern usually have subcategories that further group the pages, according to values of the class attribute. For example, ALBUMS BY ARTIST has subcategories MILES DAVIS ALBUMS, THE BEATLES ALBUMS, . . . We then identify the value of the attribute in the subcategory names. In many cases, like the example presented in Figure 15.5, NP_1 appears in the subcategory name—**albums** *by artist* → *Miles Davis* **albums**. It is then easy to identify

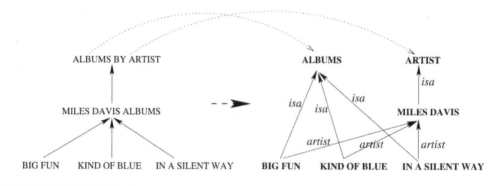

FIGURE 15.5. Example of Relations and Some of Their Instances Inferred from "by" Categories.

the attribute value (Miles Davis for artist), and we add the relation instance MILES DAVIS *is_a* ARTIST, as shown in Figure 15.5.

Not all situations follow the patterns described above: The category HEADS OF GOVERNMENT BY COUNTRY is an example. Subcategories of this category include PRIME MINISTERS OF CANADA, CHANCELLORS OF GERMANY. In this case we start processing the attribute first (NP_2):

1 if the attribute is a category in Wikipedia, collect the pages it subsumes (P_{ai}) as possible attribute values;

2 if a P_{ai} appears in the subcategory name, it serves as confirmation that this is a possible attribute value and we add the links P_{ai} *is_a* NP_2 and P_i *is_a* NP_1 for each page P_i subsumed by the "by" category;

3 extract the remainder of the subcategory name as an instance of NP_1.

In the example above, NP_1 = *heads of government*, NP_2 = *country*. We expand COUNTRY[10] to all its pages and test whether any of them appear in the name of the subcategory PRIME MINISTERS OF CANADA. We thus identify P_{ai} = *Canada*, and add the links CANADA *is_a* COUNTRY (step 2) and PRIME MINISTER *is_a* HEADS OF GOVERNMENT (step 3). For all pages P_i under HEADS OF GOVERNMENT BY COUNTRY, the relation instances P_i *is_a* HEADS OF GOVERNMENT are added (step 2).

The Algorithm

Using the information obtained from processing the category names as detailed above, we induce knowledge which is added to the original category and article network. This process is sketched out in Algorithm 15.2. In the preceding discussion we have presented category types based on the type of relation they encode. In the algorithm the ordering is in reverse order of the specificity of the matching pattern, meaning that more constraining patterns are applied first.

ALGORITHM 15.2. Deconstructing Wikipedia Categories

Input:
W–a Wikipedia dump
R–a set of relational nouns

Output:
R_1–a set of binary relation instances

1: W_C = the set of categories from W
2: R_1 = {}
3: **for** $w \in W_C$ **do**
4:     P = set of pages under w
5:     **if** w matches "NP_1 by NP_2" **then**
6:         // Class attribute categories
7:         $R_1 = R_1 \cup$ PROCESSBYCATEGORY(w)
8:         $R_1 = R_1 \cup$ EXTRACTCLASSATTRIBUTES(w, W)
9:     **else**
10:         **if** w matches "r (of|of the) [NP]" or "[NP] r", where $r \in R$ **then**
11:             // Explicit relation category, relational nouns
12:             $R_1 = R_1 \cup \{P_i \, r \, [NP] \mid \forall P_i \in P\}$
13:         **else**
14:             **if** w matches "NP_1 VBN IN NP_2" **then**
15:                 // Explicit relation category, verb–prep combination
16:                 $R_1 = R_1 \cup \{(P_i \, [VBN \, IN] \, NP_2), (P_i \, is\_a \, NP_1) \mid \forall P_i \in P\}$
17:             **else**
18:                 **if** w matches "NP_1 IN NP_2" **then**
19:                     // Partly explicit relation category
20:                     r = DetermineRelation(IN, NP_1, NP_2)
21:                     $R_1 = R_1 \cup \{(P_i \, r \, NP_2), (P_i \, is\_a \, NP_1) \mid \forall P_i \in P\}$
22:                 **else**
23:                     **if** w is a complex noun compound **then**
24:                         // Implicit relation category
25:                         C = ExtractConstituents(w)
26:                         $C = \{NP_x, NP^h\}$, NP^h is the dominant (head) constituent of w
27:                         $R_1 = R_1 \cup \{(P_i \, related\_to \, NP_x), (P_i \, is\_a \, NP^h) \mid \forall P_i \in P\}$
28: **return** R_1

To apply the aforementioned rules, the category names are processed with the POS tagger and parser developed by the Stanford NLP group.[11]

The result of this first stage of the process is a network with a heterogeneous mixture of nodes: Some represent categories, some pages, some strings obtained after splitting category names. To obtain the WikiNet version whose statistics we included in this paper, at this point of processing we had a network with 70 540 640 edges and 3 885 940 nodes.

Propagating Infobox Relations

In the previous step the information encoded in Wikipedia's category names was used to induce relations and their corresponding instances. Some category names provide only very general clues and general relations, such as *temporal* or *spatial*. For practical reasons it may be useful to have more specific relations. To obtain them we look at links between category names and information in the infoboxes: The category name encodes the categorization/grouping criterion that is respected by all of the subsumed pages, while the infoboxes contain a summary of the most important information in the corresponding pages and the categorization criterion may be part of that.

We hypothesize a connection between the information encoded in category names and the information summarized in infoboxes, and use this to propagate relations from infoboxes through the category network, as shown in Figure 15.6. Let us have a closer look at this example. First, the category name deconstruction step splits the string Military equipment of the Soviet Union into two parts: Military equipment and Soviet Union. It then proposes a rather generic *spatial* relation based on the preposition of and the fact that Soviet Union has a corresponding article whose ancestor is the GEOGRAPHY category. In the final step of the category deconstruction process, we have added the relation instances (P_i *spatial* SOVIET UNION) for all pages P_i subsumed by the category MILITARY EQUIPMENT OF THE SOVIET UNION. We would now like to find a more informative relation to replace the generic *spatial* in the relation instances mentioned before. Several of the articles under the category MILITARY EQUIPMENT OF THE SOVIET UNION contain infoboxes,[12] in which we find Soviet Union as the value of the attribute *place-of-origin*. This attribute becomes the relation, and the previously extracted relation instances are replaced by (P_i *place-of-origin* Soviet Union) for all pages P_i subsumed by the category MILITARY EQUIPMENT OF THE SOVIET UNION. This can be seen as propagating a relation first from the pages that contain infoboxes to the category which subsumes them, and then from this parent category to all the other page siblings that did not have an infobox.

Working "on top" of an existing network introduces an important difference and advantage relative to work that extracts knowledge from open texts: A piece of extracted knowledge—a

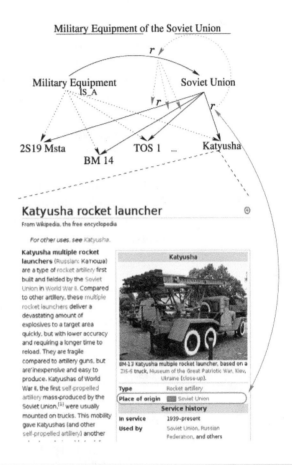

FIGURE 15.6. Some articles under a Wikipedia category contain infoboxes with hand-picked relations, from which we can determine the relation that holds between the corresponding concept and the concepts derived from its parent category, and then propagate these relations in the network.

predicate–arguments tuple—is immediately connected to other such facts, and it has a context. Because of this, every piece of information we add to this network has an impact on its neighbours, and, depending on its type, its influence can reach far. This happens when establishing the connection between the information in infoboxes for some pages and their parent categories—it impacts their siblings.

In other words, r is a candidate relation for the constituents pair (NP^h, NP_i) corresponding to category C, if it is associated with the same value V in all infoboxes in which it appears under C, and if V is compatible with NP_i. Two values are compatible if they are identical, paraphrases of each other, or are connected in a systematic way—V is an instance or a concept more specific than the one corresponding to NP_i, or for locations for example V *part-of* NP_i (a specific location in Europe is compatible with EUROPE). This predicate can become more specialized as more relation instances are added to the fact base.

Algorithm 15.3 shows the processing steps for linking a category name with information in the infoboxes of its subsumed pages and for propagating the induced relations to the page–category links.

The result of this processing step is a network consisting of the same nodes and edges as in the previous processing step, with the difference that the names of certain edges are now changed, according to the information in the infoboxes.

ALGORITHM 15.3. Linking to Infoboxes and Propagating Relations

---

Input:
W–a Wikipedia dump
R_1–a set of relations extracted in the category name processing step

Output:
R_2–a set of binary relations

1: W_c = the set of categories from W
2: $R_2 = R_1$
3: **for** w W_c, $w \mapsto \{NP_1, \ldots, NP_j\}$ according to the previous deconstruction step **do**
4:    P is the set of pages subsumed by w
5:    build set of candidates $R = \{r_i \mid (r_i, NP_x) \in P_j\}$–the set of attributes which are associated with one of the category's constituents NP_x extracted from infoboxes from pages $P_j \in P$
6:    **if** $|R| = 1$ and matching constituent is NP_x **then**
7:      $r \in R$
8:      **for** $P_j \in P$ **do**
9:         replace relations $(P_j \ r_x \ NP_x)$ in R_2 with $(P_j \ r \ NP_x)$
10:    **else**
11:      **if** $|R| > 1$ and matching constituent is NP_x **then**
12:         **if** all relations in R are compatible **then**
13:            **for** $P_j \in P$ **do**
14:               replace relations $(P_j \ r_x \ NP_x)$ in R_2 with $(P_j \ r \ NP_x)$
15: **return** R_2

Building a Concept Network

Mapping Relation Arguments to Concepts

Up until this point we have built a heterogeneous network based on various types of information in Wikipedia. Now this network will be transformed into a concept network. In works using Wikipedia as a source of knowledge, categories and articles are considered to represent concepts [36,25]. We start from this premise as well, and constrain it to eliminate redundancy—there should only be one node representing a concept. Mapping onto one node articles and categories that refer to the same concept (e.g. CITIES and CITY) or are homonyms (there is a ROME article and a category) is trivial. A more complex issue arises when mapping the fragments resulting from deconstructing the category names onto the original Wikipedia nodes—a prerequisite for the final node mapping step.

The category CHEMISTRY ALBUMS, for example, is split into two parts: *Chemistry* and *albums*, both of which are ambiguous with respect to the nodes corresponding to articles or categories in the network. *Chemistry*, for example, can refer to the science, the band, various albums and songs. To determine the correct corresponding article or category we compute a connectivity score that counts the number of times each of these potential referents is linked to from pages subsumed by the category CHEMISTRY ALBUMS. Formally, if the fragment NP_X of a category C is ambiguous, we collect the possible nodes (articles/categories) N_i that NP_X can refer to, and all pages P_j subsumed by C. We choose as an interpretation for NP_X the node N_i towards which there are the most hyperlinks (outlinks) in the pages P_j:

$$NP_X \mapsto N = \operatorname*{argmax}_{Ni} \sum_{P_j \text{ subsumed\_by } C} outlink(P_j, N_i)$$

$$outlink(P_j, N_i) = \begin{cases} 1 & \exists \text{ a link from page } P_j \text{ to } N_i; \\ 0 & \text{otherwise} \end{cases}$$

Note that only the strings obtained by splitting the category names are ambiguous, whereas the article and category nodes are not ambiguous in the network (i.e. each node has a unique title and ID extracted from the Wikipedia dump).

This disambiguation step impacts the number of relation instances extracted in the previous step, because some of the arguments of the relation instances could not be linked to a node in the network. This step and duplicate filtering reduces the set to 49 931 266 unique instances.

Extracting Alternative Lexicalizations

Following WordNet's example, which separates synsets and their lexicalizations, in the newly created network nodes are replaced with numeric IDs, and then each ID is associated with the corresponding node's name. More lexicalizations are added to each node through the redirect, the disambiguation and the cross-language links.

Redirect links pair a redirect page with its target. Redirect pages can be viewed as containing name variations for Wikipedia articles. They may contain morphological variants (actor, actors and actress redirect to the article ACTOR), proper synonyms (adrenaline redirects to EPINEPHRINE), paraphrases (Seinfeld, The show about nothing for the article SEINFELD (TV SERIES)) or even misspellings (Sienfeld for Seinfeld). The names of redirects are added to the ID corresponding to the article they point to.

Disambiguation links map a disambiguation page onto its possible targets. Disambiguation pages encode polysemy—the name of the source of this link applies to all possible targets. King points to the pages corresponding to the monarch, the chess piece, and many others. The name of the source of the disambiguation link is added to the IDs of all of the possible targets.

Cross-language links link an article to its variants in other languages. The corresponding names can be used as translations. For the concept ACTOR we find the following language variations through the cross-language links Schauspieler (German), Attore (Italian), etc.

The network presented here is built from the information extracted from the English version of Wikipedia (W_{en}). There were several reasons for choosing the English Wikipedia: It is the most comprehensive version, there are numerous language processing tools that allow for deeper processing of the article texts if necessary (at this point only POS tagging and head extraction were used for processing the category names), capitalization rules allow for easy and accurate extraction of named entity information. More information can be added from Wikipedia versions for other languages. We use page, redirect, disambiguation and cross-language information from other language versions (W_l) to add lexicalizations of concepts in different languages, following Algorithm 15.4. Essentially we map together pages in different languages either through existing cross-language links, or by checking for overlap in their respective cross-language links, following the "triangulation" algorithm from Wentland et al. [48].

Note that we do not aim to build a lexicon of synonyms for each concept based on cross-language links, as was done by de Melo and Weikum [7], who filter out inaccurate cross-language links. As shown before with redirect and disambiguation links, the index contains more than synonyms, reflecting the various ways a concept is lexicalized in different languages.

ALGORITHM 15.4   Adding Lexicalizations from a Wikipedia Version

---

Input:

$WikiNet = \{ID, Lex, R\}$—the current version of WikiNet consisting of:

        ID a set of concept IDs

        $Lex = \{L_{ID_x} \mid \forall\, ID_x \in ID\}$ a set of concept lexicalizations

        R the set of relation instances between (concept) IDs

W_{Lg}—the Wikipedia dump in a specific language Lg

t—a threshold for overlap in concept lexicalizations

Output:

$WikiNet'$—WikiNet enriched with additional lexicalizations

  1: $Lex' = Lex$

  2: **extract** ID_{Lg}—the set of page IDs from W_{Lg}

  3: **extract** Lex_{Lg}—the lexicalizations of pages from W_{Lg} through mapping page titles, redirect and disambiguation lexicalizations onto the corresponding page IDs

  4: **map** pages from different language versions:

  5: **for** $ID_{Lg,i} \in ID_{Lg}$ **do**

  6:     **for** $ID_j \in ID$ **do**

  7:         **compute overlap** $o_{ij} = |L_{ID_{Lg,i}} \cap L_{ID_j}|$—the size of the intersection of the lexicalizations of concepts corresponding to concepts $ID_{Lg,i}$ in language Lg and ID_j in the current version of WikiNet

  8:         **if** $\max_{ID_j, ID_j \in ID} o_{ij} > t$ **then**

  9:             $n = \mathrm{argmax}_{j,\, ID_j \in ID}\, o_{ij}$

10:             $ID_{Lg,i} \mapsto ID_n$

11:             $L'_{ID_n} = L_{ID_{Lg,i}} \cup L_{ID_n}$

12:             replace L_{ID_n} in Lex' with L'_{ID_n}

13: **return** $WikiNet' = \{ID, Lex', R\}$

Table 15.2 shows how the coverage of concepts and number of included lexicalizations changes when adding information from the German Wikipedia. Because the supplemental information comes from the German Wikipedia, it is not surprising that the highest increase is for German, but we see substantial differences for other languages as well, indicating that merging lexicalizations from different Wikipedia language versions is useful. The number of covered concepts has increased, meaning that we have established a mapping between concepts that were not linked through cross-language links; furthermore the number of lexicalizations has increased, meaning that for the existing entries we now have more lexicalization variations. The increase is much higher with respect to lexicalizations (5.13 times) than concept coverage (1.17 times), which is to be expected as there are several sources for lexicalizations (redirect, disambiguation, cross-language links), while concept coverage relies on mapping entries to each other. Other language versions are added in a similar fashion.

TABLE 15.2. Partial Language Statistics: Concept Coverage and Number of Lexicalizations in WikiNet before and after Adding Information from the German Wikipedia

Language	No. of Lexicalizations (no. of entries)	
	Before	After
English	7 239 290 (2 996 357)	7 515 310 (2 996 357)
French	523 835 (509 051)	728 349 (589 448)
German	484 688 (474 455)	2 488 983 (556 977)
Italian	384 192 (378 896)	555 452 (457 158)
. . .		
Hungarian	89 413 (87 526)	127 487 (115 558)
Romanian	89 030 (84 694)	137 582 (114 284)
Turkish	86 543 (80 429)	117 662 (103 733)
. . .		
Russian	265 062 (254 740)	415 638 (334 106)
Japanese	264 547 (263 186)	383 387 (323 239)
Chinese	154 404 (151 957)	221 398 (186 938)

The current version of WikiNet merges lexicalizations from English, Chinese, Dutch, French, German, Italian, Japanese and Korean Wikipedia dumps.

Anchor texts—the text fragments associated with hyperlinks in a page—are an additional lexicalization source. While they were shown to be useful for detecting concepts in texts [26], they are too noisy to be added to the resource.

Named Entity Information

Named entity (NE) information is an important feature of a concept. To retrieve it we use an approach similar to Bunescu and Paşca [5] for single words. For multi-word terms we resort to syntactic analysis, as detailed below. This processing is applied to texts from the English Wikipedia, and it relies on capitalization conventions for this language. Because the named entity information once extracted is attached to concepts, it becomes available in all languages that have a lexicalization for that concept.

- For single word entries w, we compute $c_{cs}(w)$ as the number of occurrences of the word (case-sensitive) in the text of its corresponding article, and $c(w)$ is its total number of occurrences (case-insensitive) in the text:

$$NE(w) = \begin{cases} TRUE : & \dfrac{c_{cs}(w)}{c(w)} < \tau \\[2ex] FALSE : & \dfrac{c_{cs}(w)}{c(w)} \geq \tau \end{cases}$$

$\tau = 0.2$

- For multi-word entries $(\bar{w})$, we match the NE information with the NE information of its syntactic head: $NE(\bar{w}) = NE(w)$, where w is the syntactic head of $\bar{w}$. This replaces [5] heuristic of assigning NE information based on capitalization only, which fails for categories like HISTORY OF EUROPE, or ECONOMY OF THE UNITED STATES OF AMERICA.

Of the 3 707 718 concepts in the network, 2 507 052 are tagged as named entities according to this method, leaving 1 200 666 common nouns/phrases.

EVALUATION

To verify the quality of the extracted network we carry out intrinsic and extrinsic evaluations of the resource. The intrinsic evaluation only looks at the resource itself; to do this we evaluate the result of each step of processing. The extrinsic evaluation looks at the resource in context, and its usefulness for specific tasks. We perform this through two tasks—semantic relatedness computation between pairs of terms and metonymy resolution.

WikiNet Overview

Before proceeding with the evaluation, we provide a summary of information regarding the latest version of WikiNet, built on the following Wikipedia dumps: 2011/01/15 English, 2011/01/11 German, 2011/02/01 French, 2011/01/30 Italian, 2011/06/28

Japanese, 2011/06/21 Korean, 2011/01/26 Dutch and 2011/06/28 Chinese.

concepts	3 707 718	
named entities	2 507 052	67.62%
(general) concepts	1 200 666	32.38%
number of languages[13]	196	
lexicalizations	128 505 704	
average lexicalization per concept	34.66	
unique strings	14 376 806	
unique strings when taking language into account	19 582 972	
relations	494	
relation instances	49 931 266	
between two named entities	13 529 382	27.09%
between a named entity and (general) concepts	31 423 078	62.93%
between two (general) concepts	4 978 806	9.97%

Detailed information about instances per relation and concepts covered for each language can be found here: http://www.h-its.org/downloads/nlp/stats.rels, http://www.h-its.org/downloads/nlp/stats.lang.

Intrinsic Evaluation

Deconstructing Wikipedia Categories

Processing the Wikipedia categories starts with loading the category network—in the form of nodes and category links extracted from Wikipedia dumps—and filtering out administrative categories (identified using keywords, e.g. stubs, articles, wikipedia). After this preprocessing, there are 277 918 categories in the network. We obtain 70 540 640 relation instances, 66 184 610 of which are distributed among the category processing steps as follows:

explicit relations categories:
    relational noun pattern: 42 823 category names had a relational noun head and express 185 relations (e.g. *alumnus_ of, president_ of, member_of, player_of, collections_of*).
    VBN IN pattern: 14 238 category names match this pattern, and express 192 relations (e.g. *caused_by, written_by, based_in*).
partly explicit categories: 172 196 category names encode partly explicit relations, most of which are assigned *temporal* or

TABLE 15.3. Classes and Attributes Extracted from Wikipedia's "by" Categories

Class	Attributes
ART	country, media, nationality, origin, period, region, type
BOOK	author, award, country, head of state or government, ideology, nationality, publisher, series, subject, university, writer, year
BUILDING	architect, area, city, community, county, country, function, grade, locality, province, region, shape, state, territory, town
MUSICIAN	band, community, ethnicity, genre, instrument, language, nationality, region, religion, state, territory
WORK	artist, author, genre, head of state or government, nationality, writer, year
WRITER	area, award, ethnicity, format, genre, language, movement, nationality, period, religion, state, territory

spatial relations in this step, to be refined in the infobox relation propagation step.

implicit relations categories: 39 049 category names give no overt information about the relation encoded. The relations in this case are generically named *related_to*, and part of these will be named in the infobox relation propagation step.

class attribute categories: 9612 categories. Processing the category names reveals 840 classes with an average of 2.27 attributes. A sample is presented in Table 15.3.

The difference of 4 356 030 instances from the total extracted is made up of category–category and category–article links. Some of these instances will be updated with more informative relations after mapping relation arguments to concepts.

Table 15.4 shows the number of (unique) extracted relation instances and evaluation results in terms of precision. For each of the two types of explicit relations—based on the VBN IN pattern, and the relational noun pattern—we extracted a random sample of 250 instances (covering different relations), which was manually annotated by two human judges. We evaluated separately *is_a* and *spatial*, which were two of the most frequent relations, by comparing against two other random samples of 250 instances annotated by two judges. For each of these four evaluation sets, the table includes two scores—one that corresponds to evaluation

TABLE 15.4. Extracted Relations and Instances for Each Category Type and Manual Evaluation Results of Some of the Most Frequent Relations

Category Type	Relation	# Categories	# Inst. Extracted	Precision	
				∩	∪
explicit		57 061	6 268 036		
	alumnus_of,	29 189	4 355 964	95.56%	97.17%
	member_of,				
	president_of,				
	player_of, . . .				
	caused_by,	17 297	1 912 072	94.37%	96.38%
	written_by,				
	based_in, . . .				
partly explicit		172 196	24 058 117		
implicit		39 049	8 144 597		
class attribute		9612	27 713 860		
	is_a		17 714 648	76.40%	84.00%
	spatial		13 087 052	87.09%	97.98%

against the intersection ∩ (instances that the annotators agree are correct) and against the union ∪ (instances that at least one annotator marks as correctly assigned).[14]

In addition to the fact that it is easier to analyze a short phrase to extract a relation rather than a sentence or even a document, analyzing category names and the category and page network for knowledge acquisition has other advantages as well. The category names express very concisely a relation which may also appear in the article, but is expressed there in a more complex manner. We took the 42 711 *member_of* relation instances discovered through category name analysis, and extracted from the Wikipedia article corpus the sentences in which the two elements of the pair appear together: 131 691 sentences. Of these, only 1985 sentences contained the word member, indicating that further processing would have been necessary to derive this particular type of information, while by analyzing category names this information is readily available.

Propagating Infobox Relations

At this point, the data consists of 70 540 640 relation instances obtained by deconstructing categories and keeping the category–

TABLE 15.5. The Most Frequent Propagated Relations

Relation	Count	Example
country	67 724	Duchy of Parma–Italy
subdivision_name	58 463	Aylmer, Quebec–Gatineau
location	40 525	Valvelspitze–South Tyrol
battles	39 425	John Paton–WWI
birth place	24 925	Franklin D. Roosevelt–New York
continent	24 228	1928 British Home Championship–Europe
region	18 590	1927 Crimean earthquakes–Crimea
genre	10 528	Cinepaint–graphics
industry	2056	Google–Internet

category and category–article links. Some of the relations' arguments correspond to Wikipedia pages, 1 049 724 of which contain instances of one of 4459 infobox types. Of the 277 918 categories deconstructed, for 42 060 a link was established between the category name (specifically, a constituent of the category name) and a value in the infobox. The link was established through 130 123 pages that contained infoboxes and an entry in the infobox corresponding to a category name constituent, for a total of 175 350 (P_j, NP_i) page–constituent links. The information was propagated to a further 544 702 pages and their 698 929 relation instances to the corresponding category name constituent, as shown graphically in Figure 15.6 (on page 245). This set of 698 929 relation instances is the result to be evaluated. Table 15.5 shows some of the most frequent relations, and their number of occurrences in this set.

The propagation step is evaluated through two methods: (i) manual evaluation of two sets of relations carried out by two judges, (ii) manual and automatic evaluation of the overlap with YAGO's fact base[15] [45].

Manual evaluation Due to the large number of relations extracted and due to variation in their frequency, we split the set of relation instances obtained through propagation into two roughly equally large subsets—one corresponding to high frequency relations (they have more than 5000 instances), and one to low frequency ones. We extracted two samples of 250 relation instances—one from each of these two subsets—which contain the same distribution of relations as the subset they represent. This allows us to analyze a wider spectrum of relations, as low frequency relations would not appear in a small random sample that maintains the distribution of relations. The high frequency sample contains the following relations[16]:

battles (8), *birth_place* (8), *country* (22), *date* (7), *founded* (6), *genre* (26), *group* (5), *headquarters* (6), *industry* (10), *language* (6), *location* (34), *nationality* (14), *occupation* (5), *place* (5), *pushpin_map* (6), *region* (5), *ship_ country* (6), *sport* (6), *subdivision_name* (24), *subdivision_type* (4), *type* (18), *work* (6), *year* (6), *years_active* (7)

and the low frequency sample (we give a partial list):

address (2), *airdate* (2), *alma_mater* (3), *area_served* (2), *artist* (2), *associated_acts* (2), *author* (4), *awards* (4), *basin_countries* (3), *birthdate* (2), *birthplace* (5), *body* (2), *born* (2), *branch* (4), *bundesland* (3), etc.

These two samples were manually annotated by two human judges. The guidelines instructed the annotators to assign a `true/false/not_relation` tag to each instance. The instances in the annotation set were grouped by relation, and before each batch corresponding to one relation was included a positive example from an infobox to help the annotators. During annotation a few issues became apparent: There are "attributes" in infoboxes which are not really attributes (e.g. *pushpin map*, *caption*) which link to the included map or image (we call these "false" relations). There were 15 instances of such relations in each of the two sample files, 14 on which the judges had agreed, and 1 on which they did not. The *pushpin map* replaced the rather general *spatial* relation assigned in the category deconstruction step. Another issue arose from wrongly categorized articles (at least in the opinion of the annotators). While the propagation process may have been correct, the relation instance was tagged "false." For example TRICIA LEIGH FISHER was assigned the *occupation* relation to CHILD ACTORS, because it was categorized under AMERICAN CHILD ACTORS. She started her acting career when she was 16 or 17, and one of the annotators considered the assigned category AMERICAN CHILD ACTORS—and consequently the induced TRICIA LEIGH FISHER *occupation* CHILD ACTORS relation instance—"false."

The results in terms of precision are presented in Table 15.6, relative to `true` tags assigned by both judges ($\cap$) or by at least one judge ($\cup$). The agreement between judges in terms of Cohen's Kappa is 0.62 for the high frequency sample, and 0.81 for the low frequency one.[17]

TABLE 15.6. Manual Annotation Results and Evaluation, on the Sample without "False" Relations (filtered)/on the Full Sample

Sample	Instances Filtered/All	Evaluation	
		∩	∪
high freq	235/250	78.3%/73.6%	86.8%/81.6%
low freq	235/250	75.7%/71.2%	77.9%/73.2%

Comparison with YAGO The versions of WikiNet and YAGO that we compare were not generated from the same Wikipedia download. To maximize the matching between the extracted relation instances and YAGO, we processed the arguments of our relations and those in YAGO by removing information in parentheses (e.g. Time (Unix) → Time), by lowercasing and by removing all blanks and all non-letter/digit characters. Additionally, we considered that a WikiNet relation instance matches a YAGO one if their arguments match, as the resources do not share the same relations. The overlap of the set of 698 929 relation instances renamed through relation propagation with YAGO's fact base is 7143 concept pairs. This small overlap shows that categories, the category structure and infoboxes are the combined source of novel information, not easily or directly accessible through the article texts or categories alone. We look in a bit more detail at the relations connecting these pairs in our approach and in YAGO. 306 YAGO relations are represented within the 7143 pairs. We consider the top 5, which cover 5854 of the pairs: *locatedIn* (3163), *wrote* (972), *directed* (757), *politicianOf* (572) and *created* (390). To the pairs assigned *created* in YAGO correspond the following relations assigned through the method presented in this paper:

artist (126), *writer* (89), *developer* (58), *director* (37), *manufacturer* (14), *producer* (12), *composer* (8).[18]

The relations assigned by propagating relations from the infoboxes are more specific than the relations in YAGO for the overlapping pairs. In the manually annotated sample we have 14 instances annotated with relations from this set. Their precision is 87.5% (both ∩ and ∪). The same phenomenon occurs for *locatedIn*—it is a rather general relation, and it corresponds to a variety of more specific spatial relations in our assignment: *subdivision_name* (1288), *prefecture* (660), *location* (257), *district* (142), *country* (46), *basin_countries* (37), *bundesland* (30),

TABLE 15.7. Evaluation Relative to the Overlap with YAGO

YAGO Relation	Overlap	Precision
full evaluation		
wrote	972	99.07%
directed	757	98.94%
estimation based on manually annotated sample		
located in	3163	86.25% ($\cup$)/83.75% ($\cap$)
created	390	87.5%

county (18). Of these, the relations *subdivision_name, location, country* also appear in the manually annotated data (80 instances), and (together) achieve a precision of 86.25% ($\cup$)/83.75% ($\cap$) (Table 15.7).

The *wrote* and *directed* YAGO relations are easily mapped onto the propagated relations: For 963 of the instances with relation *wrote* in YAGO, the inference process assigned the relation *author* (99.07%), and 749 instances of the relation *directed* have the relation *director* after propagation (98.94%).

The relation *politicianOf* is harder to evaluate. None of the relations assigned through relation propagation expresses the same relation, however they are not erroneous: *birth_place* (350), *death_place* (93), *residence* (16), *nationality* (15). These relations were represented in the manually annotated data (40 instances), and their precision was 72.5% ($\cup$)/70% ($\cap$).

Full Comparison with YAGO

In the previous subsection we evaluated the results of the infobox propagation method through a comparison with YAGO. Here we perform a full evaluation of the network at this stage as compared with YAGO's core set of facts extracted from Wikipedia. Matching our relation instances and YAGO's is done as described in the previous section. The discussion on the mapping between the two lists of relations (types) was partly done in the previous section. After this processing we compute three measures of the overlap between our relation instances (R_W) and YAGO's (R_Y), following the method of Ponzetto and Strube [37] (itself derived from Navigli and Ponzetto [30]):

Coverage is the ratio between the number of relation instances shared by the two resources, and the relation instances in the reference resource (here, YAGO)[19]:

$$Coverage(R_W, R_Y) = \frac{|R_W \cap R_Y|}{|R_Y|} = \frac{598\,782}{10\,329\,767} = 5.8\%$$

It is clear from the low overlap between the resources that each contains information that the other one does not. *Novelty* and *ExtraCoverage* quantify this:

Novelty quantifies the novelty rate of our relation instances, as the ratio between relation instances that appear only in our set, and the full size of the extracted set:

$$Novelty(R_W, R_Y) = \frac{|R_W \setminus (R_W \cap R_Y)|}{|R_W|} = \frac{49\,332\,484}{49\,931\,266} = 98.8\%$$

The Novelty of YAGO's core relations relative to our relations is:

$$Novelty(R_Y, R_W) = \frac{|R_Y \setminus (R_Y \cap R_W)|}{|R_Y|} = \frac{9\,730\,985}{10\,329\,767} = 94.2\%$$

ExtraCoverage shows the 'gain' in knowledge provided by our set of relation instances with respect to YAGO's set of facts, as the ratio between the number of relation instances found only in our set and the number of relations in YAGO:

$$ExtraCoverage(R_W, R_Y) = \frac{|R_W \setminus (R_W \cap R_Y)|}{|R_Y|} = \frac{49\,332\,484}{10\,329\,767} = 477.5\%$$

The ExtraCoverage of YAGO's core with respect to our resource is:

$$ExtraCoverage(R_Y, R_W) = \frac{|R_Y \setminus (R_Y \cap R_W)|}{|R_W|} = \frac{9\,730\,985}{49\,931\,266} = 19.5\%$$

These measures show that the resources are not redundant, they introduce additional knowledge relative to each other.

A particular surprise in the comparison with YAGO was the low overlap in relation instances (598 782). Our analysis shows that this is due to several factors: (i) the use of a different Wikipedia version, leading to missed matches due to changes in the article names; (ii) the *instanceOf* relation in YAGO link a Wikipedia entity to a WordNet synset, which will not match WikiNet relations; (iii) the overlap between WikiNet and YAGO consists mostly of category–category links, and there is a small number of relations that link two named entities common to the two resources.

Partial Comparison with DBpedia

DBpedia [3] is a very large repository that transforms all the structured information that Wikipedia provides into a large database. It also includes links to other resources and a classification of entities into a manually defined ontology based on infobox types. While DBpedia is based on the automatic reformatting of already existing (and structured) information in Wikipedia, in building our resource the purpose was to uncover information that is not explicitly given. Because DBpedia contains the explicit information in Wikipedia—including category–category, category–article links and relations extracted from infoboxes—we can perform a partial comparison between WikiNet and DBpedia by evaluating the differences in structure between WikiNet and Wikipedia. This way we can also avoid an imperfect mapping between the two resources. Because we started with Wikipedia's category–category and category–article links, we first evaluate how many relation instances we add to this initial structure by deconstructing categories. 69.81% of the relation instances obtained after processing category names are novel. We further test how many of these novel relation instances appear in an infobox—2.91% (2.03% of the total number of relation instances) appear in an infobox (917 999 instances). This means that 66.65% of the relations in WikiNet are novel both with respect to the category structure and with respect to the information in the infoboxes. On the other hand, we do not explicitly add relations from the infoboxes, as these are available directly and can, as such, be added, as long as they connect two Wikipedia pages, and do not express a value (e.g. Germany *area* 357 021 km^2).

Relations

The version of WikiNet described here has 454 relations. A partial histogram is presented in Figure 15.7.

Compared to other resources built from Wikipedia, WikiNet has more relations. DBpedia and YAGO are based on the explicit information in Wikipedia, and as such their relation sets consist of the attributes in infoboxes. YAGO also identifies a small number of specific categories that provide relational information, such as 1975 BIRTHS, categories starting with Countries in . . . , Rivers of . . . , Attractions in . . . , and exploit them as a source of the following relations: *bornInYear, diedInYear, establishedIn, locatedIn, writtenInYear, politicianOf, hasWonPrize*. In the first stage of processing, the relation instances extracted by WikiNet are not explicit in Wikipedia, but rather encoded in the category names. They cover relational nouns, verb–preposition phrases, plus a small number

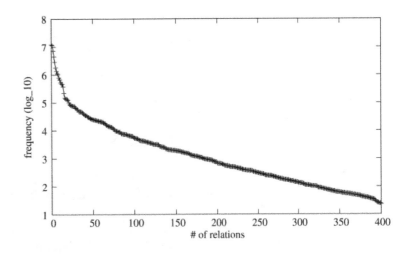

FIGURE 15.7. Partial Relations Histogram on a Log_{10} Scale.

of general and structural relations (*is_a*, *temporal*, *spatial*, *sub-cat_is_a*, *related_to*, *category*). Some of the relations extracted through this process are unique to WikiNet—e.g. *caused_by*, . . . The comparison with YAGO shows that for the same pairs, the relations in WikiNet are more fine-grained.

Named Entity Information

We evaluate the results of the named entity (NE) identification process against the manually annotated data used to evaluate HeiNER,[20] which reimplements the Bunescu and Paşca [5] heuristics. The data and manual annotation statistics are presented in detail in Wentland et al. [48]. Two judges annotated a dataset containing 2000 NE candidates from Wikipedia, and three judges annotated a second set of 2000 candidates. In both cases a candidate is considered a true NE if at least two judges tag it as such. Comparison with our NE tags results in the following precision scores: 94.42% against set 1 and 96.16% against set 2, for an average of 95.29%.[21] Wentland et al. [48] report an average precision of 95% for HeiNER.

Extrinsic Evaluation

The evaluation of the individual processing steps was shown as we progressed through the network building process. In this section we show the results of an extrinsic evaluation of the complete network, through semantic relatedness computation and metonymy resolution. These two tasks assess different aspects of the network. In relatedness computations the information provided by the structure is "compacted" in a numeric score. In metonymy resolution we use the structure of the network explicitly, by mining for specific relations.

Semantic Relatedness

One of the basic tasks for which a lexical/knowledge resource is used in NLP is establishing the similarity or relatedness between terms. The suitability of a resource is assessed based on word pairs previously annotated by human judges, such as Rubenstein and Goodenough's 65 noun pairs [42] (R&G), and Miller and Charles (M&C) 30 pairs subset of R&G [24]. High correlation between similarity and relatedness scores automatically computed on a resource and manually assigned scores is usually considered evidence of the high quality of a resource.

Previously used resources include WordNet and Roget's Thesaurus, and most methods for computing similarity and relatedness have been designed by taking these resources' specific attributes (structure, size) into account. Budanitsky and Hirst [4] present a comprehensive comparison of existing methods with their own for such computations. Recently Tsatsaronis et al. [46] proposed a new method for similarity computations in WordNet. Ponzetto and Strube [35,37], Milne and Witten [25], Gabrilovich and Markovitch [10,11] propose methods for semantic similarity/relatedness computation based on Wikipedia.

In comparison with WordNet and Roget's Thesaurus and even with WikiTaxonomy [36,37], WikiNet is larger by an order of magnitude, and has many more relation instances (two orders of magnitude) and more varied relations. To deal with this structure and size, we implemented a novel metric. The structure is still a network, so the new methods still rely on connecting nodes in this network. From the methods implemented for WordNet we have learned that not all concepts are treated the same: For establishing similarity, nodes in the WordNet *is_a* hierarchy are considered more "important" the more specific they are, or the higher their information content relative to a corpus [41]. This observation is particularly relevant to our network, where nodes representing concepts such as PEOPLE or CITIES have hundreds of thousand of instances. When computing paths between concepts, expanding such a node causes a massive growth in the number of partial paths, which makes the computation very expensive both in terms of time and of CPU. On the other hand, such nodes do serve to connect many different concepts, and should be taken into account, as should the concepts they relate to through relations other than *is_a*.

To connect two nodes in the network while keeping the computation within a reasonable amount of time, the number of partial paths must be kept small. There are two ways to control this: have an upper bound on the number of steps taken from the starting node, and control the paths taken from each node reached. The upper bound for the path length between any two nodes is $2 * maxDepth$, where $maxDepth = 16$ is the maximum depth of the network[22] computed with respect to the original category hierarchy. This translates to an upper bound of 32 in the number of expansion steps.

To control the multiplication of partial paths, we also impose a bound on which nodes to expand, and how. For example, in searching for paths we would not want to expand a node with all of its instances, especially for nodes that have thousands or even hundreds of thousands of children. But we would want to follow links that lead to their supercategories, or superconcepts, for instance. Because of this, the bound imposed on expanding concepts is as follows: For each node N_x with relations r_{xi}, and relation counts $c_{r_{xi}}$, relations of the type r_{xi} are expanded if and only if $c_{r_{xi}} \leq \tau_r$ where τ_r is a threshold determined empirically. In our experiments we set $\tau_r = 10$.

Computing Relatedness

To compute the similarity between two terms we proceed as usually done, by determining all possible concepts the terms may refer to, and then choosing the pair with the highest similarity score. The similarity score is computed by taking all paths between the corresponding starting nodes into account. To develop the similarity measure we used the 30 pairs in the Miller and Charles ($M\&C$) set. We experimented with various formulas, starting from those developed for WordNet. The formula that gave best results is presented, justified and evaluated in the remainder of the section. We make no claim that this is the best measure; it should rather be considered a lower bound. To compute the similarity, nodes closest to the lower level of the hierarchy (and thus more specific) and those closest to the edges of the path have a higher value. The value decreases as we go higher up in the hierarchy, and further from the starting nodes. A path's value is lower the longer it is and the higher up in the hierarchy its nodes are.

$$sim(n_x, n_y) = \frac{\sum_{path_{(n_x, n_y)} \in Paths(n_x, n_y)} value(path_{(n_x, n_y)})}{\left| Paths(n_x, n_y) \right|}$$

$Paths(n_x, n_y) = \{path(n_x, n_y)\}$ is the set of paths from n_x to n_y, and $value(path_{(n_x, n_y)})$ is the value of the path, computed as follows:

$$value(path_{(n_x, n_y)}) = \frac{1}{1 + \sum_{n_i \in path_{(n_x, n_y)}} value(n_i, path_{(n_x, n_y)})}$$

where $value(n_i, path_{(n_x, n_y)})$ is the value of node n_i on path $path_{(n_x, n_y)}$:

$$value(n_i, path_{(n_x, n_y)}) = \frac{ic(n_i)}{D - depth(n_i) + level(n_i, path_{(n_x, n_y)}) + 1}$$

D is the maximum depth of the category hierarchy, $depth(n_i)$ is the depth of the node n_i in this hierarchy, $level(n_i, path_{(n_x, n_y)})$ is the distance from n_i to the closest of n_x or n_y, and $ic(n_i)$ is an approximation of the information content for node n_i, computed in the same manner as done by Ponzetto and Strube [36]:

$$ic(n_i) = 1 - \frac{\log(hypo(n_i) + 1)}{\log(|Wkn|)}$$

$|Wkn|$ is the number of nodes in WikiNet, and $hypo(n_i)$ is the number of hyponyms of node ni, computed as the number of pages subsumed by ni in Wikipedia's category network.

In using similarity/relatedness measures between word pairs it is assumed that choosing the highest score leads to the correct disambiguation of the words in the pair (e.g. [4]). In previous work on evaluating WordNet, Wikipedia or other resources relative to similarity or relatedness computations, the issue of disambiguation has been disregarded, and the focus has been on obtaining good correlation scores with the human judges. In our case the assumption that words in a pair disambiguate each other to the correct senses does not hold. WikiNet is highly interconnected and contains numerous lexicalization variations for the included concepts. Because of this, all measures overestimate similarity/relatedness, because for most term pairs there are senses that are close or closely connected in the network. To evaluate the properties of the network built we separate the two tasks—disambiguating the concepts, and evaluating the similarity/relatedness measure against the manually assigned scores. Two judges have manually assigned concept IDs to the words in the Miller and Charles (M&C) and the Rubenstein and Goodenough (R&G) lists. More than one ID was allowed, and only IDs that had associated the particular term as a lexicalization were allowed as options. This caused some problems for the word journey, for example, whose best sense (as trip or voyage) cannot be retrieved from the information extracted from the Wikipedia dump: *Journey* is a disambiguation page, and while the first sentence is very helpful for the human reader (A **journey** is a trip or voyage), it does not contain a hyperlink to either of these concepts.

The disambiguated versions produced by the two human judges for each of *M&C* and *R&G* were intersected. The fact that for both data sets each word had at least one sense (ID) upon which the annotators agreed allows us to directly use the intersective annotations, without further need for adjudication. The results on the gold standards thus obtained and on the non-annotated data are presented in Table 15.8.

One of the strengths of the resource is its multilinguality. To test this feature we used the German version of the *R&G* lists— *G* [12]. We had fewer German lexicalizations of concepts than English ones; this reduced the number of possible ambiguities, which is reflected in the relatively high scores for this data set even without disambiguating annotations. Eight words from the *G* data did not appear in the multilingual index: Grinsen and Mittagsstunde (do not appear in the German Wikipedia), Irrenhaus had no overlap through cross-language links, and Schnur, Bursche, Fahrt

TABLE 15.8. Evaluation of Similarity on the Miller and Charles, Rubenstein and Goodenough and Gurevych Sets

Resource	Dataset		Pearson	Spearman
WikiNet	*M&C*	disambig	0.86	0.83
		raw	0.59	0.58
WikiTaxonomy		raw	0.87	0.79
WordNet		raw	0.86	0.86
WikiNet	*R&G*	disambig	0.70	0.67
		raw	0.66	0.64
WikiTaxonomy		raw	0.78	0.75
WordNet		raw	0.88	0.86
WikiNet	*G*	disambig	0.72	0.72
		raw	0.62	0.63
WikiTaxonomy		raw	0.69	–
GermaNet		raw	0.76	–

do not have an appropriate sense. This leaves 45 pairs (out of the original 65) for which both terms had concept correspondents in WikiNet, and 51 pairs when manually disambiguated and the judges assigned a sense to Irrenhaus.

The best previous results on semantic similarity/relatedness based on Wikipedia were reported on WikiTaxonomy by Ponzetto and Strube [37]. Using a taxonomy built based on the category network, they report highest results for Resnik's information content-based measure—0.87 (Pearson) and 0.79 (Spearman) for *M&C* and 0.78 (Pearson) and 0.75 (Spearman) for *R&G*, computed without manual disambiguation on a 2008 version of Wikipedia with 337 741 categories and 2 276 274 articles. Since then the resource has grown, and it is now bigger, more connected and has more ambiguities. A direct comparison based on the 2009/07/13 English Wikipedia dump was not possible. The best results based on WordNet for *R&G* are 0.8614 (Spearman) and 0.876 (Pearson), and for *M&C* 0.856 (Spearman) and 0.864 (Pearson) [46].

We tested WikiNet on the German version of the Rubenstein and Goodenough word pairs. On this data set Ponzetto and Strube [35] report 0.69 Pearson correlation on WikiTaxonomy, while the best score on GermaNet—the German version of WordNet—was 0.76 [12]. The reported scores were computed on the pairs for which both terms had an entry in Wikipedia.

WikiNet's high scores on the manually disambiguated data is additional (to the intrinsic evaluation) proof of the quality of its underlying structure. On the other hand, the relatively low scores on non-disambiguated data—the more realistic setting in which WordNet is the clear winner—shows that more information is needed to disambiguate terms. The semantic similarity task between two words out of context is artificial, as it assumes that the two words disambiguate each other, and the correct senses are the ones closest according to the similarity/relatedness metric. This, however, does not hold in a resource like WikiNet, with highly interconnected concepts. To better assess WikiNet we use it in an NLP task, which we describe in the following section.

Metonymy Resolution

Metonymies are figures of speech whereby the speaker is "using one entity to refer to another that is related to it." [15]—e.g. in the news article sentence 'Buckingham Palace announced at 8am on Friday that the Queen had bestowed the title of Duke of Cambridge on her grandson.', Buckingham Palace stands for the representative of the Queen whose official residence is the palace.

The task of metonymy resolution implies identifying the correct interpretation of a term in context. For example, the interpretation of the term New Zealand in the text fragment shown in Figure 15.8 is not literal—as the country New Zealand—rather it stands in for a sports team representing the country in a sporting event.

The most common view of metonymies is that they violate semantic constraints in their immediate context. To resolve metonymies one must detect violated constraints, usually from those imposed by the verbs on their arguments [8,13,40]. Most of the recent work on metonymy resolution (for an overview see [21]) relies on syntactic clues from the local sentential context of a potentially metonymic word (PMW) to determine which interpretation (reading) is most appropriate. In the example from Figure 15.8, the noun kicker suggests a `place-for-people` reading, because sports teams have kickers, rather than countries. Previously, Markert and Hahn [19] have shown that global context is useful in detecting metonymies that do not violate selectional restrictions. In this case one can use referential cohesion relations. At the time comprehensive knowledge bases were not available to

```
<sample id="samp369">

<bnc:title> [Title unknown/unassigned] </bnc:title>

<par>

If the Lions trip here is to be worthwhile in terms of Test results and
tour morale it is essential that this one is a victory. New Zealand have
not played together as a unit since last August in South Africa, where they
narrowly beat the Springboks. "Ten months is a long time to be apart and
then to be brought together to compete against such a good, experienced
team as the Lions," said Grant Fox, <annot><location reading="metonymic"
metotype="place-for-people" notes="ORG, sports, team"> New Zealand </location>
</annot>'s masterly goal kicker. Fox's kicking is crucial to the All
Black's game but there are inevitably, other great and experienced winners
around him.

</par>

</sample>
```

FIGURE 15.8. Sample Data from the Metonymy Resolution Task at SemEval 2007.

help establish such relations. We test the usefulness of WikiNet for this task.

We use the data for the metonymy task at SemEval 2007 [21], in which the PMW are names of countries and companies. The data comes partitioned into training and testing (for country PMWs 925 training and 908 testing instances, for company PMWs 1090/842). As shown in Figure 15.8, there is a larger context surrounding the PMW than just the corresponding sentence. We explore this for global constraints on the interpretation of the target word. The starting point is the system described in [28], which uses, as other work does, selectional preferences imposed by the grammatical context to decide on the correct interpretation.

To incorporate encyclopedic knowledge, we first identify concepts in the given paragraph surrounding a PMW using the existing lexicalizations in WikiNet. Solving ambiguities is done implicitly (albeit not necessarily very accurately) in the processing steps presented in Algorithm 15.5.

ALGORITHM 15.5. Extracting Concepts for Metonymy Resolution

Input:
$T = \{t_i\}$—the set of texts given for each instance in the data *WikiNet*
υ—a threshold for related concepts frequency within a paragraph
τ—a threshold for concept (feature) frequency in the data set

Output:
C—a list of concepts
1: $C = \{\}$
2: **for** $t_i \in T$ **do**
3:    $C_i = \{\}$
4:    **for** $ck \in WikiNet$ **do**
5:       $C_{ik} = \{\}$
6:       **if** c_k appears in t_i **then**
7:          $C_{ik} = C_{ik} \cup \{c_k\} \cup \{c_j \mid (c_k, R, c_j) \in WikiNet\}$
8:       $C_i = C_i \cup \{c_j \mid c_j \text{ appears in at least } \upsilon C_{ik}\}$
9:    $C = C \cup \{c_j \mid c_j \text{ appears in at least } \tau C_i\}$
10: **return** C

The purpose of the υ threshold is to compensate for the rather simple disambiguation algorithm: If a concept is related to at least υ other (potential) concepts in the given context, it is more probable that it is an appropriate concept for this context. For the experiments described later in the paper $\upsilon = 3$—it is the smallest value that counters possible noise in connectivity in WikiNet and cohesiveness of the context (in terms of concepts). The τ threshold is used to filter features for the machine learning stage. Features infrequent across instances would cause overfitting. We arbitrarily choose $\tau = 5$.

We consider the identified concepts as global context features, and added them to the features described in [28]: the syntactic features proposed in [20] and selectional preference features.

The features described above are used to represent each instance in the data. We used the Weka implementation of Support Vector Machine (SMO) [49] (default settings) to build a model for each metonymy type. The task had three settings: coarse—distinguish between literal and non-literal interpretations; medium—distinguish between literal, metonymic or mixed interpretations; fine—distinguish between all possible interpretations (a small number or prespecified possible interpretations) for the potentially metonymic word.

Table 15.9 shows the (non-zero) results obtained, in all three task settings, for the two types of PMWs—locations and organizations. *Base* shows the class distribution, the *Selectional preferences* columns show the results obtained using selectional preferences (described in detail in [28]), and the + *WikiNet information* shows the results obtained by adding the concepts identified in the paragraph surrounding the PMW to the selectional preference features. Including the encyclopedic knowledge from WikiNet shows consistent improvement in terms of precision and recall, especially for the non-literal interpretations. Because of the relatively small number of instances with a non-literal interpretation, the improvement does not appear to be statistically significant.

The evaluation shows that global context is useful in interpreting PMWs despite the simple concept identification approach used.

WIKINET IN CONTEXT

The work described in this paper fits within the rather vast and intensively explored areas of knowledge acquisition and ontology induction. Unlike the majority of other such work which involves Wikipedia, our approach does not tie Wikipedia to additional resources, but is instead focused on generating a self-contained, easily renewable resource. We review the most closely related work in decreasing order of the similarity of either the approach or resource generated.

Ponzetto and Strube [35,37] build on the category network from Wikipedia and induce *is_a* links based on several criteria: head matching, modifier matching, structural analysis of shared categories and pages between two linked categories, and patterns

TABLE 15.9. Accuracy (acc), Precision (f), Recall (r) and F-score (f) for Detecting Metonymic Interpretations

Task	Base		Selectional Preferences				+ WikiNet Information			
	acc	f	acc	p	r	f	acc	p	r	f
LOCATION—coarse	79.4		85.6				86.2			
literal		79.4		87.9	94.9	91.3		88.1	95.6	91.7
non-literal		20.6		71.5	49.7	58.7		74.6	50.3	60.1
LOCATION—medium	79.4		85.2				85.9			
literal		79.4		87.9	94.9	91.3		88.1	95.6	91.7
metonymic		18.4		70.1	53.3	60.5		73.6	53.3	61.8
mixed		2.2		33.3	5.0	8.7		40.0	10.0	16.0
LOCATION—fine	79.4		84.4				85.1			
literal		79.4		87.9	94.9	91.3		88.1	95.6	91.7
place-for-people		15.5		64.3	57.4	60.7		67.5	57.4	62.1
mixed		2.2		33.3	5.0	8.7		40.0	10.0	16.0
ORGANIZATION—coarse	61.8		74.2				75.4			
literal		61.8		74.5	88.7	80.9		75.4	89.2	81.8
non-literal		38.2		73.5	50.9	60.2		75.3	53.1	62.3
ORGANIZATION—medium	61.8		71.7				73.3			
literal		61.8		74.5	88.7	80.9		75.4	89.2	81.8
metonymic		31.0		65.8	50.2	56.9		68.4	54.0	60.4
mixed		7.2		50.0	19.7	28.2		57.1	19.7	29.3
ORGANIZATION—fine	61.8		70.3				71.7			
literal		61.8		74.5	88.7	80.9		75.4	89.2	81.8
org-for-members		19.1		59.3	55.3	57.2		61.8	58.4	60.1
org-for-product		8.0		68.8	32.8	44.4		66.7	35.8	46.6
org-for-facility		2.0		60.0	18.8	28.6		83.3	31.3	45.5
org-for-name		0.7		45.5	83.3	58.8		50.0	83.3	62.5
mixed		7.2		50.0	20.0	28.6		57.1	20.0	29.6

indicative of *is_a* relations and *not_is_a* relations. The result is WikiTaxonomy, with 208 208 *is_a* relations, evaluated at 84.0% F-score.

DBpedia[23] [1,3] converts Wikipedia's content into structured knowledge using information from Wikipedia's relational database tables and the structured information in infoboxes, and connects it to a variety of other resources, such as Freebase, WordNet, OpenCyc and more. The DBpedia dataset covers approximately 3.64 million entities, 1.83 million of which are classified into a shallow ontology consisting of 170 classes.[24] This ontology was built by manually organizing the most frequently used infobox templates from Wikipedia into a hierarchy. A distinguishing feature of DBpedia is live extraction: Its database is continuously updated whenever a Wikipedia article is changed. DBpedia offers a web-based interface to its database.

YAGO [47] also extracts information from Wikipedia, and links it to GeoNames and WordNet's hierarchies to take advantage of WordNet's manually produced taxonomy. In addition to structured information in Wikipedia, facts representing relations of 100 types are extracted from specific categories that provide relational information, such as 1975 BIRTHS, categories starting with Countries in . . . , Rivers of . . . , Attractions in . . . ,. These are used as a source of the following relations: *bornInYear, diedInYear, establishedIn, locatedIn, writtenInYear, politicianOf, hasWonPrize*. Accuracy is estimated based on a small sample of manually annotated relation instances out of the approximately 10 million extracted, and lies between $90.84 \pm 4.28\%$ and $98.72 \pm 1.30\%$. YAGO's core knowledge base (derived from Wikipedia) contains approximately 11 million relations, while the full system covers 460 million. Distinguishing characteristics of YAGO are its accompanying search engine NAGA, and SOFIE, a logical reasoning mechanism for expanding YAGO with information from open texts and for checking internal consistency of the resource when adding external facts.

MENTA [6] is a multilingual extension of the core YAGO knowledge base. It extracts entities from Wikipedia versions in all available languages, linking them through cross-language links, category–category and category–article links, and links them to WordNet. Evaluated on random samples between 104 and 322 instances, the accuracy of subclass and instance-of links to WordNet ranges between 83.38% and 92.30%. The resource covers 5.4 million entities.

BabelNet [30] is an automatically built resource that integrates WordNet and Wikipedia. It is obtained by disambiguating Wikipedia articles relative to WordNet senses, by adding different language information using the corresponding crosslanguage links, and by adding synonyms using redirect links and selected output from a machine translation system. The current version includes lexicalizations of existing WordNet synsets in 6 languages. In version 1.0.1, BabelNet contains 83 156 merged Wikipedia/WordNet entities, and provides 2 955 552 additional multilingual "babel-synsets." Because of the Wikipedia–WordNet mapping, BabelNet can take advantage of WordNet's clean hierarchy.

The largest ongoing project for acquiring knowledge from general texts is the Machine Reading project at the University of Washington [39]. One of the goals of the project is to induce a large scale ontology, which is now pursued through multiple interacting threads: rely on Wikipedia for annotated data from which to learn models for acquiring relations from open text [2,51,52], jointly perform knowledge extraction, ontology induction and population via recursive relational clustering [38]. Kylin [50] uses the existing infoboxes and their corresponding articles as sources of training data, to learn how to fill in infobox templates for articles which do not have such structured information. For four concepts, Wu and Weld [50] obtain precision between 73.9% and 97.3%, and recall between 60.5% and 95.9%. Read the Web[25] is a Never-Ending Language Learning (NELL) project at Carnegie Mellon University [16]. It has an iterative approach of adding more and more facts extracted from open text. As of yet, its results are not at the level of the Machine Reading project, with 978 383 facts extracted.

Nguyen et al. [32] filter article sentences, parse and analyze them for entity detection and keyword extraction. These elements are used to learn how to detect instances of previously seen relations, with 37.76% F-score.

Snow et al. [44] present an approach for automatically inducing semantic taxonomies, which relies on combining evidence from heterogeneous relations to derive the structure with the highest probability. This approach can be used to build a taxonomy from scratch, or to expand upon an existing one, such as WordNet. This approach is based on representing word pairs through lexico-syntactic patterns that capture how the pair is connected in sentences in the corpus. Because it deals with open texts, the method must address the sense disambiguation task as well. For 10 000 added hyponyms, precision was 84% (evaluated on a random sample of 100 pairs), for 20 000 precision was 68% (also on a sample of 100 pairs).

Navigli et al. [31] also investigate the automatic induction of semantic taxonomies from a given corpus. The process involves first obtaining a terminology from the corpus, which is then used iteratively to obtain taxonomic relations and new potential terms from the texts. In the final step, the graph is trimmed based on connectivity information and the restrictions imposed by taxonomic relations.

Freebase[26] is a large online collaborative knowledge base, originally populated with information from Wikipedia, MusicBrainz, and other online resources, open for editing by human contributors. Compared to DBpedia and YAGO, Freebase is structured as a graph, with entities as nodes and edges representing the links between them. It consists of approximately 22 million entities (called topics in Freebase),[27] which are grouped into types (e.g. people, places), and which can have associated attributes (e.g. birth date). While it does have multilingual content, there are no explicit links between the same concept in different languages.

ProBase[28] [53] is a probabilistic taxonomy automatically built from a corpus of 1.68 billion web pages and uses two years' worth of search log data for filtering concepts. Taxonomy induction starts with Hearst patterns for detecting *is_a* relations in the corpus, which are used to detect the concepts, distinguish their senses, and establish *is_a* links between them. ProBase contains 2 653 872 concepts, 16 218 369 distinct concept–instance pairs, and 4 539 176 distinct concept–subconcept pairs (20 757 545 *is_a* pairs in total).

Related to our work on deriving class attributes, Paşca [34] processes search engine queries to obtain similar information. The idea is that when writing a query, users have some elements of a relation on which they require further information—such as *side effects* for the class *drugs*, or *wing span* for the class *aircraft model*. From extensive logs of even noisy queries, a weakly supervised system can acquire large sets of relevant class attributes. Similarity between automatically ranked class attributes and manually assigned correctness labels on a sample of extracted attributes for the 40 classes considered range from 90% precision for 10 attributes to 76% for 50.

Compared to WikiTaxonomy, DBpedia, MENTA, and Babel-Net, in building WikiNet we have revealed implicit knowledge in Wikipedia, and used it to derive novel connections between entities in Wikipedia. YAGO processes a limited number of specific name patterns to derive novel information, although not on the same scale as WikiNet. We also worked under the assumption that each manually generated resource (such as Wikipedia, WordNet, OpenCyc) was built according to its own principles and captures different aspects of linguistic or encyclopedic knowledge. Because of this, we aimed for WikiNet to be self-contained, and endowed it with the type of knowledge that research in the natural language processing field has shown to be useful and desirable (such as a taxonomy backbone).

Deriving a resource like WikiNet has both advantages and disadvantages. The disadvantage is that, while it can serve as a starting point for further development, WikiNet is limited to the information included in Wikipedia. There are, however, multiple advantages: (i) we do not need to rely on external resources for the set of entities to be extracted or to validate the type of relations that are extracted; (ii) the structure arises through the building process, and combines the "folksonomy" that is the backbone of Wikipedia with a structure that arises from the knowledge decoded from the category names; (iii) it is clear how the extracted relations fit in the network and we do not have the problem of disambiguating terms extracted from text to their corresponding concepts; (iv) multilinguality. Thanks to the connection between languages in WikiNet, information easily obtained through one language can be ported to others. An example of this is the named entity information, which based on the article texts and the conventions of capitalization in English can be obtained with high accuracy, whereas for German this would not be as easy, because nouns in German are capitalized.

The work presented here was developed based on observations about the types of information that appear in Wikipedia specifically, and the way those types of information interact. However, some of the lessons learned are more general. We have learned how knowledge can be propagated throughout a network by connecting different pieces of individual information. This provides interesting avenues for further knowledge acquisition: A novel entity discovered in open text can first be classified under existing categories in Wikipedia, which then triggers the addition of links to the rest of the network through the relations implicit in the newly assigned parent categories. We have also learned that knowledge may come from unconventional, and probably "unintentional," sources. In Wikipedia's case, these sources are the category names (there may be others as well). Such situations may arise in processing other repositories of (manually built) information where knowledge is implicitly coded, for example, in directory names in a file hierarchy or in class names in manual annotations.

A question that we cannot yet answer is what is the impact of the structure—which is derived exclusively from the English Wikipedia—when applying the resource to NLP tasks in different languages, as we do not know to what extent ontologies are language specific. We can only speculate that encyclopedic knowledge, the kind reorganized into WikiNet, is less prone to cultural biases.

CONCLUSIONS

This paper described the construction of a multilingual, large scale resource, based on exploiting several facets—some obvious, some less so—of Wikipedia. Compared to related work in the domain of knowledge acquisition/ontology induction, the approach presented and the resource built has both advantages and disadvantages. Its main advantages are the rapid derivation of a large multilingual resource, easy to regenerate on new versions of Wikipedia. It can serve both English and languages poorer in resources, either as a stable resource or as a starting point for ontology population. Compared to WordNet, WikiNet has high coverage of named entities, and named entity lexicalizations in various languages are a useful resource for machine translation. Another advantage is the ability to port information—such as named entity—from one language to another. The main disadvantage is that WikiNet is not complete, and in the long run it is only a seed—although a large one—for further knowledge acquisition.

We plan to explore methods for enriching WikiNet with information extracted from open text, following an approach similar to the one for propagating information from infoboxes, by first linking (classifying) a novel entity to Wikipedia's categories, and then linking it to the rest of the network through the relations implied in its newly assigned parent categories. Future work plans also include further exploring WikiNet's use for different tasks, including coreference resolution and text alignment. Identifying common concepts in different language texts should arise naturally from WikiNet's structure. The resource is freely available for download,[29] together with a tool kit—WikiNetTK[30]—for visualization and various methods to facilitate embedding the world knowledge encoded in WikiNet into applications [14]. The scripts used to build WikiNet are also available at the WikiNet download site.

Acknowledgements

We thank the reviewers for their detailed and constructive comments, and the Klaus Tschira Foundation, Heidelberg for financial support. This work has also been partially supported by the EC-funded project CoSyne (FP7-ICT-4-24853).

Notes

1. http://www.geneontology.org.
2. http://www.nlm.nih.gov/research/umls/.
3. This article builds upon and expands [27,29]. It expands on this previous work by using a list of relational nouns extracted from NOMLEX. It presents a new method for computing semantic relatedness between a pair of terms, and its evaluation with standard data sets. It presents experiments on embedding the resource

into an NLP task, in particular metonymy resolution. WikiNet can be downloaded from http://www.h-its.org/english/research/nlp/download/wikinet.php.

4. The statistics reported in this paper refer to the WikiNet built starting from the English Wikipedia dump of 2011/01/15, and adding several other language versions.

5. Wikipedia dumps are available from http://download.wikimedia.org/. We use the pages-article.xml.bz2 file.

6. http://nlp.cs.nyu.edu/meyers/nombank/nombank.1.0/NOMLEX-plus.1.0.

7. Sans Serif is used for patterns and words, *italics* for relations, SMALL CAPS for Wikipedia categories and pages, BOLD SMALL CAPS for concepts. Part of speech tags and grammatical categories are capitalized.

8. VBN is the part of speech tag for participles, and IN is the part of speech tag for prepositions in the Penn Treebank POS tag set [43].

9. http://nlp.stanford.edu/software/tagger.shtml.

10. Wikipedia categories are usually in plural. Before extracting the pages we transform Y to its plural form.

11. http://www-nlp.stanford.edu/software/.

12. When processing a category, we consider all subsumed articles, including those subsumed by subcategories.

13. We include in the table only statistics for the 196 languages that have at least 1000 terms represented in the resource.

14. Cohen's κ on the four manually annotated data sets are 0.82, 0.73, 0.76 and 0.25 respectively (following the order in Table 15.4). However, the datasets are generated based on the system's output (the instances are randomly selected from the system's output), and as such are biased, which may lead to higher random agreement between the judges than would otherwise be expected in a purely random collection of relation instances, that both the system and the judges would then annotate.

15. http://www.mpi-inf.mpg.de/yago-naga/yago/downloads.html.

16. The list formatting is *relation (frequency)*.

17. Again, these numbers should be taken with the proverbial grain of salt. The samples are biased because they are extracted after the infobox propagation step, and as such the agreement between judges may be higher than random. See also note 14.

18. We show only the most frequent relations, which cover the majority of the pairs.

19. For our version of YAGO (downloaded 11/12/2009), we have counted 10 329 767 relation instances between Wikipedia concepts.

20. http://heiner.cl.uni-heidelberg.de.

21. For set 1 there were 8 instances for which we could not identify a corresponding entry in WikiNet's index of concepts, and for set 2 there were 16 such cases. This situation arises from the fact that a non-ambiguous name in the version used by Wentland et al. [48] has become ambiguous in our version.

22. For the 2009/07/13 English Wikipedia version.
23. http://dbpedia.org.
24. December 2011.
25. http://rtw.ml.cmu.edu/rtw/.
26. http://www.freebase.com.
27. December 2011.
28. http://research.microsoft.com/en-us/projects/probase.
29. http://www.h-its.org/english/research/nlp/download/wikinet.php.
30. http://sourceforge.net/projects/wikinettk/.

References

1. S. Auer, C. Bizer, J. Lehmann, G. Kobilarov, R. Cyganiak, Z. Ives, DBpedia: A nucleus for a Web of open data, in: Proceedings of the 6th International Semantic Web Conference and 2nd Asian Semantic Web Conference, Busan, Korea, November 11–15, 2007, pp. 722–735.
2. M. Banko, M. J. Cafarella, S. Soderland, M. Broadhead, O. Etzioni, Open information extraction from the Web, in: Proceedings of the 20th International Joint Conference on Artificial Intelligence, Hyderabad, India, 6–12 January 2007, pp. 2670–2676.
3. C. Bizer, J. Lehmann, G. Kobilarov, S. Auer, C. Becker, R. Cyganiak, S. Hellmann, DBpedia—A crystallization point for the Web of data, Journal of Web Semantics 7 (2009) 154–165.
4. A. Budanitsky, G. Hirst, Evaluating WordNet-based measures of semantic distance, Computational Linguistics 32 (1) (2006) 13–47.
5. R. Bunescu, M. Paşca, Using encyclopedic knowledge for named entity disambiguation, in: Proceedings of the 11th Conference of the European Chapter of the Association for Computational Linguistics, Trento, Italy, 3–7 April 2006, pp. 9–16.
6. G. de Melo, G. Weikum, MENTA: Inducing multilingual taxonomies from Wikipedia, in: Proceedings of the ACM 19th Conference on Information and Knowledge Management (CIKM 2010), Toronto, Ont., Canada, 26–30 October 2010, pp. 1099–1108.
7. G. de Melo, G. Weikum, Untangling the cross-lingual link structure of Wikipedia, in: Proceedings of the 48th Annual Meeting of the Association for Computational Linguistics, Uppsala, Sweden, 11–16 July 2010, pp. 844–853.
8. D. C. Fass, met*: A method for discriminating metonomy and metaphor by computer, Computational Linguistics 17 (1) (1991) 49–90.
9. C. Fellbaum (Ed.), WordNet: An Electronic Lexical Database, MIT Press, Cambridge, MA, 1998.
10. E. Gabrilovich, S. Markovitch, Computing semantic relatedness using Wikipedia-based explicit semantic analysis, in: Proceedings of the 20th International Joint Conference on Artificial Intelligence, Hyderabad, India, 6–12 January 2007, pp. 1606–1611.
11. E. Gabrilovich, S. Markovitch, Wikipedia-based semantic interpretation for natural language processing, Journal of Artificial Intelligence Research 34 (2009) 443–498.

12. I. Gurevych, H. Niederlich, Accessing GermaNet data and computing semantic relatedness, in: Companion Volume to the Proceedings of the 43rd Annual Meeting of the Association for Computational Linguistics, Ann Arbor, Mich., 25–30 June 2005, pp. 5–8.

13. J. R. Hobbs, M. E. Stickel, D. E. Appelt, P. Martin, Interpretation as abduction, Artificial Intelligence 63 (1993) 69–142.

14. A. Judea, V. Nastase, M. Strube, WikiNetTk—A tool kit for embedding world knowledge in NLP applications, in: Proceedings of the IJCNLP 2011 System Demonstrations, Chiang Mai, Thailand, 9 November 2011, pp. 1–4.

15. G. Lakoff, M. Johnson, Metaphors We Live By, University of Chicago Press, Chicago, IL, 1980.

16. N. Lao, T. M. Mitchell, W. W. Cohen, Random walk inference and learning in a large scale knowledge base, in: Proceedings of the 2011 Conference on Empirical Methods in Natural Language Processing, Edinburgh, UK, 27–29 July 2011, pp. 529–539.

17. M. Lauer, Designing statistical language learners: Experiments on noun compounds, Ph.D. thesis, Macquarie University, Dept. of Computing, Sydney, Australia, 1995.

18. D. B. Lenat, R. Guha, K. Pittman, D. Pratt, M. Shepherd, Cyc: Towards programs with common sense, Communications of the ACM 33 (8) (1990) 30–49.

19. K. Markert, U. Hahn, Metonymies in discourse, Artificial Intelligence 135 (1/2) (2002) 145–198.

20. K. Markert, M. Nissim, Comparing knowledge sources for nominal anaphora resolution, Computational Linguistics 31 (3) (2005) 367–401.

21. K. Markert, M. Nissim, SemEval-2007 Task 08: Metonymy resolution at SemEval-2007, in: Proceedings of the 4th International Workshop on Semantic Evaluations (SemEval-1), Prague, Czech Republic, 23–24 June 2007, pp. 36–41.

22. O. Medelyan, D. Milne, C. Legg, I. H. Witten, Mining meaning from Wikipedia, International Journal of Human–Computer Interaction 67 (9) (2009) 716–754.

23. A. Meyers, C. Macleod, R. Yangarber, R. Grishman, L. Barrett, R. Reeves, Using NOMLEX to produce nominalization patterns for information extraction, in: Proceedings of the COLING-ACL '98 Workshop on The Computational Treatment of Nominals, Montréal, Québec, Canada, 16 August 1998, pp. 25–32.

24. G. A. Miller, W. G. Charles, Contextual correlates of semantic similarity, Language and Cognitive Processes 6 (1) (1991) 1–28.

25. D. Milne, I. H. Witten, An effective, low-cost measure of semantic relatedness obtained from Wikipedia links, in: Proceedings of the Workshop on Wikipedia and Artificial Intelligence: An Evolving Synergy at AAAI-08, Chicago, Ill., 13 July 2008, pp. 25–30.

26. D. Milne, I. H. Witten, Learning to link with Wikipedia, in: Proceedings of the ACM 17th Conference on Information and Knowledge Management (CIKM 2008), Napa Valley, Cal., USA, 26–30 October 2008, pp. 1046–1055.

27. V. Nastase, M. Strube, Decoding Wikipedia category names for knowledge acquisition, in: Proceedings of the 23rd Conference on the Advancement of Artificial Intelligence, Chicago, IL, 13–17 July 2008, pp. 219–224.

28. V. Nastase, M. Strube, Combining collocations, lexical and encyclopedic knowledge for metonymy resolution, in: Proceedings of the 2009 Conference on Empirical Methods in Natural Language Processing, Singapore, 6–7 August 2009, pp. 910–918.

29. V. Nastase, M. Strube, B. Börschinger, C. Zirn, A. Elghafari, WikiNet: A very large scale multi-lingual concept network, in: Proceedings of the 7th International Conference on Language Resources and Evaluation, La Valetta, Malta, 17–23 May 2010.

30. R. Navigli, S. P. Ponzetto, BabelNet: Building a very large multilingual semantic network, in: Proceedings of the 48th Annual Meeting of the Association for Computational Linguistics, Uppsala, Sweden, 11–16 July 2010, pp. 216–225.

31. R. Navigli, P. Velardi, S. Faralli, A graph-based algorithm for inducing lexical taxonomies from scratch, in: Proceedings of the 22nd International Joint Conference on Artificial Intelligence, Barcelona, Spain, 19–22 July 2011, pp. 1872–1877.

32. D. P. Nguyen, Y. Matsuo, M. Ishizuka, Relation extraction from Wikipedia using subtree mining, in: Proceedings of the 22nd Conference on the Advancement of Artificial Intelligence, Vancouver, B.C., Canada, 22–26 July 2007, pp. 1414–1420.

33. I. Niles, A. Pease, Towards a standard upper ontology, in: Proceedings of the International Conference on Formal Ontology in Information Systems, Ogunquit, Maine, 17–19 October 2001, pp. 2–9.

34. M. Paşca, Organizing and searching the World Wide Web of facts—Step two: Harnessing the wisdom of the crowds, in: Proceedings of the 16th World Wide Web Conference, Banff, Canada, 8–12 May 2007, pp. 101–110.

35. S. P. Ponzetto, M. Strube, Deriving a large scale taxonomy from Wikipedia, in: Proceedings of the 22nd Conference on the Advancement of Artificial Intelligence, Vancouver, B.C., Canada, 22–26 July 2007, pp. 1440–1445.

36. S. P. Ponzetto, M. Strube, Knowledge derived from Wikipedia for computing semantic relatedness, Journal of Artificial Intelligence Research 30 (2007) 181–212.

37. S. P. Ponzetto, M. Strube, Taxonomy induction based on a collaboratively built knowledge repository, Artificial Intelligence 175 (9/10) (2011) 1737–1756.

38. H. Poon, J. Christensen, P. Domingos, O. Etzioni, R. Hoffmann, C. Kiddon, T. Lin, X. Ling, Mausam, A. Ritter, S. Schoenmackers, S. Soderland, D. Weld, F. Wu, C. Zhang, Machine reading at the University of Washington, in: Proceedings of the NAACL HLT 2010 First International Workshop on Formalisms and Methodology for Learning by Reading, Los Angeles, CA, 6 June 2010, pp. 87–95.

39. H. Poon, P. Domingos, Unsupervised ontology induction from text, in: Proceedings of the 48th Annual Meeting of the Association for

Computational Linguistics, Uppsala, Sweden, 11–16 July 2010, pp. 296–305.

40. J. Pustejovsky, The generative lexicon, Computational Linguistics 17 (4) (1991) 209–241.

41. P. Resnik, Using information content to evaluate semantic similarity in a taxonomy, in: Proceedings of the 14th International Joint Conference on Artificial Intelligence, Montréal, Canada, 20–25 August 1995, vol. 1, 1995, pp. 448–453.

42. H. Rubenstein, J. B. Goodenough, Contextual correlates of synonymy, Communications of the ACM 8 (10) (1965) 627–633.

43. B. Santorini, Part of speech tagging guidelines for the Penn Treebank Project, http://www.cis.upenn.edu/~treebank/home.html, 1990.

44. R. Snow, D. Jurafsky, A.Y. Ng, Semantic taxonomy induction from heterogeneous evidence, in: Proceedings of the 21st International Conference on Computational Linguistics and 44th Annual Meeting of the Association for Computational Linguistics, Sydney, Australia, 17–21 July 2006, pp. 801–808.

45. F. Suchanek, G. Kasneci, G. Weikum, YAGO: A large ontology from Wikipedia and WordNet, Elsevier Journal of Web Semantics 6 (3) (2008) 203–217.

46. G. Tsatsaronis, I. Varlamis, M. Vazirgiannis, Text relatedness based on a word thesaurus, Journal of Artificial Intelligence Research 37 (2010) 1–39.

47. G. Weikum, G. Kasneci, M. Ramanath, F. Suchanek, Database and information-retrieval methods for knowledge discovery, Communications of the ACM 52 (4) (2009) 56–64.

48. W. Wentland, J. Knopp, C. Silberer, M. Hartung, Building a multilingual lexical resource for named entity disambiguation, translation and transliteration, in: Proceedings of the 6th International Conference on Language Resources and Evaluation, Marrakech, Morocco, 26 May–1 June 2008.

49. I. H. Witten, E. Frank, Data Mining: Practical Machine Learning Tools and Techniques, 2nd edition, Morgan Kaufmann, San Francisco, CA, 2005.

50. F. Wu, D. Weld, Automatically semantifying Wikipedia, in: Proceedings of the ACM 16th Conference on Information and Knowledge Management (CIKM 2007), Lisbon, Portugal, 6–9 November 2007, pp. 41–50.

51. F. Wu, D. Weld, Automatically refining the Wikipedia infobox ontology, in: Proceedings of the 17th World Wide Web Conference, Beijing, China, 21–25 April 2008.

52. F. Wu, D. Weld, Open information extraction using Wikipedia, in: Proceedings of the 48th Annual Meeting of the Association for Computational Linguistics, Uppsala, Sweden, 11–16 July 2010, pp. 118–127.

53. W. Wu, H. Li, H. Wang, K.Q. Zhu, Towards a probabilistic taxonomy of many concepts, Tech. Rep. MSR-TR-2011-25, Microsoft Research Asia, 2011.

UNIT 3

There Is Never Enough Research and Development

CHAPTER 16

■ ■ ■

Questions and Answers on the Singularity: The Singularity Is Near, When Humans Transcend Biology

Ray Kurzweil

So what is the Singularity?

Within a quarter century, nonbiological intelligence will match the range and subtlety of human intelligence. It will then soar past because of the continuing acceleration of information-based technologies, as well as the ability of machines to instantly share their knowledge. Intelligent nanorobots will be deeply integrated in our bodies, our brains, and our environment, overcoming pollution and poverty, providing vastly extended longevity, full-immersion virtual reality incorporating all of the senses (like "The Matrix"), "experience beaming" (like "Being John Malkovich"), and vastly enhanced human intelligence. The result will be an intimate merger between the technology-creating species and the technological evolutionary process it spawned.

And that's the Singularity?

No, that's just the precursor. Nonbiological intelligence will have access to its own design and will be able to improve itself in an increasingly rapid redesign cycle. We'll get to a point where technical progress will be so fast that unenhanced human intelligence will be unable to follow it. That will mark the Singularity.

When will that occur?

I set the date for the Singularity—representing a profound and disruptive transformation in human capability—as 2045. The nonbiological intelligence created in that year will be one billion times more powerful than all human intelligence today.

Why is this called the Singularity?

The term "Singularity" in my book is comparable to the use of this term by the physics community. Just as we find it hard to see beyond the event horizon of a black hole, we also find it difficult to see beyond the event horizon of the historical Singularity. How can we, with our limited biological brains, imagine what our future civilization, with its intelligence multiplied trillions-fold, will be capable of thinking and doing? Nevertheless, just as we can draw conclusions about the nature of black holes through our conceptual thinking, despite never having actually been inside one, our thinking today is powerful enough to have meaningful insights into the implications of the Singularity.

Okay, let's break this down. It seems a key part of your thesis is that we will be able to capture the intelligence of our brains in a machine.

Indeed.

So how are we going to achieve that?

We can break this down further into hardware and software requirements. In the book, I show how we need about 10 quadrillion (10^{16}) calculations per second (cps) to provide a functional equivalent to all the regions of the brain. Some estimates are lower than this by a factor of 100. Supercomputers are already at 100 trillion (10^{14}) cps, and will hit 10^{16} cps around the end of this decade. Several supercomputers with 1 quadrillion cps are already on the drawing board, with two Japanese efforts targeting 10 quadrillion cps around the end of the decade. By 2020, 10 quadrillion cps will be available for around $1,000. Achieving the hardware requirement was controversial when my last book on this topic, *The Age of Spiritual Machines*, came out in 1999, but is now pretty much of a mainstream view among informed observers. Now the controversy is focused on the algorithms.

And how will we recreate the algorithms of human intelligence?

To understand the principles of human intelligence we need to reverse-engineer the human brain. Here, progress is far greater than most people realize. The spatial and temporal (time) resolution of brain scanning is also progressing at an exponential rate, roughly doubling each year, like most everything else having to do with information. Just recently, scanning tools can see individual interneuronal connections, and watch them fire in real time. Already, we have mathematical models and simulations of a couple dozen regions of the brain, including the cerebellum, which comprises more than half the neurons in the brain. IBM is now creating a simulation of about 10,000 cortical neurons, including tens of millions of connections. The first version will simulate the electrical activity, and a future version will also simulate the relevant chemical activity. By the mid 2020s, it's conservative to conclude that we will have effective models for all of the brain.

So at that point we'll just copy a human brain into a supercomputer?

I would rather put it this way: At that point, we'll have a full understanding of the methods of the human brain. One benefit will be a deep understanding of ourselves, but the key implication is that it will expand the toolkit of techniques we can apply to create artificial intelligence. We will then be able to create non-biological systems that match human intelligence in the ways that humans are now superior, for example, our pattern-recognition abilities. These superintelligent computers will be able to do things we are not able to do, such as share knowledge and skills at electronic speeds.

By 2030, a thousand dollars of computation will be about a thousand times more powerful than a human brain. Keep in mind also that computers will not be organized as discrete objects as they are today. There will be a web of computing deeply integrated into the environment, our bodies and brains.

You mentioned the AI tool kit. Hasn't AI failed to live up to its expectations?

There was a boom and bust cycle in AI during the 1980s, similar to what we saw recently in e-commerce and telecommunications. Such boom-bust cycles are often harbingers of true revolutions; recall the railroad boom and bust in the 19th century. But just as the Internet "bust" was not the end of the Internet, the so-called "AI Winter" was not the end of the story for AI either. There are hundreds of applications of "narrow AI" (machine intelligence that equals or exceeds human intelligence for specific tasks) now permeating our modern infrastructure. Every time you send an email or make a cell phone call, intelligent algorithms route the information. AI programs diagnose electrocardiograms with an accuracy rivaling doctors, evaluate medical images, fly and land airplanes, guide intelligent autonomous weapons, make automated investment decisions for over a trillion dollars of funds, and guide industrial processes. These were all research projects a couple of decades ago. If all the intelligent software in the world were to suddenly stop functioning, modern civilization would grind to a halt. Of course, our AI programs are not intelligent enough to organize such a conspiracy, at least not yet.

Why don't more people see these profound changes ahead?

The primary failure is the inability of many observers to think in exponential terms. Most long-range forecasts of what is technically feasible in future time periods dramatically underestimate the power of future developments because they are based on what I call the "intuitive linear" view of history rather than the "historical exponential" view. My models show that we are doubling the paradigm-shift rate every decade. Thus the 20th century was gradually speeding up to the rate of progress at the end of the century; its achievements, therefore, were equivalent to about twenty years of progress at the rate in 2000. We'll make another twenty years of progress in just fourteen years (by 2014), and then do the same again in only seven years. To express this another way, we won't experience one hundred years of technological advance in the 21st century; we will witness on the order of 20,000 years of progress (again, when measured by the rate of progress in 2000), or about 1,000 times greater than what was achieved in the 20th century.

The exponential growth of information technologies is even greater: we're doubling the power of information technologies, as measured by price-performance, bandwidth, capacity and many other types of measures, about every year. That's a factor of a thousand in ten years, a million in twenty years, and a billion in thirty years. This goes far beyond Moore's law (the shrinking of transistors on an integrated circuit, allowing us to double the price-performance of electronics each year). Electronics is just one example of many. As another example, it took us 14 years to sequence HIV; we recently sequenced SARS in only 31 days.

So this acceleration of information technologies applies to biology as well?

Absolutely. It's not just computer devices like cell phones and digital cameras that are accelerating in capability. Ultimately, everything of importance will be comprised essentially of information technology. With the advent of nanotechnology-based manufacturing in the 2020s, we'll be able to use inexpensive table-top devices to manufacture on-demand just about anything from very inexpensive raw materials using information processes that will rearrange matter and energy at the molecular level.

We'll meet our energy needs using nanotechnology-based solar panels that will capture the energy in .03 percent of the sunlight that falls on the Earth, which is all we need to meet our projected energy needs in 2030. We'll store the energy in highly distributed fuel cells.

I want to come back to both biology and nanotechnology, but how can you be so sure of these developments? Isn't technical progress on specific projects essentially unpredictable?

Predicting *specific* projects is indeed not feasible. But the result of the overall complex, chaotic evolutionary process of technological progress *is* predictable.

People intuitively assume that the current rate of progress will continue for future periods. Even for those who have been around long enough to experience how the pace of change increases over time, unexamined intuition leaves one with the impression that change occurs at the same rate that we have experienced most recently. From the mathematician's perspective, the reason for this is that an exponential curve looks like a straight line when examined for only a brief duration. As a result, even sophisticated commentators, when considering the future, typically use the current pace of change to determine their expectations in extrapolating progress over the next ten years or one hundred years. This is why I describe this way of looking at the future as the "intuitive linear" view. But a serious assessment of the history of technology reveals that technological change is exponential. Exponential growth is a feature of any evolutionary process, of which technology is a primary example.

This has also been true of biological evolution. Indeed, technological evolution emerges from biological evolution. You can examine the data in different ways, on different timescales, and for a wide variety of technologies, ranging from electronic to biological, as well as for their implications, ranging from the amount of human knowledge to the size of the economy, and you get the same exponential—not linear—progression. For the price-performance of computing, this goes back over a century, well before Gordon Moore was even born.

Aren't there are a lot of predictions of the future from the past that look a little ridiculous now?

Yes, any number of bad predictions from other futurists in earlier eras can be cited to support the notion that we cannot make reliable predictions. In general, these prognosticators were not using a methodology based on a sound theory of technology evolution. I say this not just looking backwards now. I've been making accurate forward-looking predictions for over twenty years based on these models.

But how can it be the case that we can reliably predict the overall progression of these technologies if we cannot even predict the outcome of a single project?

Predicting which company or product will succeed is indeed very difficult, if not impossible. The same difficulty occurs in predicting which technical design or standard will prevail. For example, how will the wireless-communication protocols Wimax, CDMA, and 3G fare over the next several years? However, we find remarkably precise and predictable exponential trends when assessing the overall effectiveness (as measured in a variety of ways) of information technologies. And as I mentioned above, information technology will ultimately underlie everything of value.

But how can that be?

We see examples in other areas of science of very smooth and reliable outcomes resulting from the interaction of a great many unpredictable events. Consider that predicting the path of a single molecule in a gas is essentially impossible, but predicting the properties of the *entire* gas—comprised of a great many chaotically interacting molecules—can be done very reliably through the laws of thermodynamics. Analogously, it is not possible to reliably predict the results of a specific project or company, but the overall capabilities of information technology, comprised of many chaotic activities, can nonetheless be dependably anticipated through what I call "the law of accelerating returns."

What will the impact of these developments be?

Radical life extension, for one.

Sounds interesting, how does that work?

Three great overlapping revolutions that go by the letters "GNR," which stand for genetics, nanotechnology, and robotics. Each will provide a dramatic increase to human longevity, among other profound impacts. We're in the early stages of the genetics—also called biotechnology—revolution right now. Biotechnology is providing the means to actually change your genes: not just designer babies but designer baby boomers. We'll also be able to rejuvenate all of your body's tissues and organs by transforming your skin cells into youthful versions of every other cell type. Already, new drug development is precisely targeting key steps in the process of atherosclerosis (the cause of heart disease), cancerous tumor formation, and the metabolic processes underlying each major disease and aging process. The biotechnology revolution is already in its early stages and will reach its peak in the second decade of this century, at which point we'll be able to overcome most major diseases and dramatically slow down the aging process.

That will bring us to the nanotechnology revolution, which will achieve maturity in the 2020s. With nanotechnology, we will be able to go beyond the limits of biology, and replace your current "human body version 1.0" with a dramatically upgraded version 2.0, providing radical life extension.

And how does that work?

The "killer app" of nanotechnology is "nanobots," which are blood-cell sized robots that can travel in the bloodstream destroying pathogens, removing debris, correcting DNA errors, and reversing aging processes.

Human body version 2.0?

We're already in the early stages of augmenting and replacing each of our organs, even portions of our brains with neural implants, the most recent versions of which allow patients to download new software to their neural implants from outside their bodies. Each of our organs will ultimately be replaced. For example, nanobots could deliver to our bloodstream an optimal set of all the nutrients, hormones, and other substances we need, as well as remove toxins and waste products. The gastrointestinal tract could be reserved for culinary pleasures rather than the tedious biological function of providing nutrients. After all, we've already in some ways separated the communication and pleasurable aspects of sex from its biological function.

And the third revolution?

The robotics revolution, which really refers to "strong" AI, that is, artificial intelligence at the human level, which we talked about earlier. We'll have both the hardware and software to recreate human intelligence by the end of the 2020s. We'll be able to improve these methods and harness the speed, memory capabilities, and knowledge-sharing ability of machines.

We'll ultimately be able to scan all the salient details of our brains from inside, using billions of nanobots in the capillaries. We can then back up the information. Using nanotechnology-based manufacturing, we could recreate your brain, or better yet reinstantiate it in a more capable computing substrate.

Which means?

Our biological brains use chemical signaling, which transmit information at only a few hundred feet per second. Electronics is already millions of times faster than this. In the book, I show how one cubic inch of nanotube circuitry would be about one hundred million times more powerful than the human brain. So we'll have more powerful means of instantiating our intelligence than the extremely slow speeds of our interneuronal connections.

So we'll just replace our biological brains with circuitry?

I see this starting with nanobots in our bodies and brains. The nanobots will keep us healthy, provide full-immersion virtual reality from within the nervous system, provide direct brain-to-brain communication over the Internet, and otherwise greatly expand human intelligence. But keep in mind that nonbiological intelligence is doubling in capability each year, whereas our biological intelligence is essentially fixed in capacity. As we get to the 2030s, the nonbiological portion of our intelligence will predominate.

The closest life extension technology, however, is biotechnology, isn't that right?

There's certainly overlap in the G, N and R revolutions, but that's essentially correct.

So tell me more about how genetics or biotechnology works.

As we are learning about the information processes underlying biology, we are devising ways of mastering them to overcome disease and aging and extend human potential. One powerful approach is to start with biology's information backbone: the genome. With gene technologies, we're now on the verge of being able to control how genes express themselves. We now have a powerful new tool called RNA interference (RNAi), which is capable of turning specific genes off. It blocks the messenger RNA of specific genes, preventing them from creating proteins. Since viral diseases, cancer, and many other diseases use gene expression at some crucial point in their life cycle, this promises to be a breakthrough technology. One gene we'd like to turn off is the fat insulin receptor gene, which tells the fat cells to hold on to every calorie. When that gene was blocked in mice, those mice ate a lot but remained thin and healthy, and actually lived 20 percent longer.

New means of adding new genes, called gene therapy, are also emerging that have overcome earlier problems with achieving precise placement of the new genetic information. One company I'm involved with, United Therapeutics, cured pulmonary hypertension in animals using a new form of gene therapy and it has now been approved for human trials.

So we're going to essentially reprogram our DNA.

That's a good way to put it, but that's only one broad approach. Another important line of attack is to regrow our own cells, tissues, and even whole organs, and introduce them into our bodies without surgery. One major benefit of this "therapeutic cloning" technique is that we will be able to create these new tissues and organs from versions of our cells that have also been made younger—the emerging field of rejuvenation medicine. For example, we will be able to create new heart cells from your skin cells and introduce them into your system through the bloodstream. Over time, your heart cells get replaced with these new cells, and the result is a rejuvenated "young" heart with your own DNA.

Drug discovery was once a matter of finding substances that produced some beneficial effect without excessive side effects. This process was similar to early humans' tool discovery, which was limited to simply finding rocks and natural implements that could be used for helpful purposes. Today, we are learning the precise biochemical pathways that underlie both disease and aging processes, and are able to design drugs to carry out precise missions at the molecular level. The scope and scale of these efforts is vast.

But perfecting our biology will only get us so far. The reality is that biology will never be able to match what we will be capable of engineering, now that we are gaining a deep understanding of biology's principles of operation.

Isn't nature optimal?

Not at all. Our interneuronal connections compute at about 200 transactions per second, at least a million times slower than electronics. As another example, a nanotechnology theorist, Rob Freitas, has a conceptual design for nanobots that replace our red blood cells. A conservative analysis shows that if you replaced 10 percent of your red blood cells with Freitas' "respirocytes," you could sit at the bottom of a pool for four hours without taking a breath.

If people stop dying, isn't that going to lead to overpopulation?

A common mistake that people make when considering the future is to envision a major change to today's world, such as radical life extension, as if nothing else were going to change. The GNR revolutions will result in other transformations that address this issue. For example, nanotechnology will enable us to create virtually any physical product from information and very inexpensive raw materials, leading to radical wealth creation. We'll have the means to meet the material needs of any conceivable size population of biological humans. Nanotechnology will also provide the means of cleaning up environmental damage from earlier stages of industrialization.

So we'll overcome disease, pollution, and poverty— sounds like a utopian vision.

It's true that the dramatic scale of the technologies of the next couple of decades will enable human civilization to overcome problems that we have struggled with for eons. But these developments are not without their dangers. Technology is a double edged sword—we don't have to look past the 20th century to see the intertwined promise and peril of technology.

What sort of perils?

G, N, and R each have their downsides. The existential threat from genetic technologies is already here: the same technology that will soon make major strides against cancer, heart disease, and other diseases could also be employed by a bioterrorist to create a bioengineered biological virus that combines ease of transmission, deadliness, and stealthiness, that is, a long incubation period. The tools and knowledge to do this are far more widespread than the tools and knowledge to create an atomic bomb, and the impact could be far worse.

So maybe we shouldn't go down this road.

It's a little late for that. But the idea of relinquishing new technologies such as biotechnology and nanotechnology is already being advocated. I argue in the book that this would be the wrong strategy. Besides depriving human society of the profound benefits of these technologies, such a strategy would actually make the dangers worse by driving development underground, where responsible scientists would not have easy access to the tools needed to defend us.

So how do we protect ourselves?

The overall message is that we need to give a higher priority to preparing protective strategies and systems. We need to put a few more stones on the defense side of the scale. I've given testimony to Congress on a specific proposal for a "Manhattan" style project to create a rapid response system that could protect society from a new virulent biological virus. One strategy would be to use RNAi, which has been shown to be effective against viral diseases. We would set up a system that could quickly sequence a new virus, prepare a RNA interference medication, and rapidly gear up production. We have the knowledge to create such a system, but we have not done so. We need to have something like this in place before its needed.

Ultimately, however, nanotechnology will provide a completely effective defense against biological viruses.

*But doesn't nanotechnology have its own
self-replicating danger?*

Yes, but that potential won't exist for a couple more decades. The existential threat from engineered biological viruses exists right now.

*Okay, but how will we defend against
self-replicating nanotechnology?*

There are already proposals for ethical standards for nanotechnology that are based on the Asilomar conference standards that have worked well thus far in biotechnology. These standards will be effective against unintentional dangers. For example, we do not need to provide self-replication to accomplish nanotechnology manufacturing.

But what about intentional abuse, as in terrorism?

We'll need to create a nanotechnology immune system—good nanobots that can protect us from the bad ones.

Blue goo to protect us from the gray goo!

Yes, well put. And ultimately we'll need the nanobots comprising the immune system to be self-replicating. The nanobot immune system we put in place will need the ability to self-replicate. That's basically the same "lesson" that biological evolution learned.

Ultimately, however, strong AI will provide a completely effective defense against self-replicating nanotechnology.

Okay, what's going to protect us against a pathological AI?

Yes, well, that would have to be a yet more intelligent AI.

This is starting to sound like that story about the universe being on the back of a turtle, and that turtle standing on the back of another turtle, and so on all the way down. So what if this more intelligent AI is unfriendly? Another even smarter AI?

History teaches us that the more intelligent civilization—the one with the most advanced technology—prevails.

Aren't there limits to exponential growth? You know the story about rabbits in Australia—they didn't keep growing exponentially forever.

There are limits to the exponential growth inherent in each paradigm. Moore's law was not the first paradigm to bring exponential growth to computing, but rather the fifth. In the 1950s they were shrinking vacuum tubes to keep the exponential growth going and then that paradigm hit a wall. But the exponential growth of computing didn't stop. It kept going, with the new paradigm of transistors taking over. Each time we can see the end of the road for a paradigm, it creates research pressure to create the next one. That's happening now with Moore's law, even though we are still about fifteen years away from the end of our ability to shrink transistors on a flat integrated circuit. We're making dramatic progress in creating the sixth paradigm, which is three-dimensional molecular computing.

But isn't there an overall limit to our ability to expand the power of computation?

Yes, I discuss these limits in the book. The ultimate 2 pound computer could provide 10^{42} cps, which will be about 10 quadrillion (10^{16}) times more powerful than all human brains put together today. And that's if we restrict the computer to staying at a cold temperature. If we allow it to get hot, we could improve that by a factor of another 100 million. And, of course, we'll be devoting more than two pounds of matter to computing. Ultimately, we'll use a significant portion of the matter and energy in our vicinity. So, yes, there are limits, but they're not very limiting.

And when we saturate the ability of the matter and energy in our solar system to support intelligent processes, what happens then?

Then we'll expand to the rest of the Universe.

Which will take a long time I presume.

Well, that depends on whether we can use wormholes to get to other places in the Universe quickly, or otherwise circumvent the speed of light. If wormholes are feasible, and analyses show they are consistent with general relativity, we could saturate the universe with our intelligence within a couple of centuries. But regardless of speculation on wormholes, we'll get to the limits of computing in our solar system within this century. At that point, we'll have expanded the powers of our intelligence by trillions of trillions.

Getting back to life extension, isn't it natural to age, to die?

Other natural things include malaria, Ebola, appendicitis, and tsunamis. Many natural things are worth changing. Aging may be "natural," but I don't see anything positive in losing my mental agility, sensory acuity, physical limberness, sexual desire, or any other human ability.

In my view, death is a tragedy. It's a tremendous loss of personality, skills, knowledge, relationships. We've rationalized it as a good thing because that's really been the only alternative we've had. But disease, aging, and death are problems we are now in a position to overcome.

Wait, you said that the golden era of biotechnology was still a decade away. We don't have radical life extension today, do we?

In my last book, *Fantastic Voyage, Live Long Enough to Live Forever*, which I coauthored with Terry Grossman, M.D., we describe a detailed and personalized program you can implement now (which we call "bridge one") that will enable most people to live long enough to get to the mature phase of the biotechnology evolution ("bridge two"). That in turn will get us to "bridge three," which is nanotechnology and strong AI, which will result in being able to live indefinitely.

Okay, but won't it get boring to live many hundreds of years?

If humans lived many hundreds of years with no other change in the nature of human life, then, yes, that would lead to a deep ennui. But the same nanobots in the bloodstream that will keep us healthy—by destroying pathogens and reversing aging processes—will also vastly augment our intelligence and experiences. As is its nature, the nonbiological portion of our intelligence will expand its powers exponentially, so it will ultimately predominate. The result will be accelerating change—so we will not be bored.

Won't the Singularity create the ultimate "digital divide" due to unequal access to radical life extension and superintelligent computers?

We need to consider an important feature of the law of accelerating returns, which is a 50 percent annual deflation factor for information technologies, a factor which itself will increase. Technologies start out affordable only by the wealthy, but at this stage, they actually don't work very well. At the next stage, they're merely expensive, and work a bit better. Then they work quite well and are inexpensive. Ultimately, they're almost free. Cell phones are now at the inexpensive stage. There are countries in Asia where most people were pushing a plow fifteen years ago, yet now have thriving information economies and most people have a cell phone. This progression from early adoption of unaffordable technologies that don't work well to late adoption of refined technologies that are very inexpensive is currently a decade-long process. But that too will accelerate. Ten years from now, this will be a five year progression, and twenty years from now it will be only a two- to three-year lag.

This model applies not just to electronic gadgets but to anything having to do with information, and ultimately that will be mean everything of value, including all manufactured products. In biology, we went from a cost of ten dollars to sequence a base pair of DNA in 1990 to about a penny today. AIDS drugs started out costing tens of thousands of dollars per patient per year and didn't work very well, whereas today, effective drugs are about a hundred dollars per patient per year in poor countries. That's still more than we'd like, but the technology is moving in the right direction. So the digital divide and the have-have not divide is diminishing, not exacerbating. Ultimately, everyone will have great wealth at their disposal.

Won't problems such as war, intolerance, environmental degradation prevent us from reaching the Singularity?

We had a lot of war in the 20th century. Fifty million people died in World War II, and there were many other wars. We also had a lot of intolerance, relatively little democracy until late in the century, and a lot of environmental pollution. All of these problems of the 20th century had no effect on the law of accelerating returns. The exponential growth of information technologies proceeded smoothly through war and peace, through depression and prosperity.

The emerging 21st century technologies tend to be decentralized and relatively friendly to the environment. With the maturation of nanotechnology, we will also have the opportunity to clean up the mess left from the crude early technologies of industrialization.

But won't there still be objections from religious and political leaders, not to mention the common man and woman, to such a radical transformation of humanity?

There were objections to the plow also, but that didn't stop people from using it. The same can be said for every new step in technology. Technologies do have to prove themselves. For every technology that is adopted, many are discarded. Each technology has to demonstrate that it meets basic human needs. The cell phone, for example, meets our need to communicate with one another. We are not going to reach the Singularity in some single great leap forward, but rather through a great many small steps, each seemingly benign and modest in scope.

But what about controversies such as the stem cell issue? Government opposition is clearly slowing down progress in that field.

I clearly support stem cell research, but it is not the case that the field of cell therapies has been significantly slowed down. If anything, the controversy has accelerated creative ways of achieving the holy grail of this field, which is transdifferentiation, that is, creating new differentiated cells you need from your own cells—for example, converting skin cells into heart cells or pancreatic Islet cells. Transdifferentiation has already been demonstrated in the lab. Objections such as those expressed against stem cell research end up being stones in the water: the stream of progress just flows around them.

Where does God fit into the Singularity?

Although the different religious traditions have somewhat different conceptions of God, the common thread is that God represents unlimited—infinite—levels of intelligence, knowledge, creativity, beauty, and love. As systems evolve—through biology and technology—we find that they become more complex, more intelligent and more knowledgeable. They become more intricate and more beautiful, more capable of higher emotions such as love. So they grow exponentially in intelligence, knowledge, creativity, beauty, and love, all of the qualities people ascribe to God without limit. Although evolution does not reach a literally infinite level of these attributes, it does accelerate towards ever greater levels, so we can view evolution as a spiritual process, moving ever closer to this ideal. The Singularity will represent an explosion of these higher values of complexity.

So are you trying to play God?

Actually, I'm trying to play a human. I'm trying to do what humans do well, which is solve problems.

But will we still be human after all these changes?

That depends on how you define human. Some observers define human based on our limitations. I prefer to define us as the species that seeks—and succeeds—in going beyond our limitations.

Many observers point out how science has thrown us off our pedestal, showing us that we're not as central as we thought, that the stars don't circle around the Earth, that we're not descended from the gods but rather from monkeys, and before that earthworms.

All of that is true, but it turns out that we are central after all. Our ability to create models—virtual realities—in our brains, combined with our modest-looking thumbs, are enabling us to expand our horizons without limit.

CHAPTER 17

■ ■ ■

Comment: The Role of Technology in Society and the Need for Historical Perspective

A. Hunter Dupree

The unique contribution the historian of technology and society can hope to make is to inject a chronological dimension. Hence historians are not likely to fit well among those who see technology either as an unalloyed blessing or as an unmitigated curse. Historians have, despite a lack of firm methodological assumptions, been piling up empirical evidence that technology has been a well-recognized factor in social change not only back to the Industrial Revolution but also back at least to Olduvai Gorge and the end of the Pleistocene glaciation. However, the most unlikely conclusion they could possibly draw from this chronological sequence is the one which Mesthene attributes to them—that technology as such is not worthy of special notice. Perhaps the econometricians have rubbed out the acceleration of productivity since the 1880s and have denied a change in time period between invention and adoption of technological components in recent decades. The historian is interested in precisely those social, cultural, psychological, and political effects which render the conclusions of the econometricians elegant exercises, beautiful in their way but divorced from the choices which men and women fixed in time have always had to make.

For the understanding of contemporary society, technology is worthy of such special notice that a program on technology and society cannot afford to overlook the possibility that important elements in the present interaction between technology and society took shape long before the 20th century. Even if one accepts Mesthene's proposition that the contemporary situation is qualitatively different from that of past societies, the way is still open to use the new insights our present technology and plight give us to reexamine the past with eyes better focused to understand the nature of technology in its interactions with society in any period. Two leading ideas of the present scene—the systems approach and ecological balance—have the possibility of combining to elucidate the nature of technology and innovation, but these ideas need a long time span to test themselves adequately.

The framework of the history of technology as now practiced is the child of the Industrial Revolution and the patent system. The effect of the patent was to focus the history of technology on the individual inventor as the potential entrepreneur-innovator and also to focus on the individual mechanical device rather than the system as the unit of innovation. The structuring of the whole concept of technological change around discrete mechanical arrangements as the unit of innovation has persisted to the present and was almost unchallenged until recently. Since almost every systems innovation has certain crucial components without which it could not operate and certain components which were already available from the existing stock of technology, the patent-inventor-invention formulation has a certain utility. Thomas A. Edison was dealing with a systems problem in substituting electricity for gas lighting in the early 1880s, but he rightly focused on the invention of the high-resistance incandescent filament in a glass-enclosed vacuum as the component which was most dramatically necessary for the whole system to operate. Therefore he found it most persuasive and also most in tune with the patent system of reward and development to describe himself as the inventor of the discrete component. The history of technology has labored mightily to trace the history of some of the thousands of components and to unravel the thorny problems of priority and prestige involved in the title *inventor*. Yet even another generation of industrious work on such a program would still be unable to help Mesthene very much in unraveling the relation of technology to society in the late 20th century, the period of the greatest multiplicity of components.

Therefore let us ask the Harvard Program on Science and Technology to take its expertise in the modern arts back along the chronological axis of history sufficiently far to get a perspective on the systems approach applied to technology itself. Let us imagine the improbable—a historian possessed of both the systems approach and ecology. Let him try to define technology. He would take a look at Mesthene's definition, "the organization of knowledge for practical purposes," and, without changing it essentially, say that technology is man's codified ways of doing things to the environment. Such definitions abound in the literature, but they need translating into terms understandable in the late 20th century by technological man himself. The hypothetical qualified modern historian of technology (not myself, but one armed with anthropology, archaeology, and linguistics as well as systems analysis, ecology, and all the conventional scholarly appurtenances) might strip off all perplexities and complications to evolve a definition something like this: Technology is an information system which connects the species of biological organisms *Homo sapiens* with its environment. Skipping over the vexed problems of animal technology and the protohuman mix of tools and biological adaptation, the historian can find as far back as he can see a biological organism (a system in itself, about which we know something from present evidence) interacting with its environment, which includes both other organisms and the physical environment accessible from the surface of the planet Earth. Other organisms have reached a balance with their environment by biological adaptation, but culture, in addition to biological adaptation, has interposed itself between *Homo sapiens* and his environment.

Although one might conceivably see this ecological position of man in several ways—for instance, as an energy transfer system—the presence of language and society even at the earliest horizon makes the information system the closest analogue of technology. Not only does the human individual take in information through his senses, process it, and read out behavior which is adapted to the environment, but culture provides a kind of memory unit which processes information flowing in from the environment on a scale beyond any individual and stores it for future use. The conception can apply both when most of the feedback flows from the environment, forcing man to adapt, and when in more recent situations the quantity of feedback flows the other way, producing massive changes in the environment itself. Yet even on the earliest horizon the feedback flow is a closed loop and not necessarily overbalanced in favor of the environment. Men of earlier times could cut down the cedars of Lebanon with the efficiency of a bulldozer.

The information system which is technology could not get very far without language, since the naming of things made efficient information exchange with the environment possible. Yet language is not the only carrier of technological information. Tools themselves transmit messages to their users even as energy flows through them to the environment. Society is also a carrier, for fathers, mothers, and masters pass on to sons, daughters, and apprentices information which they cannot verbalize and which is embedded in the skilled and practical eye-hand coordination of the artisan. No wonder that until the 20th century the best way to move technological information laterally in space in a short time was to transport skilled artisans.

Only from the time of the Renaissance, and even then only peripherally, did a formal information carrier in the shape of a technological literature develop. Mining was an ancient art which had gone on for centuries before Georgius Agricola's *De re metallica* (1556) and showed every evidence of continuing without the aid of that masterpiece. Although formal mathematics, for instance, seems to put in a very late appearance among artisans, tools and the products of early technology speak eloquently of narrow limits of accuracy and coordination of complex relationships by men unversed in Euclid. Indeed, some evidence indicates a chronologically continuous grid of measurement underlying Western technology from the ancient world to the present.

Since each generation of man must solve certain systems problems or perish, the technological information is embedded in culture groups around certain fundamental adaptive mechanisms—food, clothing, shelter, mobility, protection. Reticulation of an industrial technology can mask these fundamental mechanisms, but no amount of affluence can eliminate their biological base. The historian of technology has here an organizing principle for analyzing the technological information which puts his many component histories into perspective. The origin of agriculture and the coming food needs of the exploding population are all one subject because every generation must have the technological information to provide itself with food. McCormick's reaper and the horse collar of the Dark Ages have had center stage in the history of technology, but the magnificent unity of the history of corn, *Zea Mays*, in its full social setting with man, is much more in tune with an approach to technology which makes food provision a system equally present in every society.

Out of the necessity to preserve the fundamental technological systems to support life comes the immense stability (hopefully a better word than conservatism) of technological tradition. Especially if the surplus wealth of the community is low, an experimental attitude is disastrous. Furthermore, the redesign of components can only take place within the confines of a system that must maintain its adaptation with the environment. Therefore, innovation merits the suspicion of a peasant whose culture has taught him through the hard experience of his ancestors the course most likely to ensure his harvest.

Technological change is not, however, a new phenomenon. Although the system hunts for stability and, if the feedback from the environment remains steady, will tend toward a diminishing oscillation in technique as the tradition becomes set, the input from the environment is never completely free from change. Geology has seen to that, for the end of the glacial epoch forced massive technological change and systems innovation on *Homo sapiens*, making him into the innovating animal. When his ecological niche changes, the feedback into his culture computer tells him something is out of balance, and he responds not only with change but also with a search for a new equilibrium adapted to the changed condition. In this way the stability of culture and the pressure for change brought about by a fluctuation in the environment (including the changes induced by the impinging human population itself) form a tension out of which comes adaptation. Most animals have to stay with one ecological niche or become extinct or evolve new biological capability, but *Homo sapiens* developed the ability to change niches through technological adaptation long before the conventional dawn of history. No doubt the process of change often occurred over many lifetimes, and tradition could change without breaking the continuity of parent-to-child transmission in time. Yet not all technological change in earlier times was necessarily multigenerationally slow. A plow could spread far across Europe in a few years, and the cliff houses of Mesa Verde lost their inhabitants within the memory of a single generation.

Science has received so much praise and blame as the prime source of technological change in the present era that the Harvard Program on Technology and Society cannot avoid considering science as a part of its field of investigation. Mesthene almost never mentions science, to the extent of making American accomplishments in national defense and space exploration "technological successes." Yet his present era is precisely the time when, if ever, science has intruded itself onto the technological scene. Hence, the historian might carry his hypothetical analysis one step further and ask if science will yield to the viewpoint of systems analysis and ecology.

Despite many careless modern statements of the separateness of science and technology up to the late 19th century and their intimacy thereafter, the analysis at first glance makes the two appear surprisingly similar. Science, like technology, is an information system embedded in culture. It too mediates between man and his environment. It too is a social process concerned with a memory bank which stores information and passes it from one individual to another, including those in the younger generation who will take their places in an unbroken chain. It too relies heavily on language. It too has embedded in its tradition a mathematics tied to a measuring system.

Finally, science also has tools to supplement man's senses, which are in themselves carriers of information beyond the verbal and mathematical content of their readouts. Nothing has confused the historians of science and technology more than the fact that science floats on a bed of technology. As an information system it has hardware. Not only is science dependent on technology for the instruments specially made to its order, it rides along on the artifacts of general technology, as when the building of the transcontinental railroad enabled biologists to reexplore the trans-Mississippi West with great efficiency and systematic results. That example perhaps makes the same point more clearly than saying that science rides along on a rocket to explore space. The rocket is technology, but the exploration is science.

The recognition of science and technology as kindred information systems should not, however, deter the historian from seeking among the similarities for the differences which have led these two systems to maintain separate identities and at times almost to lose touch with each other. On the other hand, as at present, the two have become so intertwined that to recognize the boundary between them is the hard problem.

The first difference between science and technology that becomes apparent is a radically different emphasis on the various carriers of information within the systems. While the technological instrumentation carries a freight of information and while the organizations of science work, to an extent, on the master-apprentice pattern dominant in technology, the predominant carrier of scientific information is the corpus of formal literature. The linguistic channel and mathematical channel in the formal literature define the scope of science in any given age. Hence the long detour from the Greeks via Alexandria and the Arabs to Western Europe in the 13th century is mainly a matter of written texts.

The second difference, somehow linked with the first one, is that science is not a closed-loop feedback system. It has inputs from the environment, but it channels them into the memory bank—the formal literature—without the expectation on the part of a society that adaptive behavior must be immediately forthcoming. The process of abstraction, which the scientific information system began to accomplish in ancient times, broke the loop and relieved the system of the necessity of producing an unbroken series of adapted systems in all periods to provide an ecological niche for the species. The time span available for the processing of information within the system is greatly increased, and the number of optional solutions also greatly increased. In place of culture as a whole being the path for the information system in a reciprocating loop as in the case of technology, the scientific information system developed its own more limited and more disciplined cultural milieu in the scientific community. Solutions are stored for varying periods of time in the formal literature and then retrieved by the instructions of the scientific community when certain standards of cogency are met. Here is not the place to discuss the complicated rules of priority, verification by experiment, and achievement of consensus by which the scientific community processes information.

Suffice it to say that despite the similarities of the two systems, they had diverged significantly during the Middle Ages. When they began to interact toward the end of that time, the scientific information system received a large input from technology, and indeed the scientists without the help of the artisans of the Renaissance would have remained seriously hampered by a deficient experimental and observational capability.

By the late 19th century the two systems had again diverged significantly, and now it was the scientific information, with the dense matrix of options it had developed over three centuries, which made science a major input into technology. That they are both information systems with a common linguistic and mathematical tradition made their mating easier. At first science appeared as the bestower of components on already functioning technological systems. The atomic bomb might be viewed as the culmination of component bestowal from science to technology. In the post–World War II period, although the flow of science-oriented components has by no means ceased, the possibility that science might develop optimal systems to substitute for whole technological systems has become a reality. The gain in this situation is the number of matched components that become available rapidly and also the possibility that direct control of man-environment adaptation can be achieved on a systems basis rather than left to the closed-loop cultural interactions of technology.

The danger in the situation lies in two directions. In the first place, even the most science-based technologies are still made up to a large extent of traditional technological components, some of which have remained unchanged for centuries and are highly adapted, especially to man. They may be superior to a scorched-earth innovation in the name of progress. And, new or old, the system must continue to be respectful of the biological organism that *Homo sapiens* remains. The substitution of jet aircraft has not rendered walking obsolete. In the second place, the dynamics of the man-environment adaptation is so poorly understood that the trade-offs of gains and losses in hasty and partial innovation of science-based systems may after the fact produce social and ecological disaster.

If the Harvard Program on Technology and Society could use a modern approach to the history of technology, it might be able to go a little way toward sorting out the mix of systems—some science based and some a direct heritage of man's earliest experience—which make up the totality of 20th-century technology. It might also be able to avoid the extremes of unlimited optimism and bitter pessimism by an analysis of the middle ground of cost and benefit. An understanding of many different rates of change and the relations between them and a quest for balance in the man-environment ecological system might provide a standard of value which would restore to proud and anxious modern man a measure of both courage and repose.

Biographical Note

DR. DUPREE, professor of history at Brown University, is the author of *Asa Gray, Science in the Federal Government,* and *Science and the Emergence of Modern America.*

CHAPTER 18

■ ■ ■

Moore's Law and Technological Determinism
Reflections on the History of Technology

Paul E. Ceruzzi

Just over a year ago, the arrival in my mailbox of a book I had agreed to review triggered some thoughts about technology I had been meaning to articulate. The book was Ross Bassett's *To the Digital Age: Research Labs, Start-up Companies, and the Rise of MOS Technology* (Baltimore, 2002).[1] In it, Bassett describes the development of metal-oxide semiconductor (MOS) technology, which enabled semiconductor firms to place more and more transistors on a single silicon chip.[2] This became the basis for what is now known as Moore's law, after Gordon E. Moore. In April 1965, Moore, then the director of research and development at the semiconductor division of Fairchild Camera and Instrument Corporation, published a paper in which he observed that the number of transistors that could be placed on an integrated circuit had doubled every year since integrated circuits had been invented and predicted that that trend would continue.[3] Shortly afterward, Moore left Fairchild to cofound Intel—a company, Bassett notes, that staked its future on MOS technology.

It is important to note at the outset that Moore's law was an empirical observation; it is not analogous to, say, Ohm's law, which relates resistance to current. Moore simply looked at the circuits being produced, plotted their density on a piece of semi-log graph paper, and found a straight line. Furthermore, he made this observation in 1965, when the integrated circuit was only six years old and had barely found its way out of the laboratory. The name "Silicon Valley" did not even exist; it would be coined at the end of that decade. Nonetheless, Moore's prediction that the number of transistors that could be placed on an integrated circuit would continue to double at short, regular intervals has held true ever since, although the interval soon stretched from twelve to eighteen months.[4]

Moore's law has been intensively studied, mainly by those wondering when, if ever, fundamental physical constraints (such as the diameter of a hydrogen atom) will interrupt the straight line that Moore observed. These studies note the lengthening of the interval mentioned already: chip densities now double about every eighteen to twenty months, although no one is sure why.[5] Analysts have been predicting the failure of Moore's law for years. Interestingly, the moment of its demise seems always to be about ten years from whenever the prediction is made; that is, those writing in 1994 anticipated that it would fail in 2004, while some today put the likely date at about 2015. Obviously one of these predictions will pan out someday, but for now Moore's law is very much in force, as it has been for over forty-five years—a fact from which the lengthening of the doubling interval should not distract us. Over the same period, computer-disk memory capacity and fiber-optic cable bandwidth have also increased at exponential rates. Thus, in 2005 we see memory chips approaching a billion (10^9) bits of storage, Apple iPods with forty-gigabyte (3×10^{11} bits) disks, and local networks capable of transmitting a full-length Hollywood feature film in seconds.

But while industry analysts, engineers, and marketing people have studied Moore's law intensively, historians of science and technology have shown less interest. That is surprising, since it cuts to the heart of an issue that they have debated over the years: technological determinism.

Mel Kranzberg and his colleagues organized the Society for the History of Technology in part to foster a view of technology running counter to the notion that technology is an impersonal force with its own internal logic and a trajectory that human beings must follow. The society's founders spoke of a "contextual" approach to technology, in which the linear narrative of events from invention to application was accompanied by an understanding of the context in which those events occurred.[6] They named the society's journal *Technology and Culture* to emphasize the importance of all three words. Of course, the founding of SHOT and the establishment of *T&C* did not settle the framework for studying technology once and for all, and periodically the concept of determinism is revisited.[7] Nor did the contextual approach remain static. Led by a second generation of scholars including Thomas Parke Hughes, Wiebe Bijker, and Donald MacKenzie, it evolved into the notion (borrowed from elsewhere) of the "social construction" of technology.[8] At the risk of telescoping a complex and rich story, recall that part of the context of the founding of the Society for the History of Technology in 1957 was the Soviets' launch of *Sputnik* and its effect on the perception of U.S. and British technology.[9] The idea of free peoples choosing their destiny freely was very much on the minds of Americans and Britons, then engaged in a cold war with a nation whose citizens lacked such freedom.

I agree with and support this approach to the history of technology. But it must confront a serious challenge: the steady and unstoppable march of semiconductor density, which has led to the rapid introduction of an enormous number of new products, services, and ways of working and living. Think of all the cultural, political, and social events that have occurred in the West since 1965. Think of our understanding of the history of science and technology today compared to then. Now consider that throughout all of these years, the exponential growth of chip density has hardly deviated from its slope. Can anything other than the limit implied by Planck's constant have an effect on Moore's law?

That Moore's law plays a significant role in determining the current place of technology in society is not in dispute. Is it a determinant of our society? The public and our political leaders believe so. In the popular press, the term "technology" itself is today synonymous with "computers." Historians of technology find that conflation exasperating, as it excludes a vast array of technology-driven processes, such as textiles or food production.

The public acceptance of technological determinism is evident among the many visitors where I work, at the National Air and Space Museum, and a recent essay in this journal indicates that determinism is again very much on the minds of historians of technology as well. In "All That Is Solid Melts into Air: Historians of Technology in the Information Revolution," Rosalind Williams recounts her experiences as dean of students at the Massachusetts Institute of Technology during that institution's transition from a set of internally generated, ad hoc administrative computing systems to one supplied by a commercial vendor, SAP.[10] Williams noted that MIT faculty and administrators felt powerless to shape, much less resist, the administrative model embodied in the new software. Such feelings of powerlessness might be understandable elsewhere, but MIT faculty are supposed to be the masters of new technology—they are the ones who create the science and engineering that underpin SAP's products. How could *they* be powerless?

A close reading of Williams's essay reveals that MIT faculty and staff were not exactly passive consumers of SAP R/3. They may have conformed to the software's rigid structure, but not without a fight. The final implementation of this "reengineering," as it was called, was much more than a simple top-down process. Is that not a refutation of the notion that increases in semiconductor density drive society? If one looked instead at a liberal arts college, less technologically savvy than MIT, would the deterministic nature of computing assert itself more strongly?

Williams used her own institution and her own role as a dean as data points (although she did exclaim "There must be an easier way to do research").[11] I propose that we do the same: look not at other people and institutions but rather at ourselves, historians of technology who live and work in a digital environment and who assert the right to criticize the blind acceptance of the products of the information age. How do we, as individuals, handle the consequences of Moore's law?

I begin with the ground on which we stand—or, more accurately, the chairs in which we sit. We spend our days in offices, staring into computer screens, using software provided by corporations such as Microsoft, Adobe, AOL, Novell, Lotus. We do not design or build the hardware or write the software, nor do we have more than a rudimentary notion of how to repair either when something breaks. "Wizards" install new applications for us; we insert a disk and press "Enter." The computer recognizes when a new device is attached, a process called "plug and play." How far removed this is from the days when many of us used jacks, wrenches, screwdrivers, and other tools to replace broken or worn parts on our cars, reinstalled everything, tested it, and then drove off![12]

We are trying to have it both ways. We pass critical and moral judgment on Harry Truman for his decision to use atomic bombs against Japan, we criticize a museum for showing, out of context, the aircraft that carried the first bomb, yet we ignore our inability to exert more than a smidgen of control over technologies that affect—determine—our daily lives.[13] In her recent book *User Error,* Ellen Rose, a professor of education and multimedia at the University of New Brunswick, writes that when it comes to software people uncritically accept technology without regard to its context or social dimension.[14] This time the villains are not Harry Truman, the Air Force Association, or senior management at the Smithsonian. We are responsible. Historians of technology find determinism distasteful. Yet we validate it every day.

Consider the tools that I and my colleagues used when I began my career as a historian of technology and a teacher:

> 16 mm movies
> Triplicate 3″ × 5″ library cards (author, title, subject)
> 5″ × 8″ note cards, some with edge notches sorted by a knitting needle
> 35 mm film camera, producing color slides or 8″ × 10″ black-and-white prints
> Blackboard and chalk
> Cassette tape recorder
> Drafting table, for producing hand-drawn maps and charts
> Hewlett-Packard pocket calculator

Microfilm
Mimeograph machine
Overhead transparencies, hand drawn on the fly during a lecture
Photocopier
Preprints or offprints of published papers
Telephone, rotary dial, leased from AT&T
Typed letters, sent through U.S. mail
Typewriter, manual

Now consider the tool set we use today in our daily work of teaching, researching, and writing. This list is based on an informal look around my own office and at nearby universities in Maryland and Virginia where I have taught or lectured. For convenience I divide it into software and hardware. Strictly speaking only hardware obeys Moore's law, but in practice the advances in semiconductor technology allow for more and more complex software products, so both lists are appropriate.

Hardware	Software
Blackberry or PDA	JPEG image files
Compact disks	PDF files (plus Adobe Reader)
Cell phone	Electronic mail
Digital camera	Instant messaging or chat
DSL or cable modem	Groupware (Lotus Notes or Microsoft Outlook)
DVD player	
GPS receiver	Adobe Photoshop
MP3 player	Microsoft Excel
Laptop computer	Microsoft PowerPoint
Desktop personal computer	Microsoft Word
Scanner, with digitizing software	Worldwide Web browser
Sony MiniDisc recorder	Amazon.com
VoIP telephone	Blackboard.com
Wireless ethernet (Wi-Fi) networking device	Blogs
	Google
	HTML documents
	JSTOR
	Listservs, Usenet, or similar discussion groups
	ProQuest on-line newspaper retrieval
	QuickTime Virtual Reality
	Turnitin.com

I have probably left some out. Few readers will be enthusiastic users of every device or program or service listed on the previous page (though some will be). But I have made my point: Moore's law is at work.

Every three years, as chip capacity quadruples, a new generation of electronic products appears, along with new versions of existing software or new software products. Six years from now probably half the devices in my list of current hardware will be superseded. We see Moore's law at work in the progression of personal computer system software from CP/M to MS-DOS to Windows in its numerous versions, each integrating more and more functions (and triggering antitrust actions, to little avail). We see it, too, in the progression of personal computers, laptops, cell phones, digital cameras, MP3 players, and other devices far more powerful than the computer that accompanied Neil Armstrong, Michael Collins, and Buzz Aldrin to the Moon in 1969.[15]

It is this progression that drives the current relationship between culture and technology. Right now, many of us are abandoning film for digital photography. For those of us who took pleasure in working in a darkroom, this transition is painful. Do we have a choice? I vividly remember getting a pocket calculator and putting away my beloved slide rule.[16] It was a conscious decision that I made with an appreciation of its cultural implications. But who thinks about the wholesale transition to digital technology? Ellen Rose argues that we adopt these things en masse, without questioning them. And if we do not question them, we are at the mercy of those who produce and sell them to us. How can we espouse theories of the social shaping of technology when our daily interaction with technology is driven to such a great extent by the push of engineering?

This phenomenon seems, furthermore, without regard for the themes of gender, race, and class to which historians of technology have devoted so much attention. This journal, for example, has published an excellent study of women's involvement with programming early computers.[17] The popular press carries almost daily reports on, for example, how technologies such as the cell phone are used in less-developed countries lacking extensive wired phone infrastructure, how such technologies are differently adopted in various developed countries, how such devices are manufactured in Asia, or the outsourcing of software production to countries like India.

These are second-order examples of social construction. Silicon Valley firms frequently introduce products that fail in the marketplace, and the consumer plays a role in that process. Race, class, and gender factor into consumers' decisions. But transistor density and memory capacity never stop growing. The MIT faculty may balk at implementing a particular data-base product, but not at the doubling of chip capacity every eighteen months. It is a prerequisite for employment at MIT, Microsoft, or in Silicon Valley that one buy into the perpetuation of Moore's law. People who do not believe it must find work elsewhere.

Is this belief, then, an indication of the social construction of computing? I think not. Rather, it is an indication of the reality of technological determinism. Computing power must increase because it can.

POWERPOINT

In an earlier version of this essay I examined the debate over Microsoft PowerPoint as a possible refutation of the thesis of determinism. Many scholars have criticized this program. Edward Tufte, the well-known author of books on the visual presentation of information, is especially harsh, arguing that PowerPoint "elevates format over content, betraying an attitude of commercialism that turns everything into a sales pitch."[18] Vint Cerf, coinventor of the Internet protocols, prefers old-fashioned overhead transparencies and typically begins his public talks with the admonition, "Power corrupts; PowerPoint corrupts absolutely." For Cerf it is more of an apology; at most conferences he is the only speaker who does not use the program.[19] Originally I intended to add my own critique, but in the interval between early draft and later revision the debate was flattened by the steamroller of Moore's law. Neither Tufte nor Cerf has made the slightest dent in the adoption of PowerPoint. And if they could not, who can? Two years ago it was still possible to warn scholars not to use PowerPoint. Now that sounds like a crusty old newspaper reporter waxing nostalgic about his old Underwood (and the bottle of bourbon in the top desk drawer).

Comparing PowerPoint to Stalin, as Tufte does, does not advance the debate over technological determinism. Nor will it do to deny determinism because one uses only a fraction of the electronic devices listed above—or even none of them. In a famous and now fairly old essay titled "Why I Am Not Going to Buy a Computer," Wendell Berry raised many of the objections found in more recent critiques, albeit with a succinct eloquence that few can match.[20] One objection not found in many later commentaries that Berry nonetheless advanced was that his wife did the typing for him. That brought him a lot of criticism, of course, but no argument he could have raised would have made a difference. As Ellen Rose points out, even if one writes an essay in longhand, someone else will have to scan or key it into a computer before it can be published.[21] Who is kidding whom? All of these critiques wither before Moore's law. When I was preparing these remarks I found Berry's famous essay not by going to the library and looking for a print copy but by typing the title into Google. The full text came up in seconds. Whether Berry knows or cares that his writings can be found that way, I cannot say. Nor do I know if whoever put the essay onto the Worldwide Web did so with a sense of irony. It does not matter. That is how one retrieves information nowadays.

A common method by which scholars communicate today is via Microsoft Word files attached to e-mail messages. Most publishers and publications (including this journal) ask that manuscripts be submitted as e-mail attachments. Microsoft Word has its flaws; most of us who use it, for example, have encountered instances where the font suddenly changes, randomly, for no apparent reason.[22] Word is also a voracious consumer of memory, but thanks to Moore's law that does not matter. Attaching Word files to e-mail is simple and it works, and so the practice is ubiquitous. I compare it to the 4′8½″ railroad gauge, which experts say is slightly narrower than the optimum, in terms of engineering efficiency. That drawback is overshadowed by the virtue of being a standard.[23] But remember that the encoding of text in Word is controlled by Microsoft, and Microsoft has the right to change the code according to its needs—not ours. Indeed, Microsoft has done so in the past, and we may assume that it will do so again.[24] The same holds true of another "standard" now taking hold, Adobe's Portable Document Format (PDF). PDF files also take up a lot of memory, but that is not the problem. The coding of these files is owned by Adobe, not by the person who wrote the words or created the document. Before reading such a file, we have to look at a page of dense legalese that states that we "accept" whatever terms of use Adobe wants us to accept (I have never read it).

One response to these concerns is to adopt "open source" programs that do what Word and Acrobat do but run under some other operating system, such as Linux, and adhere to the GNU general public license. Such programs are available and their numbers are increasing. By definition, their source code is available publicly, without charge, and cannot ever come under the control of a private entity.[25] Users are encouraged to modify the software to fit their needs. The historian who learns how to write open-source code would be the present-day counterpart to one who could repair and modify his own automobile in the dim past.

But can open-source software refute the thesis that historians have no ability to control the pace of digital technology? Thus far, the number of historians of technology who use these programs is miniscule. Perhaps open source will prevail, but the movement is mature and yet has not had much effect on us.

AN INTERNAL LOGIC AT WORK

Historians need to be cautious when predicting the future—or, for that matter, assessing the present. Using ourselves as data points, as I (like Rosalind Williams) have done, is also dangerous. Yet the data are there, and it would be foolish to ignore our own actions. Readers interested in critiques of the pace of digital technology besides the ones cited here can find a range of studies.[26] I have not dwelled more on them because, like everything else, they have had no effect on Moore's law. For the same reason, I do not offer this essay as yet another critique of digitization. My goal is more modest: to ask that we step back from a social constructionist view of technology and consider that, in at least one instance, raw technological determinism is at work. Only then can we begin to make intelligent observations about the details of this process. Ross Bassett's *To the Digital Age* is one such study. There ought to be many more, and they ought to address the question of why the exponential advance of computer power is so impervious to social, economic, or political contexts.

I do not deny that the digital world we inhabit is socially constructed. I am reminded of it every time I observe the celebrity status afforded to Steve Jobs—who, by the way, was not an engineer. Biographies of individuals like Jobs tell how they willed the future into being through the strength of their personalities. One must read these biographies with care, but their arguments are valid. Studying the history of computing in the context of social, political, and economic forces makes sense. It identifies us as like-minded thinkers who do not embrace every new gadget. But if we assert the right to look at technology that way, we must also recognize that in at least one case, Moore's law, an internal logic is at work, and that it is based on old-fashioned hardware engineering that an earlier generation of historians once celebrated.

Notes

1. My review appeared in the October 2004 issue of this journal, *Technology and Culture* 45 (2004): 892–93.

2. A variant, in which PNP-type transistors alternate with NPN types, is called "complementary MOS," or CMOS, and has the advantage of requiring very little power.

3. Gordon E. Moore, "Cramming More Components onto Integrated Circuits," *Electronics*, 19 April 1965, 114–17.

4. The mathematical relationship described by Moore is $n = 2^{((y - 1959) \div d)}$, where n is the number of circuits on a chip, y is the current year, and d is the doubling time, in years. For a doubling time of eighteen months, or $d = 1.5$, this equation predicts chip densities of about one billion in 2005. Chips with that density are not yet available commercially as far as I know, but are being developed in laboratories.

5. For early discussions on this topic among the principals, see Gordon E. Moore, "Progress in Digital Integrated Electronics" (paper presented at the International Electronic Devices Meeting, Washington, D.C., 1–3 December 1975, technical digest 11–13); Robert N. Noyce, "Microelectronics," *Scientific American* 237 (September 1977): 65.

6. See, for example, Stephen H. Cutchffe and Robert C. Post, eds., *In Context: History and the History of Technology—Essays in Honor of Melvin Kranzberg* (Bethlehem, Pa., 1989).

7. See, for example, Merritt Roe Smith and Leo Marx, eds., *Does Technology Drive History? The Dilemma of Technological Determinism* (Cambridge, Mass., 1994).

8. For example, Donald MacKenzie and Judy Wajcman, eds., *The Social Shaping of Technology,* 2nd ed. (Buckingham, 1999); Wiebe Bijker, Thomas P. Hughes, and Trevor Pinch, eds., *The Social Construction of Technological Systems* (Cambridge, Mass., 1987).

9. Mel Kranzberg, "The Newest History: Science and Technology," *Science,* 11 May 1962, 463–68.

10. Rosalind Williams, "All That Is Solid Melts into Air: Historians of Technology in the Information Revolution," *Technology and Culture* 41 (2000): 641–68. See also her more recent book, *Retooling: A Historian Confronts Technological Change* (Cambridge, Mass., 2002).

11. Williams, "All That Is Solid," 641.

12. I can no longer make such repairs, as the engine and basic components of the car I now drive are inaccessible. Its ignition, fuel, brake, and other systems are all heavily computerized.

13. Robert C. Post, "A Narrative for Our Time: The *Enola Gay* 'and after that, period,'" *Technology and Culture* 45 (2004): 373–95. But see also his "No Mere Technicalities: How Things Work and Why It Matters," *Technology and Culture* 40 (1999): 607–22, which expresses Post's concerns about the way historians of technology react to claims that "life without technology isn't an option."

14. Ellen Rose, *User Error: Resisting Computer Culture* (Toronto, 2003).

15. The Apollo Guidance Computer had a read-write memory capacity of two thousand sixteen-bit words, or four thousand bytes. See the History of Recent Science and Technology project web pages

for the Apollo Guidance Computer, http://hrst.mit.edu/hrs/apollo/public/, accessed July 2005.

16. The calculator was a Hewlett-Packard HP-25C. The letter "C" meant that it used CMOS chips, novel at that time.

17. Jennifer S. Light, "When Computers Were Women," *Technology and Culture* 40 (1999): 455–83.

18. Edward Tufte, "Power Corrupts: PowerPoint Corrupts Absolutely," *Wired,* September 2003, 118–19; also Ian Parker, "Absolute Power-Point," *New Yorker,* 28 May 2001, 86–87.

19. This is the title of Tufte's article cited above, of course, but I heard Cerf use the phrase on the two occasions when we were on the same program as speakers; we were the only two who did not use PowerPoint.

20. The essay was published in print in various places, but I found it on the Worldwide Web at http://www.tipiglen.dircon.co.uk/berrynot.html (accessed July 2005).

21. Rose (n. 14, on previous page), 175. She is referring to Neil Postman, who proudly claimed that he wrote all his work by hand.

22. This happened to me as I was preparing this essay.

23. George W. Hilton, *American Narrow Gauge Railroads* (Stanford, Calif., 1990).

24. And this does not address the question whether one can still read the disk on which a document was stored.

25. Paul Ceruzzi, "A War on Two Fronts: The U.S. Justice Department, Open Source, and Microsoft, 1995–2000," *Iterations,* an on-line journal, http://www.cbi.umn.edu/iterations/ceruzzi.html (accessed July 2005). Among colleagues in SHOT, I note that Bryan Pffafenberger, of the University of Virginia, uses open source software. At home I use several open-source programs, but my employer in general does not allow them at work. GNU, a recursive acronym for "GNU's Not UNIX," is, among other things, an open-source operating system.

26. The best are written by computer-industry insiders. See, for example, Clifford Stoll, *Silicon Snake Oil: Second Thoughts on the Information Superhighway* (New York, 1996); Ben Shneiderman, *Leonardo's Laptop: Human Needs and the New Computing Technologies* (Cambridge, Mass., 2003); Steve Talbott, *The Future Does Not Compute* (Sebastopol, Calif., 1995); Thomas K. Landauer, *The Trouble with Computers: Usefulness, Usability, and Productivity* (Cambridge, Mass., 1995); Donald A. Norman, *The Invisible Computer: Why Good Products, Fail the Personal Computer Is So Complex, and Information Appliances Are the Solution* (Cambridge, Mass., 1998).

Biographical Note

PAUL CERUZZI is curator of aerospace electronics and computing at the Smithsonian's National Air and Space Museum. A second edition of his book *A History of Modern Computing* appeared in 2004.

CHAPTER 19

■■■

Case Studies of Most Common and Severe Types of Software System Failure

Sandeep Dalal[1]
Department of Computer Science and Applications
Maharshi Dayanand University, Rohtak

Dr. Rajender Singh Chhillar[2]
Department of Computer Science and Applications
Maharshi Dayanand University, Rohtak

ABSTRACT

Today a software system is an integral part of each and every business model, be it core product manufacturing, banking, healthcare, insurance, aviation, hospitality, social networking, shopping, e-commerce, education or any other domain. If any business has to be leveraged and simplified then software has to be integrated with the main stream business of any organization. Designing and development of any software system requires huge capital, a lot of time, intellectuals, domain expertise, tools and infrastructure. Though the software industry has matured quite a lot in the past decade, the percentage of software failure has also increased, which led to the loss of capital, time, good-will, loss of information, and in some cases severe failures of critical applications also lead to the loss of lives. Software could fail due to faults injected in various stages of software or product development life cycle starting from project initiation until deployment. This paper describes the case study of most common and severe types of software system failures in the Software Industry.

INTRODUCTION

Every organization starts a project with intent of deploying it successfully to perform the function specified by the client or as required by the business; however, there are reasons that this goal of the organization is not achieved due to some faults which later result in failures. This could happen due to inappropriate project initiation, planning, monitoring and control, execution or deployment of the software system. In bigger projects each phase of the product is considered to be a project, for example "requirement analysis, elicitation and validation" could be considered a project which would give feed to later stages of product development. So this is not a wrong statement to say that software failure could happen at any stage of software product development.[1,3] The software failure term is generally used when the software doesn't perform its intended function or crashes after deployment. This paper intends to study the most recent case studies pertaining to most common and severe software failures. Later in this paper we will analyze and conclude the common reason of software failures.

Software System Failure

A software system is any software product or application supporting any business. A software system could be defined as a system of intercommunicating components based on software forming part of a computer system (a combination of hardware and software). It "consists of a number of separate programs, configuration files, which are used to set up these programs, system documentation, which describes the structure of the system, and user documentation, which explains how to use the system." According to Laprie et al.,[12] "A system failure occurs when the delivered service no longer complies with the specifications, the latter being an agreed description of the system's expected function and/or service." This definition applies to both hardware and software system failures.

Focus Area of Study

A recent survey[6,7] of 800 IT managers says that 62% of total software fails, which is true. 49% of software suffered budget overruns, 47% had higher than expected maintenance costs and 41% failed to deliver the expected business value and ROI. Few software designers while designing ever thought of considering the requirements which cause threats and failures later in the stage at the time of utilizing the product for example—information security, hacking, virus threats, scaling up to the level of usage, maintainability and performance. Software projects fail for various reasons from all the domains and technologies. So this paper would consider case studies showing threats, risks and failure of software systems supporting nation security, banking and financial analysis application, aviation, medical and social networking applications which are used globally.

COMMON AND SEVERE FAILURES

Those failures which impact the lives of people or result in huge loss of capital are considered to be the most severe. The severity or impact of fault is determined on the basis of various parameters like

- **a** Number of users of the application
- **b** Involvement of monetary transactions.
- **c** Type of use of application like—Home use, National security or defense, space, missile and satellite, aviation related app, etc.
- **d** Could the application impact the lives of people if it fails.

Severity of failure could be amplified if any of the parameters mentioned above are touched by application. There could be other daily use application which could lead to discomfort if they don't function appropriately. Such applications could be any online shopping app, ticket booking app, emails, chat server, gaming and entertainment app and social networking sites. Such applications experience most common and frequent failures. Most frequent failures include non-functional issues with the application which adds uneasiness and embarrassment. These are generally home use applications. Such failures could be any of these:

- **a** Slow response from application server.
- **b** Pages are not downloading properly
- **c** Application is not compatible with the browser
- **d** Performance issues like slow access time, load time, run time.

"Electricity lets us heat our homes, cook our food, and enjoy security and entertainment. It also can kill you if you're not careful."

—"Energy Notes" (Flyer sent with San Diego Gas & Electric utility bills.)

We trust our lives to technology every day. We trust older, non-computer technologies every time we step into an elevator, a car, or a building. As the tools and technologies we use become more complex and more interconnected, the amount of damage that results from an individual disruption or failure increases, and we sometimes pay the costs in dramatic and tragic events. If a person, out for a walk, bumps into another person, neither is likely to be hurt. If both are driving cars at 60 miles per hour, they could be killed. If two jets collide, or one loses an engine, several hundred people could be killed.[8,10] Most new technologies were not very safe when first developed. If the death rate from commercial airline accidents in the U.S. were the same now as it was 50 years ago, 8,000 people would die in plane crashes each year. In some early polio vaccines, the virus was not totally inactivated. The vaccines caused polio in some children. We learn how to make improvements. We discover and solve problems. Scientists and engineers study disasters and learn how to prevent them and how to recover from them.

Learn from Failures

If American Airlines had installed GPWS (the system that warns pilots if they are headed toward a mountain) on the plane that crashed near Cali, Colombia, in 1995, they would have saved many lives. This crash triggered adoption of the GPWS. No commercial U.S. airliner has crashed into a mountain since then. Similarly, a disastrous fire led to the development of hydrants—a way to get water at the scene from the water pipes under the street. Automobile engineers used to design the front of an automobile to be extremely rigid, to protect passengers in a crash. But people died and suffered serious injuries because the car frame transmitted the force of a crash to the people. The engineers learned it was better to build cars with "crumple zones" to absorb the force of impact. Software engineering textbooks use the Cali crash as an example so that future software specialists will not repeat the mistakes in the plane's computer system.

We learn what has happened to the safety record in other technologies. The number of deaths from motor vehicle accidents in the U.S. declined from 54,633 in 1970 to roughly 42,600 in 2006 (while population and the number of cars, of course, increased). One significant factor is increased education about responsible use (i.e., the campaign against drunk driving). Another is devices that protect people when the system fails (seat belts and airbags). Yet another is systems that help avoid accidents (many of which, like airbags, use microprocessors). Examples of the latter include rear-view cameras that help drivers avoid hitting a child when backing up and night vision systems that detect obstacles and project onto the windshield an image or diagram of objects in the car's path. Yet another is electronic stability systems. These systems have sensors that detect a likely rollover, before the driver is aware of the problem, and electronically slow the engine. As use of technology, automation, and computer systems has increased in virtually all work places, the risk of dying in an on-the-job accident dropped from 39 among 100,000 workers (in 1934) to four in 100,000 in 2004. Risk is not restricted to technology and machines, it is a part of life. We are safer if we know the risks and take reasonable precautions. We are never 100% safe.

CASE STUDIES

In this section we have discussed some most common and severe types of software system failure case studies.

Case Study 1

This case study focuses on the ERP project failure in Jordan which is a developing nation. The design—reality gap model applied to a case study of partial ERP failure in a Jordanian manufacturing firm. The model analyses the situation both before and during ERP implementation.[11] It finds sizeable gaps between the assumptions and requirements built into the ERP system design, and the actual realities of the client organisation. It is these gaps and the failure to close them during implementation that underlies project failure. ERP systems are failing in developing countries. ERP (Enterprise resource planning) systems integrate financial systems, HR, logistics, and data systems across the organizations to save

TABLE 19.1. List of Some Most Common and Severe Types of Software System Failures

Software	Failure Description	Casualties
1. ERP project failure in Jordan	It finds sizeable gaps between the assumptions and requirements built into the ERP system design, and the actual realities of the client organisation	Huge loss of capital and unsatisfied clients.
2. Ariane 5	Ariane 5, Europe's newest unmanned rocket, was unintentionally destroyed seconds after launch on its maiden flight. Also destroyed was its cargo of four scientific satellites to study how the Earth's magnetic field interacts with solar winds.	10 years hard work and $100 million loss. Reputation of ESA (European Space Agency) deteriorated.
3. Therac-25	Canada's Therac-25 radiation therapy machine malfunctioned and delivered lethal radiation doses to patients	Many people dead. Many people critically injured.
4. STS-126	A software change had inadvertently shifted data in the shuttle's flight software code	"In-flight" software anomalies occurred and several automated functions failed.
5. Automated airport baggage handling (DIA)	Failure to anticipate the number of carts correctly resulted in delays in picking up bags that would undermine the system's performance goal.	Monthly maintenance cost exceeded the monthly manual investment.

money and improve decision making and customer retention. These are increasingly being used by organizations in developing nations.

Success and Failure Factors

There are few outcome elements which decide if ERP implementation is a success or failure, for example—System and Information Quality, Use and user satisfaction, Individual impact which relates to the extent to which information produced by system influences or affects the management decisions, and Organization impact which measures the effect of the information produced by the system on organizational performance. The model used for deciding success or failure is DeLone and McLean's model. It provides an appropriate framework for data gathering, analysis and presentation in relation to the outcome of an ERP project; and a framework that can be integrated easily with Heeks' three-way outcome categorisation of total failure, partial failure, and success in order to provide a final classification.

Gap analysis is done on the design and real system implemented and the analysis of gap tells that it is a failure.

Loss

It involves huge loss of capital and non-satisfaction of the client. This would also not at all solve the purpose of getting ERP software. The ignorant client remains in dark and never gets the business up to the mark with no appropriate decision making.

Case Study 2

On June 4, 1996 at 12:33 GMT (UTC), the European Space Agency launched a new rocket, Ariane 5, on its maiden unmanned flight. Ariane exploded after 40 seconds of its lift-off. Although this was an unmanned flight and therefore there were no human casualties, there is no reason to expect that the outcome would have been any different if the flight had been manned. In such an event all onflight crew and passengers would have been killed. Remember as we proceed through this case that this was a project of the very experienced European Space Agency.[1] The project cost was $7 billion. Part of the payload were four satellites, Cluster, that would engage in a scientific investigation. These satellites had taken many years to develop and cost around $100 million. They were irreplaceable.

In a report, James Gleick has said:

It took the European Space Agency (ESA) 10 years and $7 billion to produce Ariane 5, a giant rocket capable of hurling a pair of three-ton satellites into orbit with each launch and intended to give Europe overwhelming supremacy in the commercial space business. All it took to explode that rocket less than a minute into its maiden voyage last June, scattering fiery rubble across the mangrove swamps of French Guiana, was a small computer program trying to stuff a 64-bit number into a 16-bit space. One bug, one crash. Of all the careless lines of code recorded in the annals of computer science, this one may stand as the most devastatingly efficient.

The purpose of Ariane 5 was to deliver satellite to space. It was an improved version of Ariane 4. Control System of Ariane 5 was composed of:

- An inertial reference system (SRI)
- An On-Board Computer (OBC)

SRI of Ariane 5 is the same as the one in Ariane 4. Ariane 5 failed due to SRI software exception caused due to a data conversion. At the time of the failure, the software in the SRI was doing a data conversion from 64-bit floating point to 16-bit integer. The floating point number had a value greater than could be represented by a 16-bit signed integer; this resulted in an overflow software exception. It was actually a reuse error. The SRI horizontal bias module was reused from 10-year-old software, the software from Ariane 4. But this is not the full story: It is a reuse specification error. The truly unacceptable part is the absence of any kind of precise specification associated with a reusable module. The requirement that the horizontal bias should fit in 16 bits was in fact stated in an obscure part of a document. But in the code itself it was nowhere to be found! The Ariane 5 disaster was a wake-up call for the software engineering community. Proper actions should be taken to ensure such a failure does not occur again.

Case Study 3

Canadian Cancer Therapy Machine (Therac-25, 1986) Designed by Atomic Energy of Canada, Ltd. (AECL): Therac-25 was a software controlled radiation therapy machine used to treat people with cancer. Between 1985 and 1987 Therac-25 machines in four medical centers gave massive overdoses of radiation to six patients. An extensive investigation and report revealed that in some instances operators repeated overdoses because machine display indicated no dose given. Some patients received between 13,000–25,000 rads when 100–200 was needed. The result of the excessive radiation exposure resulted in severe injuries and three patients' deaths.[5]

Causes of the errors were attributed to lapses in good safety design. Specific examples are cited as failure to use safety precautions present in earlier versions, insufficient testing, and that one key resumption was possible despite an error message. The investigation also found calculation errors. For example, the set-up test used a one byte flag variable whose bit value was incremented on each run. When the routine called for the 256th time, there was a flag overflow and a huge electron beam was erroneously turned on.

An extensive investigation showed that although some latent error could be traced back for several years, there was an inadequate system of reporting and investigating accidents that made it hard to determine the root cause. The final investigations report indicates that during real-time operation the software recorded only certain parts of operator input/editing. In addition, the radiation machine required careful reconstruction by a physicist at one of the cancer centres in order to determine what went wrong.

Case Study 4

A few minutes after the Shuttle Endeavour reached orbit for STS-126 on November 14, 2008, mission control noticed that the shuttle did not automatically transfer two communications processes from launch to orbit configuration. Primary communications continued to use S-band frequencies after they should have transferred to the more powerful Ku-band. The link between the shuttle and its payload—the Payload Signal Processor (PSP)—remained configured for a radio link rather than switching automatically to the hardwired umbilical connection.

Fortunately, mission control was able to manually command both the S-band/Ku-band switch and the PSP port shift. While mission control was not able to re-instate automatic transfers during flight, they continued to monitor communications and manually operated necessary transfers for the remainder of the mission. STS-126 completed its mission successfully and returned to earth without further software problems.

While the software problems did not endanger the mission, they caught management's attention because "in-flight" software anomalies on the shuttle are rare. Software goes through rigorous reviews during development and testing to prevent this sort of problem, and most software anomalies are detected and fixed long before the shuttle leaves the ground.

Investigation found that a software change had inadvertently shifted data in the shuttle's flight software code. Because of this build defect, the software did not send configuration commands to the shuttle's Ground Command Interface Logic, and several automated functions failed.

Case Study 5

What was to be the world's largest automated airport baggage handling system, became a classic story in how technology projects can go wrong. Faced with the need for greater airport capacity, the city of Denver elected to construct a new state of the art airport that would cement Denver's position as an air transportation hub. Covering a land area of 140 Km^2, the airport was to be the largest in the United States and have the capacity to handle more than 50m passengers annually.[9] The airport's baggage handling system was a critical component in the plan. By automating baggage handling, aircraft turnaround time was to be reduced to as little as 30 minutes. Faster turnaround meant more efficient operations and was a cornerstone of the airport's competitive advantage. Despite the good intentions the plan rapidly dissolved as underestimation of the project's complexity resulted in snowballing problems and public humiliation for everyone involved. Thanks mainly to problems with the baggage system, the airport's opening was delayed by a full 16 months. Expenditure to maintain the empty airport and interest charges on construction loans cost the city of Denver $1.1M per day throughout the delay.

The embarrassing missteps along the way included an impromptu demonstration of the system to the media which illustrated how the system crushed bags, disgorged content and how two carts moving at high speed reacted when they crashed into each other.[4] When opening day finally arrived, the system was just a shadow of the original plan. Rather than automating all 3 concourses into one integrated system, the system was used in a single concourse, by a single airline and only for outbound flights. All other baggage handling was performed using simple conveyor belts plus a manual tug and trolley system that was hurriedly built when it became clear that the automated system would never achieve its goals.

Although the remnants of the system soldiered on for 10 years, the system never worked well and in August 2005, United Airlines announced that they would abandon the system completely. The $1 million per month maintenance costs exceeded the monthly cost of a manual tug and trolley system.

System at a Glance

1 88 airport gates in 3 concourses.

2 17 miles of track and 5 miles of conveyor belts.

3 3,100 standard carts 1 450 oversized carts.

4 14 million feet of wiring.

5 Network of more than 100 PCs to control flow of carts.

6 5,000 electric motors.

7 2,700 photo cells, 400 radio receivers and 59 laser arrays.

As with all failures the problems can be viewed from a number of levels. In its simplest form, the Denver International Airport (DIA) project failed because those making key decisions underestimated the complexity involved. As planned, the system was the most complex baggage system ever attempted. Ten times larger than any other automated system, the increased size resulted in an exponential growth in complexity. At the heart of the complexity lay an issue know as "line balancing." To optimize system performance, empty carts had to be distributed around the airport ready to pick up new bags. With more than 100 pickup points (check-in rows and arrival gates) each pickup needed to be fed with enough empty carts to meet its needs. The algorithms necessary to anticipate where empty carts should wait for new bags represented a nightmare in the mathematic modelling of queue behaviours. Failure to anticipate the number of carts correctly would result in delays in picking up bags that would undermine the system's performance goals.

Failure to recognise the complexity and the risk involved contributed to the project being initiated too late. The process of requesting bids for the design and construction of the system was not initiated until summer of 1991. Based on the original project schedule, this left a little over two years for the contracts to be signed and for the system to be designed, built, tested and commissioned. The closest analogous projects were the San Francisco system and one installed in Munich. Although much smaller and simpler, those systems took two years to implement. Given the quantum leap in terms of size and complexity, completing the Denver system in two years was an impossible task.

The underestimation of complexity led to a corresponding underestimation of the effort involved. That underestimation meant that without realising it, the Project Management team had allowed the baggage system to become the airport's critical path. In order to meet the airport's planned opening date, the project needed to be completed in just two years. This clearly was insufficient time and that misjudgement resulted in the project being exposed to massive levels of schedule pressure. Many of the project's subsequent problems were likely a result of (or exacerbated by) shortcuts the team took and the mistakes they made as they tried to meet an impossible schedule.

COMMON CAUSES OF FAILURES

- Lack of clear, well-thought-out goals and specifications.
- Poor management and poor communication among customers, designers, programmers.[13]
- Incorrect steps to reproduce and improper fault assignment.[13]
- Institutional or opinionated pressures that encourage unrealistically low bids, unrealistically low budget requests, and underestimates of time requirements.
- Use of very new technology, with unknown reliability and problems, perhaps for which software developers have insufficient experience and expertise.
- Refusal to recognize or admit that a project is in trouble.

There is a common misconception that increasing reliability will increase safety. Many software-related accidents have occurred despite the software being compliant with the requirements specification. Semantic mismatch is characterized by errors that can be traced to errors in the requirements—what the computer should do is not necessarily consistent with safety and reliability.

CONCLUSION

The analysis of case studies pertaining to common and severe failures depicts that a software failure at any stage could lead to the loss of lives, financial losses, wastage of time, effort and other intangible losses like discomfort, stress, good will, reputation, confidence, peace, etc. In the current information age the application of software has penetrated in each and every industry unlike the traditional approach where software was altogether a separate entity. As software has become an integral part of every product and process, there is a need to make a full proof system so that the software failures could be avoided. There is further requirement of root cause analysis of these software failures to understand the problematic area and suggest the areas of improvement in the current process as several corrective and preventive actions need to be taken while developing products and software systems.

References

1. Gerard Le Lann. "Analysis of the Ariane 5 Flight 501 Failure—A System Engineering Perspective." Proceedings of IEEE Workshop on *Engineering of Computer-Based Systems* (ECBS '97), pp. 339–346.
2. Michael Fagan. "Advances in Software Inspections," *IEEE Transactions on Software Engineering,* Vol. 12, No. 7, July 1986.
3. J. Gray and D. Siewiorek. "High-Availability Computer Systems." *IEEE Computer,* pp. 39–48, Sept. 1991.
4. Case Study—Denver International Airport Baggage Handling System—An illustration of ineffectual decision making. *Calleam Consulting Ltd.—Why Technology Projects Fail,* 2008.
5. Delores R. Wallace and D. Richard Kuhn. "Failure Modes in Medical Device Software: An Analysis of 15 years of Recall Data," *International Journal of Reliability, Quality and Safety Engineering,* Vol. 8, No. 4, 2001.
6. Andreas Zeller and Ralf Hildebrandt. "Simplifying and Isolating Failure–Inducing Input," *IEEE Transactions on Software Engineering,* Vol. 28, No. 2, February 2002.
7. Shull, et al., 2002. "What We Have Learned about Fighting Defects," *Proceedings, Metrics 2002.* IEEE, pp. 249–258.
8. Jim Shore. "Fail Fast," *IEEE Software, September/October 2004,* http://martinfowler.com/ieeeSoftware/failFast.pdf.
9. Dr. R. de Neufville. "The Baggage System at Denver: Prospects and Lessons," *Journal of Air Transport Management,* Vol. 1, No. 4, Dec., pp. 229–236, 1994.
10. Kurt R. Linberg. "Software developer's perceptions about software project failure: a case study," *The Journal of Systems and Software 49*(1999), pp. 177–192.
11. Ala'a Hawari & Richard Heeks. "Explaining ERP Failure in Developing Countries: A Jordanian Case Study," Manchester Centre for Development Informatics Working Paper 45, 2010.
12. J.C. Laprie (ed.). *Dependability: Basic Concepts and Terminology.* Springer-Verlag, Wein, New York, 1992.
13. Sandeep, Dalal & Rajender, Chhillar. Role of Fault Reporting in Existing Software Industry, *CiiT International Journal of Software Engineering,* Vol. 4, No. 7, July 2012.

UNIT 4

Future Trends in Technology

CHAPTER 20

■ ■ ■

Dimensions of Innovation in a Technology-Intensive Economy

John H. Marburger III

The following essay is based on a Keynote Address to the OECD "High Level Meeting of the Committee for Scientific and Technology Policy," Oslo, March 4, 2008, on the topic "Adjusting Policy to New Dimensions in Science, Technology and Innovation." The objective of the talk was to point out the difficulty of linking specific policies to specific measures of successful innovation, while nevertheless identifying broad policy characteristics that foster innovation.

Innovation is a defining human activity. Why it should now be a topic of the greatest interest to policy makers deserves some explanation. Precursors can be seen in an interest in the conditions for promoting "invention" that first appeared well before the industrial revolution, particularly in England, and was an important theme in the rise of America's economic strength through the nineteenth century. Innovation, by almost any definition has been associated with American economic culture for more than two centuries. What is different now? What are the special conditions that have reawakened interest in innovation, and what can we learn from them to enhance this fundamental human activity?

The explosive pace of nineteenth-century innovation, particularly in the United States and Great Britain, continued into the twentieth despite the debilitating impact of global warfare and associated large-scale economic and social disruption in the first half-century. But wars and economic depression took their toll, arguably slowing the application of extraordinary scientific discoveries that began at the turn of the century. As World War II ended, widely disparate patterns of industrial development disadvantaged all but a few nations—primarily the wartime antagonists—in the subsequent cold war period of growing technical innovation. The superpowers emerged from the war convinced of the need for state-supported technical innovation in the name of national security. Arms races, space races, and ideologically based geopolitical competition engendered remarkable innovations through policies that gave little attention to market forces, much too little in the case of centrally planned economies. As the cold war ended, however, the innovation landscape had already begun to rearrange itself in response to four decades of uneasy but relatively stable world-wide economic conditions, fed by a combination of wartime technology and cold war-enhanced innovations funded particularly by the United States, Germany, and Japan. New market-oriented economies emerged in the "Asian Tigers" to seize opportunities created by the rapidly developing information technology, falling transportation costs, and generally cheap energy. The demise of the Soviet Union released new political and economic forces whose effect seems to have been a further rapid globalization of technical capability, leading journalist Tom Friedman to observe famously in 2005 that, when it comes to economic competitiveness, *The World Is Flat.*

As the twenty-first century dawned, the former superpowers struggled to reorient priorities from cold war national security to economic competitiveness. All the older developed nations faced a new reality in which the same forces that powered intense globalization and competition a century earlier were once again in play, but in a vastly expanded international field. From a broad historical perspective, the emphasis on innovation for economic competitiveness is old news. The world is shaking off a near century-long geopolitical pathology that distorted the natural evolution of economic competition among nations, and now we are returning to what looks very much like nineteenth-century competitive conditions. Two features, however, are genuinely new: the number of national players—particularly the hugely populated Asian countries—and the revolution in information technology that is as profound in its effect on world economic conditions as the development of navigation in the sixteenth century or the introduction of powered machinery in the nineteenth. Innovation is just as important for national economic competitiveness today as it was more than a century ago, but globalization and the information revolution add a complexity that perhaps justifies an evolution if not a revolution in innovation policy.

The strongly technical flavor of the information revolution is one of several leading factors in the tendency today to link innovation to science through technology. Others include the widely shared hope that urgent societal problems such as environmental and health impacts of continued population growth may be solved or mitigated by science-driven technologies. It is well to keep in mind, however, that innovation is not necessarily a technical—nor technology a scientific—phenomenon. Linking science, technology, and innovation into an overall policy framework may suggest that we know more about how these activities are related than we really do. This very common linkage implicitly conveys a now discredited linear progression from scientific research to technology creation to innovative products. More nuanced pictures break these complex activities down into components that interact with each other in a multi-dimensional socio-technological-economic network. One analysis of this sort, Donald Stokes' now classic *Pasteur's Quadrant*, offers two dimensions—knowledge-inspired and use-inspired—which intersect in "Pasteur's Quadrant" of use-inspired basic research. More than two dimensions are probably needed to capture the complex modes of research and their interactions.

That technical innovation can be independent of science is amply demonstrated by the history of machinery for textile production in the eighteenth century. The advanced state of patent and copyright law in England compared with other countries gave strong incentives to English inventors and investors, but the newly emerging physical sciences had little impact. Indeed, the first practical weaving machine (patented 1785) was invented by Edmund Cartwright, a minister of the Church of England, poet and book reviewer, who wrote "As I had never before turned my thoughts to anything mechanical, either in theory or in practice, nor had even seen a loom at work, or knew anything of its construction, you will readily suppose that my first loom must have been a most rude piece of machinery." He was motivated by a chance conversation in a public house where a textile expert remarked that no one could ever build a practical weaving machine. According to his own account, Cartwright was inspired by an exhibition in London of "an automaton figure which played at chess." But clearly Cartwright's mind was prepared by his formal education, which included mathematics among the usual classical subjects.

While England's intellectual property laws were important to these innovations, so was the tradition of weaving in Western England that owed much to the displacement of a large population of textile workers from France following the revocation of the Edict of Nantes in 1685. As their industry grew, the means of production changed, not, at first, because of machinery, but because of innovations in the organization of work. The factory system emerged along with, and slightly ahead of, the early machines. It is worth mentioning that American efforts to match the quality of English machine-woven goods failed repeatedly until an experienced English textile plant manager, Samuel Slater, immigrated in 1789, bringing details of the perfected machinery with him. England, of course, had strong laws forbidding transfer of this technology beyond its borders, and Slater had left the country surreptitiously. Industrial espionage, intellectual property theft, and vigorous patent litigation were constant features of the industrial revolution, as they are today.

I mean these tales from history to illustrate components of the complex innovation ecology that are familiar to us today: an effective legal regime of intellectual property protection, an immigration policy that welcomes skilled workers, availability of investment capital, attention to the organization and management of work, and the prospect of profit from one's ingenuity. These are not exactly science policies, and they are not entirely technology policies. They are innovation policies, and they were clearly important factors in the early lead established by both America and Great Britain in the industrialization of the nations that dominated global trade and manufacturing by the end of the nineteenth century.

Science did eventually become an important source of inspiration and guidance to new technologies that supported broad innovation. Among technical innovators at the turn of the century those best prepared to benefit from advanced science had been educated in Europe. American science grew rapidly during the twentieth century, but remained weak in theoretical subjects that would become so important during and after World War II. This weakness was repaired by an influx of brilliant scientists from Europe during the middle third of the century, propelled by a dreadful intolerance not unlike that which drove France's textile workers to England two and a half centuries earlier.

Science feeds technology in two different modes: it delivers novel empirically-rooted phenomena that might lead to a technology platform that supports broad innovations, and it provides theoretical tools and methods that assist engineering analysis and design. The discovery and development of quantum mechanics in the interval between the world wars made it possible to trace the origin (if not the detailed understanding) of nearly all technically important physical phenomena up to that time *and thereafter*. This aspect of completeness in the relevant physical sciences is not widely appreciated, but that is what makes it possible to direct "basic" research into areas likely to be important in applications. It is possible today to identify areas of "basic" science in which investigations are likely to produce socially relevant results. This is what makes "Pasteur's Quadrant" a real option for guiding national investments in research. Many scientists complain that "directed basic research" is an oxymoron because no one can know in advance what useful thing might be discovered in a laboratory. That is true in a more narrow sense than scientists usually admit. Surely no one expected that monatomic layers of graphene could be manufactured by peeling with Scotch Tape, a 2004 observation that won its discoverers a Nobel prize in 2010. But scientists knew thin layers of carbon would likely have technical applications. The research may have been "curiosity driven," but the researchers did not choose graphene randomly for their subject. They were arguably working in Pasteur's Quadrant despite their disregard of particular applications.

What about the "pure" research (Bohr's Quadrant)? Does work on cosmology or string theory have any relevance for innovation? Bohr himself, a founding father of quantum mechanics, deployed his remarkable theory of atomic structure to elucidate the eminently useful periodic table of chemical elements. That was in 1921. Today we know quantum theory is the most well-verified physical theory ever constructed, and no one expects its predictions of human scale phenomena will fail in the future. The frontiers of size and energy where cosmology and string theory lie are far beyond any phenomenon of human relevance. And yet, our ability to probe these frontiers is limited by technology. Two things are interesting about innovative technologies for basic research. First, the drivers of technology at the frontiers are not the same as those societal necessities that are the typical mothers of invention. Direct attacks on any problem are likely to lead to incremental advances. Research at the technology-limited frontier of "pure" science can produce "out of the box" advances unlike anything motivated directly by practical problems. The second interesting thing is that basic science attracts very bright young people whose passion for discovery is uncannily powerful. The combination of "out of the box" technical needs and exceptionally motivated innovators can lead to profoundly novel innovations.

In the 1990s particle physicists at Columbia University struggled to calculate implications of a theory of strong nuclear forces (QCD) that presents formidable computational challenges. Existing computer architectures were too inefficient, so they designed a microprocessor specifically for "lattice gauge calculations." When they consulted IBM engineers to help optimize the design, the engineers saw in it the possibility of an entirely new and broadly useful architecture that they rapidly incorporated in a new generation of computers. In 2004 the new machine, "Blue Gene/L," recovered the "world's fastest supercomputer" title from Japan's NEC "Earth Simulator" that had been introduced with much fanfare only 2 years before. And it was a particle physicist at CERN who famously created an approach to using the Internet, the World Wide Web, that solved a technical need, but also transformed the Internet from a specialist tool to an extraordinary technology platform that has supported a new universe of innovations.

Necessity is said to be the mother of invention, but in all human societies "necessity" is a mix of culturally conditioned perceptions and the actual physical necessities of life. The concept of need, of what is wanted, is the ultimate driver of markets and an essential dimension of innovation. And as the example of the World Wide Web shows, need is very difficult to identify before it reveals itself in a mass movement. Today, the generation of perceived need is itself a matter of innovation. Innovation has this chicken-and-egg quality that makes it extremely hard to analyze. We all know of visionaries who conceive of a society totally transformed by their invention, and who are bitter that the world has not embraced their idea. Sometimes we think of them as crackpots, or simply unrealistic about what it takes to change the world. We practical people necessarily view the world through the filter of what exists and fail to anticipate disruptive change. Nearly always we are surprised by the rapid acceptance of a transformative idea. If we truly want to encourage innovation through government policies, we are going to have to come to grips with this deep unpredictability of the mass acceptance of a new concept. Works analyzing this phenomenon are widely popular under titles like *The Tipping Point* by Malcolm Gladwell or more recently the book by N.N. Taleb called *The Black Swan*, among others.

The innovations of interest to us here are those that become integrated into economies. What causes them to be adopted depends on their ability to satisfy some perceived need by consumers, and that perception may be an artifact of marketing, or fashion, or cultural inertia, or ignorance. Some of the largest and most profitable industries in the developed world—entertainment, automobiles, clothing and fashion accessories, health products, children's toys, grownups' toys!—depend on perceptions of need that go far beyond the utilitarian and are notoriously difficult to predict. And yet, these industries clearly depend on sophisticated and rapidly advancing technologies to compete in the marketplace. But they do not depend only upon technology. Technologies are part of the environment for innovation, or in a popular and very appropriate metaphor—part of the *innovation ecology*.

This complexity of innovation and its ecology is conveyed in Chapter One of a currently popular best-seller in the U.S. called *"Innovation Nation"* by the American innovation guru, John Kao, formerly on the faculty of the Harvard Business School:

"I define it [innovation]," writes Kao, "as the ability of individuals, companies, and entire nations to continuously create their desired future. Innovation depends on harvesting knowledge from a range of disciplines besides science and technology, among them design, social science, and the arts. And it is exemplified by more than just products; services, experiences, and processes can be innovative as well. The work of entrepreneurs, scientists, and software geeks alike contributes to innovation. It is also about the middlemen who know how to realize value from ideas. Innovation flows from shifts in mind-set that can generate new business models, recognize new opportunities, and weave innovations throughout the fabric of society. It is about new ways of doing and seeing things as much as it is about the breakthrough idea."

This is not your standard OECD-type definition. Gurus, of course, do not have to worry about leading indicators and predictive measures of policy success. Nevertheless some policy guidance can be drawn from this high level "definition," and I will do so later.

The first lesson to be drawn from these examples is that the *structural* aspects of "science, technology, and innovation" are imperfectly defined, complex, and poorly understood. There is still much work to do to identify measures, develop models, and test them against actual experience before we can say we really know what it takes to foster innovation. There is a second lesson about the *temporal* aspects: all three of these complex activities are changing with time. Science of course always changes through the accumulation of knowledge, but it also changes through revolutions in its theoretical structure, through its ever-improving technology, and through its evolving sociology. Technology has its own intrinsic time scales, both long and short as it exploits the available science and builds out infrastructure like roads and power grids that enable a host of short-lived applications. Today, the pace of change in both science and technology is strongly impacted by the rapidly changing information technology.

An important contributor to the unpredictable temporal quality of innovation is the increasing role of market forces in making technology accessible. Technology today often flows from research and development laboratories but the ability of technology to influence both science and innovation depends strongly on its *commercial* adoption. Commercial-scale manufacturing drives down the costs of technology so it can be exploited in an ever-broadening range of applications by an ever-broadening community of innovators. The mass market for precision electromechanical devices like cameras, printers, and disk drives is the basis for new scientific instrumentation and also for further generations of products that integrate hundreds of existing components in new devices and business models like the Apple iPod and video games, not to mention improvements in old products like cars and telephones. Innovation is changing too as it expands its scope beyond individual products to include all or parts of systems such as supply chains, and inventory control, as in the Wal-Mart phenomenon. Apple's iPod does not stand alone; it is integrated with iTunes software and novel arrangements with media providers.

With one exception, however, technology changes more slowly than it appears because we encounter basic technology platforms in a wide variety of relatively short-lived products. Technology is like a language that innovators use to express concepts in the form of products and business models that serve (and sometimes create) a variety of needs, some of which fluctuate with fashion. The exception to the illusion of rapid technology change is the pace of information technology, which is no illusion. It has fulfilled Moore's Law for more than half a century, and it is a remarkable historical anomaly arising from the systematic exploitation of the understanding of the behavior of microscopic matter following the discovery of quantum mechanics. The pace would be much less without a continually evolving market for the succession of smaller and higher capacity products. It is not at all clear that the market demand will continue to support the increasingly expensive investment in fabrication equipment for each new step up the exponential curve of Moore's Law. The science is probably available to allow many more capacity doublings if markets can sustain them.

I worry about the psychological impact of the rapid advance of information technology. I believe it has created unrealistic expectations about all technologies and has encouraged a somewhat casual attitude among policy makers toward the capability of science and technology to deliver solutions to difficult social problems. This is certainly true of what may be the greatest technical challenge of all time—the delivery of energy to large developed and developing populations without adding greenhouse gases to the atmosphere. The challenge of sustainable energy technology is much more difficult than many people currently seem to appreciate. I am afraid that time will make this clear.

Structural complexities and the intrinsic dynamism of science and technology pose challenges to policy makers, but they seem almost manageable compared with the challenges posed by extrinsic forces. Among these are the complex processes of globalization and the impact of global economic development on the environment. The latter, expressed quite generally through the concept of "sustainability" is likely to be a component of much twenty-first-century innovation policy. Measures of development, competitiveness, and innovation need to include sustainability dimensions to be realistic over the long run. Development policies that destroy economically important environmental systems, contribute to harmful global change, and undermine the natural resource basis of the economy are bad policies. Sustainability is now an international issue because the scale of development and the globalization of economies have environmental and natural resource implications that transcend national borders.

From the policy point of view, globalization is a not a new phenomenon. Science has been globalized for centuries and we ought to be studying it more closely as a model for effective responses to the globalization of our economies. What is striking about science is the strong imperative to share ideas through every conceivable channel to the widest possible audience. If you had to name one chief characteristic of science, it would be empiricism. If you had to name two, the other would be open communication of data and ideas. The power of open communication in science cannot be overestimated. It has established, uniquely among human endeavors, an absolute global standard. And it effectively recruits talent from every part of the globe to labor at the science frontiers. The result has been an extraordinary legacy of understanding of the phenomena that shape our existence. Science is the ultimate example of an open innovation system.

Science practice has received much attention from philosophers, social scientists, and historians during the past half-century, and some of what has been learned holds valuable lessons for policy makers. It is fascinating to me how quickly countries that provide avenues to advanced education are able to participate in world science. The barriers to a small but productive scientific activity appear to be quite low and whether or not a country participates in science appears to be discretionary. A small scientific establishment, however, will not have significant direct economic impact. Its value at early stages of development is indirect, bringing higher performance standards, international recognition, and peer role models for a wider population. A science program of any size is also a link to the rich intellectual resources of the world scientific and technical communities. The indirect benefit of basic scientific research to a developing country far exceeds its direct benefit, and policy needs to recognize this. It is counterproductive to base support for science in such countries on a hoped-for direct economic stimulus through science-driven technical products. Small country science programs can, however, feed relevant technical solutions to regional issues such as public health and poor agricultural practices in the face of inadequate logistical infrastructure.

Keeping in mind that the innovation ecology includes far more than science and technology, it should be obvious that within a small national economy, innovation can thrive on a very small indigenous science and technology base. But innovators, like scientists, do require access to technical information and ideas. Consequently, policies favorable to innovation will create access to education and encourage free communication with the world technical community. Anything that encourages awareness of the marketplace and all its actors on every scale will encourage innovation.

This brings me back to John Kao's definition of innovation. His vision of "the ability of individuals, companies, and entire nations to continuously create their desired future" implies conditions that create that ability, including most importantly educational opportunity. The notion that "innovation depends on harvesting knowledge from a range of disciplines besides science and technology" implies that innovators must know enough to recognize useful knowledge when they see it, and that they have access to knowledge sources across a spectrum that ranges from news media and the Internet to technical and trade conferences. If innovation truly "flows from shifts in mind-set that can generate new business models, recognize new opportunities, and weave innovations throughout the fabric of society," then the fabric of society must be somewhat loose-knit to accommodate the new ideas. Innovation is about risk and change, and deep forces in every society resist both of these. A striking feature of the U.S. innovation ecology is the positive attitude toward failure, an attitude that encourages risk-taking and entrepreneurship.

All this gives us some insight into what policies we need to encourage innovation. Innovation policy is broader than science and technology policy, but the latter must be consistent with the former to produce a healthy innovation ecology. Innovation requires a predictable social structure, an open marketplace, and a business culture amenable to risk and change. It certainly requires an educational infrastructure that produces people with a global awareness and sufficient technical literacy to harvest the fruits of current technology. What innovation does not require is the creation by governments of a system that defines, regulates, or even rewards innovation except through the marketplace or in response to evident success. Some regulation of new products and new ideas is required to protect public health and environmental quality, but innovation needs lots of freedom. Innovative ideas that do not work out should be allowed to die so the innovation community can learn from the experience and replace the failed attempt with something better.

Do we understand innovation well enough to develop policy for it? If the policy addresses very general infrastructure issues such as education, economic and political stability and the like, the answer is perhaps. If we want to measure the impact of specific programs on innovation, the answer is no. Studies of innovation are at an early stage where anecdotal information and case studies, similar to John Kao's book—or the books on *Business Week's* top ten list of innovation titles—are probably the most useful tools for policy makers.

I have been urging increased attention to what I call the science of science policy—the systematic quantitative study of the subset of our economy called science and technology—including the construction and validation of micro- and macro-economic models for science and technology activity. International organizations, and particularly OECD, have been valuable players in this enterprise, and can do much to encourage deeper knowledge of the innovation ecology and thus provide better tools for policy makers. The deep effort OECD is now making to gather global information about innovation and its ecology is a welcome and valuable enterprise that must continue over a long period of time to be successful. Eventually we may learn enough to create reliable indicators by which we can judge the health of our global innovation ecosystem. For now, we should have confidence in the insights gained from centuries of experience with innovation. We know it requires a critical mass of broadly educated individuals interacting in a relatively stable and open socio-economic environment that encourages open communication and entrepreneurialism. All the apparatus of intellectual property protection, government regulation for public and environmental health and sustainability, and access to capital are part of this environment that are targets of ongoing public policy. How each of these parts contributes to the ultimate set of innovation indicators is likely to be different among the multitude of different niches in the rich and changing global ecology of human behavior.

CHAPTER 21

■■■

Information Technology: The Shadow Web

Julian Dibbell

Governments and corporations have more control over the Internet than ever. Now digital activists want to build an alternative network that can never be blocked, filtered or shut down.

IN BRIEF

The Internet was designed to be a decentralized system: every node should connect to many others. This design helped to make the system resistant to censorship or outside attack. Yet in practice, most individual users exist at the edges of the network, connected to others only through their Internet service provider (ISP). Block this link, and Internet access disappears. An alternative option is beginning to emerge in the form of wireless mesh networks, simple systems that connect end users to one another and automatically route around blocks and censors. Yet any mesh network needs to hit a critical mass of users before it functions well; developers must convince potential users to trade off ease of use for added freedom and privacy.

Just after midnight on January 28, 2011, the government of Egypt, rocked by three straight days of massive antiregime protests organized in part through Facebook and other online social networks, did something unprecedented in the history of 21st-century telecommunications: it turned off the Internet. Exactly how it did this remains unclear, but the evidence suggests that five well-placed phone calls—one to each of the country's biggest Internet service providers (ISPs)—may have been all it took. At 12:12 a.m. Cairo time, network routing records show, the leading ISP, Telecom Egypt, began shutting down its customers' connections to the rest of the Internet, and in the course of the next 13 minutes, four other providers followed suit. By 12:40 a.m. the operation was complete. An estimated 93 percent of the Egyptian Internet was now unreachable. When the sun rose the next morning, the protesters made their way to Tahrir Square in almost total digital darkness.

Both strategically and tactically, the Internet blackout accomplished little—the crowds that day were the biggest yet, and in the end, the demonstrators prevailed. But as an object lesson in the Internet's vulnerability to top-down control, the shutdown was alarmingly instructive and perhaps long overdue.

Much has been made of the Internet's ability to resist such control. The network's technological origins, we are sometimes told, lie in the cold war–era quest for a communications infrastructure so robust that even a nuclear attack could not shut it down. Although that is only partly true, it conveys something of the strength inherent in the Internet's elegantly decentralized design. With its multiple, redundant pathways between any two network nodes and its ability to accommodate new nodes on the fly, the TCP/IP protocol that defines the Internet should ensure that it can keep on carrying data no matter how many nodes are blocked and whether it's an atom bomb or a repressive regime that does it. As digital-rights activist John Gilmore once famously said, "The Internet interprets censorship as damage and routes around it."

That is what it was designed to do anyway. And yet if five phone calls can cut off the Internet access of 80 million Egyptians, things have not worked quite that way in practice. The Egyptian cutoff was only the starkest of a growing list of examples that demonstrate how susceptible the Internet can be to top-down control. During the Tunisian revolution the month before, authorities had taken a more targeted approach, blocking only some sites from the national Internet. In the Iranian postelection protests of 2009, Iran's government slowed nationwide Internet traffic rather than stopping it altogether. And for years China's "great firewall" has given the government the ability to block whatever sites it chooses. In Western democracies, consolidation of Internet service providers has put a shrinking number of corporate entities in control of growing shares of Internet traffic, giving companies such as Comcast and AT&T both the incentive and the power to speed traffic served by their own media partners at the expense of competitors.

What happened, and can it be fixed? Can an Internet as dynamically resilient as the one Gilmore idealized—an Internet that structurally resists government and corporate throttles and kill switches—be recovered? A small but dedicated community of digital activists are working on it. Here is what it might look like.

■ ■ ■

It's a dazzling summer afternoon at the Wien-Semmering power plant in Vienna, Austria. Aaron Kaplan has spent the past seven minutes caged inside a dark, cramped utility elevator headed for the top of the plant's 200-meter-high exhaust stack, the tallest structure in the city. When Kaplan finally steps out onto the platform at its summit, the surrounding view is a panorama that takes in Alpine foothills to the west, green Slovakian borderlands in the east and the glittering Danube straight below. But Kaplan did not come here for the view. He walks straight to the platform's edge to look instead at four small, weatherized Wi-Fi routers bolted to the guardrail.

These routers form one node in a nonprofit community network called FunkFeuer, of which Kaplan is a co-founder and lead developer. The signals that the routers beam and pick up link them, directly or indirectly, to some 200 similar nodes on rooftops all over greater Vienna, each one owned and maintained by the user who installed it and each contributing its bandwidth to a communal, high-speed Internet connection shared almost as far and wide as Kaplan, from the top of the smokestack, can see.

FunkFeuer is what is known as a wireless mesh network. No fees are charged for connecting to it; all you need is a $150 hardware setup ("a Linksys router in a Tupperware box, basically," Kaplan says), a roof to put your equipment on and a line-of-sight connection to at least one other node. Direct radio contact with more than a few other nodes isn't necessary, because each node relies on its immediate neighbors to pass along any data meant for nodes it cannot directly reach. In the network's early months, soon after Kaplan and his friend Michael Bauer started it in 2003, the total number of nodes was only about a dozen, and this bucket brigade transmission scheme was a sometimes spotty affair: if even one node went down, there was a good chance the remainder could be cut off from one another or, crucially, from the network's uplink, the one node connecting it to the Internet at large. Keeping the network viable around the clock back then "was a battle," Kaplan recalls. He and Bauer made frequent house calls to help fix ailing user nodes, including one 2 a.m. rooftop session in the middle of a –15 degree Celsius snowstorm, made bearable only by the mugs of hot wine ferried over by Kaplan's wife.

As the local do-it-yourself tech scene learned what FunkFeuer offered, however, the network grew. At somewhere between 30 and 40 nodes, it became self-sustaining. The network's topology was rich enough that if any one node dropped out, any others that had been relying on it could always find a new path. The network had reached that critical density at which, as Kaplan puts it, "the magic of mesh networking kicks in."

Mesh networking is a relatively young technology, but the "magic" Kaplan talks about is nothing new: it is the same principle that has long underpinned the Internet's reputation for infrastructural resilience. Packet-switched store-and-forward routing—in which every computer connected to the network is capable not just of sending and receiving information but of *relaying* it on behalf of other connected computers—has been a defining architectural feature of the Internet since its conception. It is what creates the profusion of available transmission routes that lets the network simply "route around damage." It is what makes the Internet, theoretically at least, so hard to kill.

If the reality of the Internet today more closely matched the theory, mesh networks would be superfluous. But in the two decades since the Internet outgrew its academic origins and started becoming the ubiquitous commercial service it is now, the store-and-forward principle has come to play a steadily less meaningful role. The vast majority of new nodes added to the network in this period have been the home and business computers brought online by Internet service providers. And in the ISP's connection model, the customer's machine is never a relay point; it's an end point, a terminal node, configured only to send and receive and only to do so via machines owned by the ISP. The Internet's explosive growth, in other words, has not added new routes to the network map so much as it has added cul-de-sacs, turning ISPs and other traffic aggregators into focal points of control over the hundreds of millions of nodes they serve. For those nodes there is no routing around the damage if their ISP goes down or shuts them off. Far from keeping the Internet tough to kill, the ISP, in effect, becomes the kill switch.

What mesh networks do, on the other hand, is precisely what an ISP does not: they let the end user's machine act as a data relay. In less technical terms, they let users stop being merely Internet consumers and start being their own Internet providers *[see box on next page]*. If you want a better sense of what that means, consider how things might have happened on January 28 if Egypt's citizens communicated not through a few ISPs but by way of mesh networks. At the very least, it would have taken a lot more than five phone calls to shut that network down. Because each user of a mesh network owns and controls his or her own small piece of the network infrastructure, it might have taken as many phone calls as there were users—and much more persuading, for most of those users, than the ISPs' executives needed.

■ ■ ■

The Perils of Centralized Networks

As Facebook-fueled protests threatened the Egyptian government last year, the Internet disappeared. Records show that each of Egypt's major Internet providers dropped users' connections within a few minutes of one another. The only system that did not disappear was the Noor Group, which happens to serve the Egyptian stock exchange. It was shut down four days later.

Active Internet Connections

Internet Service Providers
— Telecom Egypt
— Link Egypt
— Etisalat Misr
— Raya Telecommunications
— Internet Egypt
— Noor Group

Midnight (Jan. 28, 2011)   12:30 A.M.   1:00 A.M.   10:45 P.M. (Jan. 31)

Traditional Hub-and-Spoke Networks
Nowadays individual Internet users depend on a single connection to reach the global network: that of their Internet service provider (ISP), any one of which might serve millions of individuals. If a single ISP goes down, all its customers will find themselves in digital darkness.

Normal Operations
Communication path
User
ISP

ISP Shutdown
Customers are disconnected

Decentralized Mesh Networks
In a mesh network, each user has the capability to receive and send information and to relay information on behalf of other connected computers. In this setup, an ISP shutdown might slow communications, but the shadow network would keep them alive, routing information around the primary hubs.

Normal Operations
Shadow network
User hub

ISP Shutdown
Mesh users remain connected

At 37 years old, Sascha Meinrath has been a key player in the community mesh-networking scene for about as long as there has been a scene. As a graduate student at the University of Illinois, he helped to start the Champaign-Urbana Community Wireless Network (CUWiN), one of the first such networks in the U.S. Later, he co-organized a post-Katrina volunteer response team that set up an ad hoc mesh network that spanned 60 kilometers of the disaster area, restoring telecommunications in the first weeks after the hurricane. Along the way, he moved to Washington, D.C., intent on starting a community wireless business but instead ending up being "headhunted," as he puts it, by the New America Foundation, a high-powered think tank that hired Meinrath to generate and oversee technology initiatives. It was there, early last year, that he launched the Commotion wireless project, an open-source wireless mesh-networking venture backed by a $2-million grant from the U.S. State Department.

The near-term goal of the project is to develop technology that "circumvents any kill switch and any sort of central surveillance," Meinrath says. To illustrate the idea, he and other core Commotion developers put together what has been called a prototype "Internet in a suitcase": a small, integrated package of wireless communications hardware, suitable for smuggling into a repressive government's territory. From there, dissidents and activists could provide unblockable Internet coverage. The suitcase system is really just a rough-and-ready assemblage of technologies already well known to mesh-networking enthusiasts. Any sufficiently motivated geek could set one up and keep it working.

The long-term question for Meinrath and his colleagues is, "How do you make it so easy to configure that the other 99.9 percent of nongeek humanity can do it?" Because the more people use a mesh network, the harder it is to kill.

In one way, this is numerically self-evident: a mesh network of 100 nodes takes less effort to shut down, node by node, than a mesh of 1,000 nodes. Perhaps more important, a larger mesh network will tend to contain more links to the broader Internet. These uplinks—the sparsely distributed portal nodes standing as choke points between the mesh and the rest of the Internet—become less of a vulnerability as the mesh gets bigger. With more uplinks safely inside the local mesh, fewer everyday communications face disruption should any one link to the global network get cut. And because any node in the mesh could in principle become an uplink using any external Internet connection it can find (dial-up ISP, tethered mobile phone), more mesh nodes also mean a greater likelihood of quickly restoring contact with the outside world.

Size matters, in a word. Thus, in mesh-networking circles, the open question of mesh networks' scalability—of just what size they can grow to—has tended to be a pressing one. Whether it is even theoretically possible for mesh networks to absorb significant numbers of nodes without significantly bogging down remains controversial, depending on what kind of numbers count as significant. Just a few years ago some network engineers were arguing that mesh sizes could never grow past the low hundreds of nodes. Yet currently the largest pure-mesh networks have node counts in the low four digits, and dozens of community networks thrive, with the biggest of them using hybrid mesh-and-backbone infrastructures to reach node counts as high as 5,000 (like the Athens Wireless Metropolitan Network in Greece) and even 15,000 (like Guifi.net in and around Barcelona). The doubt that lingers is whether it is *humanly* possible for mesh networks to grow much bigger, given how most humans feel about dealing with technologies as finicky and complicated as mesh networks.

Unlike most open-source technologies, which tend to downplay the importance of a user-friendly interface, the mesh movement is beginning to realize how critical it is for its equipment to be simple. But if Commotion is not alone in seeking to make mesh networks simpler to use, the key simplification it proposes is a uniquely radical one: instead of making it easier to install and run mesh-node equipment in the user's home or business, Commotion aims to make it unnecessary. "The notion is that you can repurpose cell phones, laptops, existing wireless routers, et cetera," Meinrath explains, "and build a network out of what's already in people's pockets and book bags." He calls it a "device as infrastructure" network, and in the version he envisions, adding one more node to the mesh would require all the effort of flipping a switch. "So in essence, on your iPhone or your Android phone, you would push a button and say, yes, join this network," he says. "It needs to be that level of ease."

■■■

Imagine a world, then, in which mesh networks have finally reached that level—finally cleared the hurdle of mass usability to become, more or less, just another app running in the background. What happens next? Does the low cost of do-it-yourself Internet service squeeze the commercial options out of the market until the last of the ISPs' hub-and-spoke fiefdoms give way to a single, world-blanketing mesh?

Even the most committed supporters of network decentralization aren't betting on it. "This type of system, I think, will always be a poor man's Internet," says Jonathan Zittrain, a Harvard Law School professor and author of *The Future of the Internet: And How to Stop It.* Zittrain would be happy to see the mesh approach succeed, but he recognizes it may never match some of the efficiencies of more centrally controlled networks. "There are real benefits to centralization," he says, "including ease of use." Ramon Roca, founder of Guifi.net, likewise doubts mesh networks will ever put the ISPs out of business—and for that matter, doubts such networks will ever take much more than 15 percent of the market from them. Even at that low a rate of penetration, however, mesh networks can serve to "sanitize the market," Roca argues, opening up the Internet to lower-income households that otherwise could not afford it and spurring the dominant ISPs to bring down prices for everybody else.

As welcome as those economic effects might be, the far more important civic effects—mesh networking's built-in resistances to censorship and surveillance—need a lot more than a 15 percent market share to thrive. And if it is clear that market forces alone are not going to get that number up much higher, then the question is, What will?

Typically, when markets fail to deliver a social good, the first place that gets looked to for a fix is government. In this case particularly, that is not a bad place to start looking. The same mesh network that routes around censorship as if it were damage can just as effectively route around actual damage, which makes mesh networks an ideal communications channel in the face of hurricanes, earthquakes and other natural disasters of the kind that governments are charged with protecting against. Zittrain contends, therefore, that it would be good policy for governments to take an active hand in spreading mesh networks not just among foreign dissidents but among their own citizens. All it might take is a requirement that cell phones sold in the U.S. come equipped with emergency mesh-networking capabilities so that they are ready to turn themselves into relay-capable nodes at the press of a button.

From a public policy perspective, Zittrain says, "it's a no-brainer to build that. And the national security and law-enforcement establishments should generally cheer it on."

The hitch, of course, is that it is just as easy to picture law-enforcement agencies denouncing any national mesh network as a place for criminals and terrorists to communicate out of earshot of the telephone and ISP companies that facilitate surveillance. Such are the complications of counting on government to support mesh networking when it is governments, often enough, that do the kind of damage mesh networks promise to help fix.

It is doubtful, then, that governments can be relied on to do the job any more than markets can. But Eben Moglen has some thoughts about what might. Moglen is a law professor at Columbia University and for many years has been the lawyer for the Free Software Foundation, a nonprofit group of digital activists. Last February, inspired partly by the news from Tunisia, he announced a project called FreedomBox. He also announced he was seeking start-up money for the project on the crowdsourced funding site Kickstarter, and he went on to raise $60,000 in five days.

As a project, FreedomBox has a number of similarities to Commotion, few of them entirely coincidental (Meinrath has a seat on the FreedomBox Foundation's technical advisory committee). Like Commotion, the project broke ground with an illustrative prototype—in this case, the FreedomBox, a networking device about the size of a small brick that costs "$149, in small quantity, and will ultimately be replaced by a bunch of hardware that is half that cost or less," Moglen says.

Again like Commotion, FreedomBox is not tied to the form of any specific gadget. Rather it's a stack of code that can go into the increasing number of networked CPUs that are piling up in our homes and lives, like "dust bunnies under people's couches," as Moglen puts it. All of these can become the infrastructure of an Internet that "rebalances privacy" and restores the vision of "a decentralized network of peers." There are IP addresses in television set-top boxes, in refrigerators—any of these, Moglen says, could be a FreedomBox. And it is not just about decentralizing the infrastructure. It is about decentralizing data, too. For Moglen, for example, the concentration of user data in cloud services such as Facebook and Google is just as much a threat to privacy and freedom of expression as the concentration of traffic in ISPs. To counteract this trend, FreedomBox will be optimized to run alternative social networks such as Diaspora that store your personal data on your machine, sharing it only with the people you choose via peer-to-peer networks.

Still, the key element in the project, Moglen says, is "the political will that is being displayed by a generation of young people who, because of their dependence on social networking, are increasingly aware of their and other people's vulnerability online." It is this earnestness he is counting on to motivate, in part, the many coders who are contributing labor to the project. It is also the one thing likeliest to push users to adopt the technology. Short of a sustained campaign of techno-activism, Moglen suggests, it's not clear what will ever wake the average user to the broad costs in eroded freedom and privacy that we pay for ease of use and other, more immediately tangible benefits.

"People underestimate the harm being done by the death of privacy pretty much in the same way that they underestimate the extraordinary multiplicative consequences of other ecologically destructive acts," such as littering and polluting, Moglen says. "It's hard for human beings to calculate ecologically. It's not a thing that the primate brain evolved to do."

This suggests that the reinvention of the Internet can never be just a matter of tweaking the technologies. It may require a political movement as broad-based and long-ranged as the environmental movement. If neither government nor markets can lead us there, maybe only a collective change of awareness will do, like the kind of change that the green movement brought about by force of will. Nobody recycled before. Now we do. Nobody uses mesh infrastructure now. Someday we might.

Even then, no single technical measure would be enough to preserve the freedoms that the Internet both evokes and embodies. That's because, ultimately, even the ideal, unkillable Internet can't, on its own, resist the social and economic forces that push to recentralize it. Mesh networking is just one way to help push back. "These mesh networks are good for communities, and the bigger they are, the better," Funkfeuer's Kaplan says. But even a single, worldwide mesh would still be at risk of retracing the evolutionary steps that led to the compromised Internet we have now. "Mesh networking is not a replacement for the Internet. It's just part of it," he says. "There's no place for utopia here."

Biographical Note

JULIAN DIBBELL has been writing about the Internet and digital culture for nearly two decades. He is author of *Play Money: Or How I Quit My Day Job and Made Millions Trading Virtual Loot* and editor of *The Best Technology Writing 2010.*

CHAPTER 22

■ ■ ■

Future Technologies, Today's Choices
Nanotechnology, Artificial Intelligence and Robotics;
A technical, political and institutional map of emerging technologies

RESEARCH AND DEVELOPMENT

Introduction

The absence of a universally accepted strict definition of nano-technology has allowed the research emphasis to broaden, encompassing many areas of work that have traditionally been referred to as chemistry or biology (DTI, 2002). Thus, the first major characteristic of activity grouped under this section is that contemporary R&D cuts across a wide range of industrial sectors. In some cases, major markets are fairly well defined. The food industry serves as a good example here, where there are significant drivers at work (pers. comm., Abid Khan, London Centre for Nanotechnology, 6 Nov 2002). To illustrate, 'smart' wrappings for the food industry (that indicate freshness or otherwise) are close to the market (Saxl, 2000). By 2006, beer packaging is anticipated by industry to use the highest weight of nano-strengthened material, at 3 million lbs., followed by meats and carbonated soft drinks. By 2011, meanwhile, the total figure might reach almost 100 million lbs. (nanotechweb.org, 2002). In other cases, important applications are identified but the eventual market impacts are more difficult to predict. For example, nanotechnology is anticipated to yield significant advances in catalyst technology. If these potential applications are realised then the impact on society will be dramatic as catalysts, arguably the most important technology in our modern society, enable the production of a wide range of materials and fuels (Saxl, 2000).

A second characteristic of current work in this area is that the kinds of materials and processes being developed are necessarily 'technology pushed': urged on by the potential impacts of nano-technology, the R&D community is achieving rapid advances in basic science and technology. This level of scientific interest is gauged by Compano and Hullman (2001) who examine the worldwide number of publications in nanotechnology in the Science Citation Index (SCI) database. They conclude that for the period between 1989 and 1998 the average annual growth rate in the number of publications is an 'impressive' 27%. This rise in interest is not confined to a small number of central repositories however (Smith, 1996). Instead, research is spread across more than 30 countries that have developed nanotechnology activities and plans (Holister, 2002). In this way, Compano and Hullman (2001) also examine the distribution of this interest. Based upon their findings, the most active is the US, with roughly one-quarter of all publications, followed by Japan, China, France, the UK and Russia. These countries alone account for 70% of the world's scientific papers on nanotechnology. In particular, for China and Russia the shares are outstanding in comparison with their general presence in the SCI database and show the significance of nanoscience in their research systems.

Novel Materials

The third major characteristic of activity grouped under this section concerns that fact that nanotechnology is primarily about making things (Holister, 2002). For this reason, most of the existing focus of R&D centres on 'nanomaterials': novel materials whose molecular structure has been engineered at the nanometre scale (DTI, 2002). Indeed, Saxl (2000) states that: *'material science and technology is fundamental to a majority of the applications of nanotechnology.'* Thus, many of the materials that follow (Table 22.1) involve either bulk production of conventional compounds that are much smaller (and hence exhibit different properties) or new nanomaterials, such as fullerenes and nanotubes (ETC Group, 2002a). The markets range of nanomaterials are considerable. Indeed, it has been estimated that, aided by nanotechnology, novel materials and processes can be expected to have a market impact of over US$340 billion within a decade (Holister, 2002).

Nanotubes

Nanotubes provide a good example of how basic R&D can take off into full-scale market application in one specific area. Described as *'the most important material in nanotechnology today'* (Holister, 2002), nanotubes are a new material with remarkable tensile strength. Indeed, taking current technical barriers into account, nanotube-based material is anticipated to become 50–100 times stronger than steel at one-sixth of the weight (Anton et al., 2001).

TABLE 22.1. Summary of the Major Nanomaterials Currently in Research and Development and Their Potential Applications

Material	Properties	Applications	Time-scale (to market launch)
Clusters of atoms			
Quantum wells	Ultra-thin layers—usually a few nanometers thick—of semiconductor material (the well) grown between barrier material by modern crystal growth technologies (Saxl, 2000). The barrier materials trap electrons in the ultra-thin layers, thus producing a number of useful properties. These properties have led, for example, to the development of highly efficient laser devices.	CD players have made use of quantum well lasers for several years. More recent developments promise to make these nanodevices commonplace in low-cost telecommunications and optics.	Current–5 years
Quantum dots	Fluorescent nanoparticles that are invisible until 'lit up' by ultraviolet light. They can be made to exhibit a range of colours, depending on their composition (Miles and Jarvis, 2001).	Telecommunications, optics.	7–8 years
Polymers	Organic-based materials that emit light when an electric current is applied to them and vice versa (pers. comm., Jenny Nelson, Imperial College London, 2 Dec 2002).	Computing, energy conversion.	?
Grains that are less than 100nm in size			
Nanocapsules	Buckminsterfullerenes are the most well known example. Discovered in 1985, these C60 particles are 1 nm in width.	Many applications envisaged e.g. nanoparticulate dry lubricant for engineering (Saxl, 2000).	Current–2 years
Catalytic nanoparticles	In the range of 1–10 nm, such materials were in existence long before it was realized that they belonged to the realms of nanotechnology. However, recent developments are enabling a given mass of catalyst to present more surface area for reaction, hence improving its performance (Hay and Shaw, 2000). Following this, such catalytic nanoparticles can often be regenerated for further use.	Wide range of applications, including materials, fuel and food production, health and agriculture (Hay and Shaw, 2000).	Current–?

(continued)

TABLE 22.1. (*Continued*)

Material	Properties	Applications	Time-Scale (to Market Launch)
Fibres that are less than 100nm in diameter			
Carbon nanotubes	Two types of nanotube exist: the single-wall carbon nanotubes, the so-called 'Buckytubes', and multilayer carbon nanotubes (Hay and Shaw, 2000). Both consist of graphitic carbon and typically have an internal diameter of 5 nm and an external diameter of 10 nm. Described as the 'most important material in nanotechnology today' (Holister, 2002), it has been calculated that nanotube-based material has the potential to become 50–100 times stronger than steel at one sixth of the weight.	Many applications are envisaged: space and aircraft manufacture, automobiles and construction. Multi-layered carbon nanotubes are already available in practical commercial quantities. Buckytubes are some way off from large-scale commercial production (Saxl, 2000).	Current–5 years
Films that are less than 100nm in thickness			
Self-assembling monolayers (SAMs)	Organic or inorganic substances spontaneously form a layer one molecule thick on a surface. Additional layers can be added, leading to laminates where each layer is just one molecule in depth (Holister, 2002).	A wide range of applications, based on properties ranging from being chemically active to being wear resistant (Saxl, 2000).	2–5 years
Nanoparticulate coatings	Coating technology is now being strongly influenced by nanotechnology. E.g. metallic stainless steel coatings sprayed using nanocrystalline powders have been shown to possess increased hardness when compared with conventional coatings (Saxl, 2000).	Sensors, reaction beds, liquid crystal manufacturing, molecular wires, lubrication and protective layers, anti-corrosion coatings, tougher and harder cutting tools (Holister, 2002).	5–15 years
Nanostructured materials			
Nanocomposites	Composites are combinations of metals, ceramics, polymers and biological materials that allow multifunctional behaviour (Anton et al., 2001). When materials are introduced that exist at the nanolevel, nanocomposites are formed (Hay and Shaw, 2000), and the material's properties—e.g. hardness, transparency, porosity—are altered.	A number of applications, particularly where purity and electrical conductivity characteristics are important, such as in microelectronics. Commercial exploitation of these materials is currently small, the most ubiquitous of these being carbon black, which finds widespread industrial application, particularly in vehicle tyres (Hay and Shaw, 2000).	Current–2 years
Textiles	Incorporation of nanoparticles and capsules into clothing leading to increased lightness and durability, and 'smart' fabrics (that change to their physical properties according to the wearer's clothing) (Holister, 2002).	Military, lifestyle.	3–5 years

This development would dwarf the improvements that carbon fibres brought to composites. Harry Kroto, who was awarded the Nobel Prize for the discovery of C60 Buckminsterfullerene, states that such advances will take *'a long, long time'* to achieve (2010 Nanospace Odyssey lecture, Queen Mary University, 6 Jan 2003), the first applications of nanotubes being in composite development. However, if such technologies do eventually arrive, the results will be awesome: they will *'be equivalent to James Watt's invention of the condenser'*, a development that kick-started the industrial revolution. The concept of the space elevator serves as a good illustration of the kind of visionary thinking that recent nanotube development has inspired. The idea of a 'lift to the stars' is not itself particularly new: a Russian engineer, Yuri Artutanov, penned the idea of an elevator—perhaps powered by a laser that could quietly transport payloads and people to a space platform—as early as 1960 (cited in Cowen 2002). However, such ideas have always been hampered by the lack of material strength necessary to make the cable attachment. The nanotube may be the key to overcoming this longstanding obstacle, making the space elevator a reality in just 15 years time (Cowen, 2002). This development, though, will rely on the successful incorporation of nanotubes into fibres or ribbons and successfully avoiding various atmospheric dangers, such as lightning strikes, micrometers, and human-made space debris.

The market impetus behind such developments, then, is clear: the conventional space industry is anticipated as the first major customer, followed by aircraft manufacturers. However, as production costs drop (currently US$20–1200/g), nanotubes are expected to find widespread application in such large industries as automobiles and construction. In fact, it is possible to conceive of a market in any area of industry that will benefit from lighter and stronger materials (Holister, 2002). It is expectations such as these that are currently fuelling the race to develop techniques of nanotube mass-production in economic quantities. The ETC Group (2002b) states that there are currently at least 55 companies involved in nanotube fabrication and that production levels will soon be reaching 1 kg/day in some companies. For example, Japan's Mitsui and Co. will start building a facility in April 2003 with an annual production capacity of 120 tons of carbon nanotubes (Fried, 2002). The company plans to market the product to automakers, resin makers and battery makers. In fact, the industry has grown so quickly that Holister (2002) believes that the number of nanotube suppliers already in existence are not likely to be supported by available applications in the years to come.

Fried (2002) also supports this contention, stating that the *'carbon nanotube field is already over-saturated'*.

Tools and Fabrication

It is a simple statement of fact that in order to make things you must first have the fabrication tools available. Therefore, many of the nanomaterials covered above are co-evolving with a number of enabling technologies and techniques. These tools provide the instrumentation needed to examine and characterize devices and effects during the R&D phase, the manufacturing techniques that will allow the large-scale economic production of nanotechnology products, and the necessary support for quality control (DTI, 2002). Because of the essential nature of this category, its influence is far greater than is reflected in the size of the economic sectors producing these products. For this reason, the tools and techniques highlighted below have a strong commercial future and the greatest number of established companies (pers. comm., Gareth Parry, Imperial College London, 22 Nov 2002). The following sections cover methods for top-down and bottom-up manufacture, software modeling and nanometrology. However, in the near future, this area will mainly feature extensions of conventional instrumentation and top-down manufacturing. More futuristic molecular scale assembly remains distant (Miles and Jarvis, 2001).

Top-down Manufacture

Scanning Probe Microscope. This is the general term for a range of instruments with specific functions. Fundamentally, a nanoscopic probe is maintained at a constant height over the bed of atoms. This probe can be positioned so close to individual atoms that the electrons of the probe-tip and atom begin to interact. These interactions can be strong enough to 'lift' the atom and move it to another place (pers. comm., Gareth Parry, Imperial College London, 22 Nov 2002).

Optical Techniques. These techniques can be used to detect movement—obviously important in hi-tech precision engineering. Optical techniques are, in theory, restricted in resolution to half the wavelength of light being used, which keeps them out of the lower nanoscale, but various approaches are now overcoming this limitation (Holister, 2002).

Lithographics.   Lithography is the means by which patterns are delineated on silicon chips and micro-electrical-mechanical systems (MEMS). Most significantly, optical lithography is the dominant exposure tool in use today in the semiconductor industry's Complementary Metal Oxide Semiconductor (CMOS) process.

Bottom-up Manufacture

The tools here support rather more futuristic approaches to large-scale production and nanofabrication based on bottom-up approaches, such as nanomachine production lines (Miles and Jarvis, 2001). This approach is equivalent to building a car engine up from individual components, rather than the less intuitive method of machining a system down from large blocks of material. Indeed, although such techniques are still in their infancy, the DTI (2002) report a recent movement away from top-down techniques towards self-assembly within the international research community. Scientists and engineers are becoming increasingly able to understand, intervene and rearrange the atomic and molecular structure of matter, and control its form in order to achieve specific aims (Saxl, 2000).

Self-assembly and Self-organisation.   Self-assembly refers to the tendency of some materials to organise themselves into ordered arrays (Anton et al., 2001). This technique potentially offers huge economies, and is considered to have great potential in nano-electronics. In particular, the study of the self-assembly nature of molecules is proving to be the foundation of rapid growth in applications in science and technology. For example, Saxl (2000) reports that the Stranski–Krastonov methods for growing self-assembly quantum dots has rendered the lithographic approach to semiconductor quantum dot fabrication virtually obsolete. In addition, self-assembly is leading to the fabrication of new materials and devices. The former area of materials consists of new types of nanocomposites or organic/inorganic hybrid structures that are created by depositing or attaching organic molecules to ultra-small particles or ultra-thin manmade-layered structures (Hay and Shaw, 2000). Similarly, the latter area of devices range from the production of new chemical and gas sensors, optical sensors, solar panels and other energy conversion devices, to bio-implants and *in vivo* monitoring. The basis of these technologies is an organic film (the responsive layer) which can be deposited on a hard, active electronic chip substrate. The solid-state chip receives signals from the organic over-layer as it reacts to changes in its environment, and processes them. The applications for these new materials and devices are summarized in Table 22.2.

Software Modeling

Molecular modelling software is another fabrication technique of wide-ranging applicability as it permits the efficient analysis of large molecular structures and substrates (Miles and Jarvis, 2001). Hence, it is much used by molecular nanotechnologists, where computers can simulate the behaviour of matter at the atomic and molecular level. In addition, computer modelling is anticipated to prove essential in understanding and predicting the behaviour of nanoscale structures because they operate at what is sometimes referred to as the mesoscale, an area where both classical and quantum physics influence behaviour (Holister, 2002).

Nanometrology

Fundamental to commercial nanotechnology is repeatability, and fundamental to repeatability is measurement. Nanometrology, then, allows the perfection of the texture at the nanometre and sub-nanometre level to be examined and controlled. This is essential if highly specialised applications of nanotechnology are to operate correctly, for example X-ray optical components and mirrors used in laser technologies (Saxl, 2000).

TABLE 22.2. Applications for New Materials and Devices Resulting from Self-Assembly and Self-Organisation

Name	Technique	Application
New materials		
Sol-gel technology (Miles and Jarvis, 2001)	Inorganic and organic component combination.	The design of different types of materials; functional coatings.
Intercalation of polymers (Miles and Jarvis, 2001)	Intercalation of polymers with other materials (DNA, drugs).	Toxicity testing, drug delivery and drug performance analysis.
Nano-emulsions (Saxl, 2000)	Nanoparticle size and composition selected.	Production of required viscosity and absorption characteristics.
Biomimetics (Anton et al., 2001)	Design of systems, materials and their functionality to mimic nature.	High strength, structural applications, such as artificial bones and teeth.
New devices		
Field-sensing devices (Saxl, 2000)	Combination of molecular films with optical waveguides and resonators.	Biosensing and optical switching.
Material-sensing devices (Saxl, 2000)	Surfaces of liquid crystals or thin membranes and other organic compounds can be used to detect molecules via structural or conductive changes.	Gas and chemical sensing.

Public Funding for Research and Development

The main reason for government interest in nanotechnology is strategic: to achieve an advantageous position so that when nanotech applications begin to have a significant effect in the world economy, countries are able to exploit these new opportunities to the full. Harper (2002), who describes the current situation as a global 'arms race', puts these ideas into perspective:

> You only have to look at how IT made a huge difference to both the US economy and US military strength to see how crucial technology is. Nanotechnology is an even more fundamental technology than IT. Not only has it the ability to shift the balance of military power but also affect the global balance of power in the energy markets.

This emphasis on military power is well founded: Smith (1996) echoes this sentiment when he speculates that it is entirely possible that much, or even most, US government research in the field is concentrated in the hands of military planners.

Levels of public investment in nanotechnology are reminiscent of a growing strategic interest: this is an area that attracts both large and small countries. Global R&D spending is currently around US$4 billion (ETC Group, 2002a), with public investment increasing rapidly (503% between 1997 and 2002 across the 'lead' countries). Table 22.3 summarises these rises.

TABLE 22.3. Worldwide Government Funding for Nanotechnology Research and Development (US$million)

Area	1997	1998	1999	2000	2001	2002	2003
US*	116	190	255	270	422	604	710
Western Europe	126	151	179	200	225	~400	NA
Japan	120	135	157	245	465	~650	NA
Others**	70	83	96	110	380	~520	NA
Total	432	559	687	825	1502	2174	NA
(% of 1997)	100	129	159	191	348	503	NA

NA: not available.

*Excluding non-federal spending e.g. California.

**'Others' includes Australia, Canada, China, Eastern Europe, the Former Soviet Union, Singapore, Taiwan and other countries with nanotechnology R&D. For example, in Mexico there are 20 research groups working independently on nanotechnology. Korea, already a world player in electronics, has an ambitious 10-year programme to attain a world-class position in nanotechnology (DTI, 2002).

The US

The US is widely considered to be the world-leader in nanoscale science research (Saxl, 2000). Certainly, in terms of leading centres for nanotechnology research, the USA dominates, with eight institutions making the DTI (2002) top list of 13. These centres are University of Santa Barbara, Cornell University, University of California at Los Angeles, Stanford University, IBM Research Laboratories, Northwestern University, Harvard University and the Massachusetts Institute of Technology (MIT). In total, more than 30 universities have announced plans for nanotech research centres since 1997 (Leo, 2001). Further, the US is widely regarded as the benchmark against which nanotechnology funding should be compared (Roman, 2002). Indeed, Howard (2002) states that, *'while other governments are investing in a range of nanotechnology research, the US effort is by far the most substantial.'* From 1985–1997 the total support for projects related to nanotechnology was estimated at US$452 million, coming in roughly equal parts from the NSF, various industrial sponsorship, and other government funding. Then in 2000, the much-heralded NNI was launched—a multi-agency program designed to provide a big funding boost for nanotechnology. There are currently 10 US government partners in the NNI. These are shown in Table 22.4.

Table 22.4 shows that the NSF and Department of Defense (DoD) are the two major recipients of investment in nanoscience and technology R&D. Indeed, the NSF has designated *'nanoscale science and engineering'* as one of its six priority areas, while the DoD has dedicated its funding to elaborating a *'conceptual template for achieving new levels of war-fighting effectiveness'* (DoD, 2002). This table provides a fairly accurate picture of current research priorities in the US. However, state funding, which can sometimes be substantial, is not included in the estimates. For example, the state of California, which is home to virtually all the work in molecular nanotechnology, has invested US$100 million in the creation of a California Nanosystems Institute. And neither are the figures static; levels of funding are anticipated to increase rapidly once the economic benefits of US funding begin to be felt, whether in new company start-up activity, or progress towards military or social goals.

Far East

Table 22.5 shows the levels of 2002 government spending on nanotechnology within five countries in the Far East. On average, these

TABLE 22.4. Breakdown of Spending on the US's National Nanotechnology Initiative from 2001–2003 (US$million)

Recipient	2001 Actual	2002 Estimate	2003 Proposed
National Science Foundation	145	199	221
Department of Defence	125	180	201
Department of Energy	78	91	139
National Aeronautics and Space Administration	0	46	49
National Institute of Health	40	41	43
National Institute of Standards and Technology	28	37	44
Environmental Protection Agency	5	5	5
Department of Transportation	0	2	2
US Department of Agriculture	0	2	5
Department of Justice	1	1	1
Total	**422**	**604**	**710**

DTI, 2002.

TABLE 22.5. Top Five Government Spending on Nanotechnology in the Far East in 2002 (US$million).

Country	Spending
Japan	750
China	200
Korea	150
Taiwan	111
Singapore	40
Total	**1251**

Roman, 2002.

figures are lower than in the US although, given the increased purchasing power in countries such as China, they may be considered as relatively high (Roman, 2002). However, while the figures given are up-to-date, the time-scales over which they operate are ambiguous.

Of all the countries shown in Table 22.5, Japan's nanotech investments are by far the greatest. Indeed, it is universally agreed that Japan has the only fully co-ordinated and funded national policy of nanotechnology research. The most prominent product of this national policy has been the Ministry of Economy, Trade and Industry (METI) programme on atomic manipulation, 1991–2001, entitled *Research and Development of Ultimate Manipulation of Molecules* (Tam, 2001). The programme was funded at the ¥25 billion level (approximately US$210 million). Of the total, US$167 million has been allocated for the development of microbots (Saxl, 2000). Nowadays, the Japanese government views the successful development of nanotechnology as key to restoration of its economy: nanotechnology is one of the four strategic platforms of Japan's second basic plan for science and technology. For example, the Japanese government has founded the Expert Group on Nanotechnology under the Japan Federation of Economic Organisations Committee on Industrial Technology. In another initiative, which it calls its 'e-Japan strategy', the Japanese government aims to become *'the world's most advanced IT nation within five years'* (IT Strategic Headquarters, 2001). Japan's government nanotechnology expenditures are given in Table 22.6.

Although the figures given in Table 22.6 are impressive, Roman (2002) believes that the annual 50% increase does cast some doubt over their accuracy. For while there is no doubt that funding will continue to increase, increasing the number of researchers available to absorb this extra funding does not seem possible on an annual basis.

European Union

All European Union (EU) member states, except Luxembourg where no universities are located, have research programmes. For

TABLE 22.6. Estimated Japanese Government Nanotechnology Research and Development Expenditures (US$million).

1997	1998	1999	2000	2001	2002	2003
120	135	157	245	465	~750	~1000

Roman, 2002.

some countries, such as Germany, Ireland or Sweden, where nanotechnology is considered of strategic importance, nanotechnology programmes have been established for several years. On the other hand, many countries have no specifically focused nanotechnology initiatives, but this research is covered within more general R&D programmes (Compano, 2001). Table 22.7 summarises the situation for the top six countries.

The European Commission (EC) funds nanoscience through its so-called Framework Program (FP). The aim of the FP6 is to produce breakthrough technologies that directly benefit the EU, either economically or socially. Under this, €1.3 billion are earmarked for *'nanotechnologies and nanosciences, knowledge-based multifunctional materials and new production processes and devices'* in the 2002–2006 FP out of a total budget of €11.3 billion. This thematic priority is only partly dedicated to nanoscience, while other thematic priorities also have a nanotechnology component. At first glance this may seem a small figure compared to the 2003 NNI budget of US$710 million (€0.72 billion). However, it does not take into account the substantial contributions made by individual member states (Compano, 2001). The UK serves as a good example of this, where public spending on nanotechnology R&D was around £30 million in 2001 (DTI, 2002), 70–80% of it from the Engineering and Physical Sciences Research Council (EPSRC). However, this is set to rise quite rapidly in 2002–2003 as the new interdisciplinary research collaborations and university technology centres start to spread.

TABLE 22.7. Top Six European Government Nanotechnology Spending from 1998–2000 (€million).

Country/Institution	1998	1999	2000
Germany	49.0	58.0	63.0
UK	32.0	35.0	39.0
European Commission	26.0	27.0	29.0
France	12.0	18.0	19.0
Netherlands	4.7	6.2	6.9
Sweden	3.4	5.6	5.8
European total	**139.8**	**164.7**	**184.0**

Compano, 2001.

CONCERNS

Introduction

Given the difficulty in foreseeing nanotechnology outcomes and estimating likelihood, it is difficult to extrapolate predictions of specific threats and risks from current trends (Anton et al., 2001). And yet, in spite of this, recent discussions of the possible dangers posed by future technologies (such as AI, genetic engineering and MNT) have made it clear that analysis of the major classes of risks of nanotechnology is warranted. Perhaps the greatest difficulty in predicting the impacts of new technologies has to do with the fact that, once the technical and commercial feasibility of an innovation is demonstrated, subsequent developments may be as much in the hands of users as in those of the innovators (NSF, 2001). As a result, new technologies can affect society in ways that were not intended by those who initiated them. Sometimes these unintended consequences are beneficial, such as spin-offs with valuable applications in fields remote from the original innovation. A good example of this concerns the early days of the Internet—the subject is covered in Part 2 of this report. Other times, intended benefits may also have unintended or 'second- order' consequences. Interestingly, while a few far-sighted scientists are focusing on potentially negative second-order impacts of future nanotech applications, virtually no one has been tracking the potentially negative impacts of nanotechnology's present-day products (ETC Group, 2002a). This section, therefore, will attempt to distinguish between these two time-frames, as well as introducing the main environmental and socio-political concerns. For the purposes of this report, 'long-term' refers to a hazard that, due to challenges associated with technological development, is unlikely to manifest itself within a 10–15 year time-frame.

Environmental Concerns

The potential impact of nanostructured particles and devices on the environment is perhaps the most high profile of contemporary concerns. Quantum dots, nanoparticles, and other throwaway nanodevices may constitute whole new classes of non-biodegradable pollutants that scientists have very little understanding of. Essentially, most nanoparticles produced today are mini-versions of particles that have been produced for a long time. Thus, the larger (micro) versions have undergone testing, while their smaller (nano) counterparts have not (ETC Group, 2002a). For example, Vicki Colvin, Executive Director of Rice University's Centre for Biological and Environmental

Nanotechnology (CBEN) has recently postulated that nanomaterials provide a large and active surface for adsorbing smaller contaminants, such as cadmium and organics. Thus, like naturally occurring colloids, they could provide an avenue for rapid and long-range transport of waste in underground water (cited in Colvin, 2002).

Infiltrating Humans

The concern that nanomaterials could bind to certain common but harmful substances in the environment, such as pesticides or PCBs, leads to the short-term worry of such materials infiltrating humans. According to the ETC Group (2002a), at a recent fact-finding meeting at the US Environmental Protection Agency (EPA), researchers reported that nanoparticles can penetrate living cells and accumulate in animal organs. In particular, the possibility of toxic elements attaching themselves to otherwise benign nanomaterials inside bacteria and finding a way into the bloodstream was acknowledged. In addition, very little work has been done in order to ascertain the possible effects of nanomaterials on living systems. One possibility is that proteins in the bloodstream will attach to the surface of nanoparticles, thus changing their shape and function, and triggering dangerous unintended consequences, such as blood clotting. A second possibility relates to the ability of nanoparticles to slip past the human immune system unnoticed, a property desirable for drug delivery, but worrying if potentially harmful substances can attach to otherwise benign nanomaterials and reside in the body in a similar manner. According to Colvin (2002), 'it is possible to speculate that nanoscale inorganic matter is generally biologically inert. However, without hard data that specifically address the issue of synthetic nanomaterials, it is impossible to know what physiological effects will occur, and, more critically, what exposure levels to recommend.' To illustrate, this report shows how nanotubes, should industry predictions be realised, are set to become relatively ubiquitous within the coming decades—such materials are already finding their way into a number of products. But it has not yet been determined what happens if, for example, large quantities of nanotubes are absorbed by the human body. One prominent concern relates to the structural similarities between nanotubes and asbestos fibres: like the latter, nanotubes fibres are long, extremely durable, and have the potential to reside in the lungs for lengthy periods of time. One recent study, conducted by the National Aeronautics and Space Administration (NASA), has shown that breathing in large quantities of nanotubes can cause damage to lungs. However, as nanotubes are essentially similar to soot, then this is not particularly surprising (The Economist, 2002). On the whole, far more experiments are required before the issue can be resolved.

Self-replication

Self-replication is probably the earliest-recognised and best-known long-term danger of MNT. This centres upon the idea that self-replicating nanorobots capable of functioning autonomously in the natural environment could quickly convert that natural environment (i.e. 'biomass') into replicas of themselves (i.e. 'nano-mass') on a global basis. Such a scenario is usually referred to as the 'grey goo' problem but perhaps more properly termed 'global ecophagy' (Freitas, 2000). The main feature that distinguishes runaway replication as a long-term environmental concern is the extreme difficulty involved in constructing machines with the adaptability of living organisms. As Freitas (2000) notes:

> 'The replicators easiest to build will be inflexible machines, like automobiles or industrial robots . . . To build a runaway replicator that could operate in the wild would be like building a car that could go off-road and fuel itself from tree sap. With enough work, this should be possible, but it will hardly happen by accident. Without replication, accidents would be like those of industry today: locally harmful, but not catastrophic to the biosphere. Catastrophic problems seem more likely to arise though deliberate misuse, such as the use of nanotechnology for military aggression' (see below).

This is not to imply, however, that the risk that molecular machines designed for economic purposes might replicate unchecked and destroy the world should be written off altogether: while the danger seems slight, even a slight risk of such a catastrophe is best avoided (Zyvex, 2002). To this end, David Forrest (1989) has produced a set of guidelines to assure that molecular machines and their products are developed in a safe and responsible manner.

Socio-political Concerns

Clearly, if scientists are successful in developing nanofabrication techniques for manufacturing nanoelectronic devices in huge volumes at very low cost, then the impact on society will be enormous. The potentially disruptive nature of nanotechnology has already been highlighted in earlier sections through its ability to generate major new paradigm shifts in how things are generated, such as a shift from top-down to bottom-up manufacturing techniques. This section further elaborates upon this and similar concerns.

Medical Ethics

The ethical questions that have been raised in recent years following the advancement of such technologies as gene therapy are similar to in scope and philosophy to nanotechnology. For example, the emergence of highly specific drug therapies, a nano-based technique that features prominently in earlier sections of this report, may result in genetic discrimination. That is, discrimination directed against an individual or family based solely on an apparent or perceived genetic variation from the 'normal' human genotype (LaVan and Langer, 2001). The major concern here lies in the end result of going down such a road: that the de-selection of characteristics judged unwanted by societies (referred to as negative eugenics) will be viewed as the right, responsible, moral thing to do, as will cures and enhancements (Wolbring, 2002). Similarly, on a longer time-scale, concerns over nanotech applications for enhancing the performance of the human body might also arise. A major question here is whether such enhancements can be forced upon people, either when in a position to make a decision for themselves or, more controversially, against their will.

The Nano-divide

If Moore's law holds and the miniaturisation of PCs continues unchecked well into the 21st Century, then it seems likely that, in the long-term, society will get to a point where people can carry computers 24 hours a day. As Chaudhari (2001) states: '*We are evolving to the point where every human being will be connected to any other human or to the vast network of information sources throughout the world by a communication system comprised of wireless and optical fibre communication links.*' A world in which information is abundant and cheap may well have serious privacy implications for those who can afford to connect. However, little consideration seems to have been given to those who will clearly not be able to afford to participate. Indeed, many nations are already witnessing an IT divide, particularly in reference to Internet usage, that correlates with inequality in the distribution of wealth. This gap is likely to be exacerbated by any impending nanotechnological revolution, forming a so-called 'nano-divide.' It is important not to underestimate the potential scale of this: the transition from a pre-nano to post-nano world could be very traumatic and could exacerbate the problem of haves vs. have-nots. Such differences are likely to be striking (Smith, 2001).

A quick glance at demographics provides some insight into what such a post-nano world might look like. According to the World Bank, the Western industrial democracies will shrink from 12.7% of today's population to 8.6% by 2025. At the same time in the developing world the population will double (cited in Jeremiah, 1995). The kinds of nanotech-inspired wonders alluded to throughout this report may only be feasible for the 8.6% of the 2025 population who live in Western industrial democracies, and the upper layer of society in the developing and non-developing world, not for the rural poor and the underside of all urban populations. In other words, *'the differences in the quality of life will be even starker than today between these two worlds'* (Jeremiah, 1995). The NSF supports these sentiments: *'Those who participate in the nano revolution stand to become very wealthy. Those who do not may find it increasingly difficult to afford the technological wonders that it engenders.'* (Roco and Bainbridge, 2001). One near-term example will be in medical care, as nanotech-based treatments may be initially expensive and hence only accessible to the very rich.

In the longer-term, campaign groups such as the ETC Group point to what they describe as the *'corporate concentration'* of *'material building blocks and processes that make everything from dams to DNA.'* This concern arises irrespective of the general doctrine in patent law that products of nature cannot be patented because the atomically-engineered elements of today are able to side-step the issue. For example, C Sixty Inc., a Toronto, Canada-based start-up exercise, has filed a series of patents, five of which have been granted, for Buckminsterfullerene. The aim of C Sixty Inc. is to corner the market with respect to this remarkable molecule and its vast potential in drug delivery. A big concern of the ETC Group (2002c) is that patenting offices (such as the US Patent and Trademark Office) understand nanotechnology, so that when approached by industry, examiners understand what are reasonable boundaries to intellectual property rights.

Destructive Uses

The potentially catastrophic but long-term danger that the deliberate misuse of nanotechnology for military aggression poses has already been sketched out above. Indeed, Howard (2002) concedes that *'once the basic technology is available, it would not be difficult to adapt it as an instrument of war or terror.'* Gsponer (2002), on the other hand, draws attention to the existing potential of nanotechnology to affect dangerous and destabilising 'refinements' of existing nuclear weapons designs—such fourth generation nuclear weapons are new types of explosives that can be developed in full compliance with the Comprehensive Test Ban Treaty (CTBT). Such developments hint at the worrying possibility of a nanotechnology arms race. Zyvex (2002) sketch out the underlying rationale for such an occurrence:

> 'It is clear that offensive weapons made using advanced nanotechnology can only be stopped by defensive systems made using advanced nanotechnology as well. If one side has such weapons and the other doesn't, the outcome will be swift and very lopsided. This is just a specific instance of the general rule that technological superiority plays an important and often critical role in determining the victor in battle. Clearly, we will need much further research into defensive systems as this technology becomes more mature.'

Public Acceptance of Nanotechnology

In spite of the concerns highlighted above, both precautionary principle and industry advocates agree that there is time to create dialogue and consensus that could prevent the kind of confrontations occurring that plagued the development of biotechnology. In this way, the objective of industry is to launch pre-emptive strikes against any problems with public acceptance of nanotechnology that might arise down the line (Gorman, 2002). The earliest example of this is the Foresight Institute, a think-tank founded in 1986 primarily to facilitate public understanding and discussion of the policy issues surrounding the development and deployment of nanotechnology. More recently, nanotech researchers have been urged to build on the example of the Ethical and Social Implications (ELSI) project (an interdisciplinary effort within the Human Genome Project). That is, to *take a hard look at potential ethical and cultural issues, but follow through much more carefully and get out ahead of the public* (Paul Thompson, Professor of Ethics at Purdue University, quoted in Leo, 2001). Indeed, the NNI has long acknowledged a need to integrate societal studies and dialogues concerning the perceived dangers of nanotechnology with its investment strategy, and the resulting White House Fact Sheet (2000) promised that the impact nanotechnology has on society from legal, ethical, social, economic, and workforce preparation perspectives would be studied. These aims have already been realised to some extent. For example, the 2001 NSF report entitled *Implications of Nanoscience and Nanotechnology* takes a long, hard look at a range of hypothetical social ramifications (Roco and Bainbridge, 2001).

This industry strategy has been received with mixed reaction. Some commentators, such as Ho (2002a), have praised scientists for informing the public with *'clarity and candour.'* Others, on the other hand have not been nearly so generous in their assessment. Herrera (2002), for example, sums up the present state of the nanotech industry as being comparable to a *'sitting duck'*, just as biotech was during the 1990s, because it is not taking the issue of public acceptance seriously. Herrera continues: *'Ask members of the nanotechnology community if there are any obvious or potential controversies that they should be watching for, and they will say 'no' . . . Scientists think about ethics but they don't let it interfere with their work.'*

At present, the majority of controversy in this area surrounds the interaction of nanomaterials with the environment and their implications for human health. Vicki Colvin of CBEN believes that *'scientists' experience with other particulate matter argues for a thorough examination of how nanoparticles might react in mammalian systems when they are inhaled or when there is skin exposure'* (cited in Schultz, 2002). In addition, nanotech manufacturing processes need to be examined for potential health impacts, for example the solvents used in the gases produced in the manufacture of carbon nanotubes. Outside of manufacturing, researchers should investigate the possible consequences of nanoparticles entering and accumulating in the food chain. Indeed, some of the ongoing work by CBEN, and other organisations such as NASA and the EPA, has been alluded to above. However, it is becoming increasingly clear that this work alone is not sufficient for the scope of these issues. As Colvin (2002) notes:

> 'It is critical that more organisations and people devote time and money to these questions. This requires a change in the current climate: of the [US$710 million in funding for the NNI in the fiscal year 2003, less than [US$500,000 is devoted to the study of environmental impact. It is difficult to convince scientists, or funding managers, to support environmental impact studies. The immediate payback for research that demonstrates ways of using nanomaterials to cure disease, for example, is greater than the reward for uncovering that a nanomaterial may cause disease.'

One way in which prevailing industry attitudes may be influenced is through the idea that information about unintended effects (whatever its conclusions), rather than alarming investors, in fact reassures, thus increasing the likelihood that viable nanotechnology products are developed. Most importantly, hard data on the environmental effects of nanomaterials could go a long way to building the public's trust (Colvin, 2002). This is in contrast to, for example, the controversy that surrounded the pesticide DDT in the 1960s and early 1970s: by refusing to acknowledge the demonstrable environmental harm caused by DDT, the US chemical industry lost a controversial but effective product, particularly for control of mosquitoes and mosquito-borne diseases.

The Regulation Debate

The precautionary approach upholds that regulatory action may be taken, based on the possibility of significant environmental damage, even before there is conclusive, scientific evidence that the damage will occur (European Environment Agency, 2003). Perhaps the most vigorous example of this concerns the ETC Group, who have called for a global moratorium on the manufacture of nanomaterials until such a time when their interactions with living systems are more fully understood (McCullagh, 2002). Such an appeal is well-placed within this precautionary worldview, and nano-advocates have had to respond quickly with a number of forceful counterarguments. Many of these claims stem from the diversity of envisaged nanotech applications and products (i.e. essentially a vast array of very small components), the difficulties of defining nanotechnology, and its broad interdisciplinary scope. Indeed, the convergence of a wide number of scientific disciplines within the field of nanotechnology certainly complicates the practicalities of enforcing such a ban, especially when one considers that pushing research underground may increase either the danger of deliberate misuse, or at least the difficulty of ensuring that usage remains within responsible boundaries.

As an alternative, nano-enthusiasts advocate a more modest regulation structure combined with robust civilian research. Such an approach would focus work on the potential risks and benefits of nanotechnology, whilst ensuring that safe practices are exported to developing countries. (Indeed, it is in the interests of developing countries to adopt good practice, otherwise investment will flop). Thus, such a regime should be based on the monitoring of the sale of such technologies, rather than control. This situation is analogous to biotechnology: the DNA experience, for example, suggests that a combination of self-regulation and government co-ordination can answer legitimate safety concerns while allowing scientific research to flourish (Reynolds, 2002). Thus, while there is no way of knowing, *a priori*, the unintended and higher order consequences of nanotechnology, the participation of environmental and social scientists in the field may allow for important issues to be identified earlier, the right questions to be raised, and necessary corrective actions to be taken. It does seem likely that some form of regulatory control will be necessary to assure that nanotechnology is developed safely—*'safe designs, safe procedures and methods to test for potentially hazardous assemblers can be incorporated into standards by consensus of interested parties'* (Forrest, 1989). The greatest danger, however, appears to be intentional abuse of the technology, so certain aspects of development should be performed in a secure environment.

CONCERNS

Introduction

The fields of strong AI and robotics are generally regarded as controversial because of their far-reaching social, ethical, and philosophical implications. Research managers are in no doubt that such controversy has affected the funding environment for AI and the objectives of many research programmes (NRC, 1999). However, in general, less attention is paid to the implications of weak AI, even though many of the applications of this field, as demonstrated above, are in operation today. In other words, it should be recognised that many of the concerns described below do not rely on the long-term development of strong AI as popularly imagined. As for the section on nanotechnology then, this section, as well as considering the connotations of AI, will attempt to distinguish between short- and long-term concerns that advancements in this area will surely bring.

Predictive Intelligence

According to Kirsner (2002), the technology world's big debate for 2003 will centre on predictive intelligence. This aspect of AI, already touched upon above, concerns the ability to use software running on powerful computers to analyze information about ones prior behaviour. In the private sector, companies are already using predictive intelligence to analyze data profiles and solve more mundane business problems. These include Epsilon—a database marketing company based in the US, which have been combing through transactional data since the 1980s to help its customers market more effectively—along with other projects designed to identify which customers are more likely to spend the most money (Kirsner, 2002).

The most dramatic example of this is provided by the US DoD, which has established a research group to develop technology for information gathering and analysis on a huge scale. Its goal is to mine data sources all over the world—including government and commercial stores of personal information—to look for terrorists and terrorist threats (Anthes, 2002). This programme includes the recently-established controversial Total Information Awareness (TIA) office which aims to 'revolutionize the ability of the US to detect, classify and identify foreign terrorists, decipher their plans, and take timely action to pre-empt and defeat terrorist acts.' The tools which the TIA intends to develop to achieve this rely to a large extent on new AI technologies. These include 'entity extraction from natural language text' and 'biologically inspired algorithms for agent control.' Furthermore, one of the TIA's 13 subdivisions, the Human Identification at a Distance (HumanID) programme, is releasing contracts for face, iris and gait recognition. Another of the subdivisions, FutureMap, will concentrate on market-based techniques for avoiding surprise and predicting future events (Hertzberg, 2002).

A second programme, called Evidence Extraction and Link Discovery (EELD), aims to develop technology for *automated discovery, extraction and linking of sparse evidence contained in large amounts of classified and unclassified data sources'* (Anthes, 2002). In order to achieve this, EELD will have to develop detection capabilities to extract relevant data and relationships about people, organisations and activities from huge volumes of data.

Apart from the sheer ambitiousness of the programmes, TIA and EELD have generated concern mainly in relation to their implications for infringing individual and group privacy, and the possibility of such information being handled carelessly or even leading to malevolence. Indeed, it only takes a moment of reflection to consider that nearly everyone in modern society has at least one fact about themselves to hide. And yet, in spite of these well-founded concerns, both the TIA and EELD are already in active development; in response, Hertzberg (2002) recommends that, at a minimum, a temporary shutdown of the EELD system pending some sort of congressional review and the creation of safeguards is highly desirable.

AI and Robotic Autonomy

Many of the major ethical issues surrounding AI-related development hinge upon the potential for software and robot autonomy. In the short term, some commentators question whether people will really want to cede control over our affairs to an artificially intelligent piece of software, which might even have its own legal powers. Broersma (2001) believes that, while some autonomy is beneficial, absolute autonomy is frightening. For one thing, it is clear that legal systems are not yet prepared for high autonomy systems, even in scenarios that are relatively simple to envisage, such as the possession of personal information. In the longer-term, however, in which it is possible to envisage extremely advanced applications of hard AI, serious questions arise concerning military conflict, and robot 'take-overs' and machine rights. Each of these is dealt with in turn below.

AI and Military Conflict

This report shows that the military interest in AI is significant. However, as pointed out above, the difficulties involved in achieving anything resembling hard AI surely mean that any such system will be subject to reliability concerns. This idea is not new; the issue is picked up by Thompson as early as 1977, who sets out his concerns regarding existing and planned uses of computer technology as part of nuclear weapons systems. More generally, it is his belief that no computer system has the capacity to reliably make decisions of the required kind and in the required circumstances, nor can one ever be constructed. This is because the complexity and sensitivity of such systems makes exhaustive characterization extremely difficult, and any resulting mistakes cannot be corrected via the usual process of use, failure and modification. More recently, the controversial US National Missile Defence programme, which is being designed using the latest AI technology, provides a second example. The system is supposed to dispense 'kill power' based on an ability to recognise incoming missiles in a matter of seconds and then decide whether to destroy, intercept or ignore them (Newquist, 1987). However, serious concerns are already being voiced based upon the workability of such a system. This is because, while testing may be possible for an autonomous tank and other weapons of the electronic battlefield, it is not feasible for National Missile Defence. Such a system can only be realistically evaluated in actual combat (Augarten, 1986). More fundamentally, significant moral difficulties arise out of human distaste for autonomous weapons. Gary Chapman (2000) summarizes this concern well:

> '[Such arms] are a revolution in warfare in that they will be the first machines given the responsibility for killing human beings without human direction or supervision. To make this more

accurate, these weapons will be the first killing machines that are actually predatory, that are designed to hunt human beings and destroy them.'

Indeed, the UCAV example provided above demonstrates that potentially, in battle, humans may be taken out of the decision-making loop and still be on the receiving end—where the 'kill power' goes.

Robot 'Take-over' and Machine Rights

Such issues of predatory machines are bound to raise concern over the scenario of AIs overtaking humankind and thus somehow competing with him. This idea has often been popularized by classic science fiction works and populist academics, such as Professor Kevin Warwick, Professor of Cybernetics at the University of Reading, UK, who has repeated his beliefs concerning robot 'take-over' on many occasions in the press, in his books, and on television and radio. Consider the following letter from Nicholas Albery (1999) of the Institute of Social Inventions. Published in New Scientist and entitled Robot Terror, Albery seeks support for the following petition:

'In view of the likelihood that early in the next millennium computers and robots will be developed with a capacity and complexity greater than that of the human brain, and with the potential to act malevolently towards humans, we, the undersigned, call on politicians and scientific associations to establish an international commission to monitor and control the development of artificial intelligence systems.'

It is this kind of claim that seems to infuriate many in the AI scientific community. Chris Malcolm (2001) of the School of Artificial Intelligence at Edinburgh University, for example, describes belief in the robot take-over scenario as 'dangerous' and 'misleading'. He points out that public overreaction to AI stems from an assumption that something which displays some of the attributes of creaturehood must possess all the attributes of creaturehood. In his words:

'Intelligence is no more enough to make a real creature than is fur and beady eyes. No matter how much intelligence is added to your word processor it is not going to sulk and refuse to edit any more letters if you don't improve your spelling . . . Our problem is that while we have got used to the idea that teddy bears are not real even though we may be in the habit of talking to them at length, we are not used to contraptions being intelligent enough to talk back, and are willing to credit them with possession of the full orchestra of creaturehood on hearing a few flute-like notes.'

Perhaps the most measured assessment of the possibility of tyrannical take-over to date stems from the work of Whitby and Oliver (2001), who, in addition to the classic worst case scenario, focus on the more subtle ideas of 'cultural reliance' and 'co-evolution'. With regard to the former, the authors conclude that: *'although not obviously misguided or incoherent, predictions of tyrannical take-over are wrong. This is due to a number of possible failsafe methods, such as buddy systems, ethical systems programming, and perhaps most importantly, humans as final arbitrators in decision making.'* In any case, it is not clear in the first place why intelligence should necessarily be regarded as synonymous with aggression. On the other hand, cultural reliance, in which humans somehow allow a position of dependency on AI and robotics to develop, and co-evolution, in which human and machine become inextricably intertwined, are regarded as more probable.

The strong public reaction to machine takeover appears, then, not to be well founded. However, if it is possible to agree, for argument's sake, that humankind will be able to create a truly intelligent machine, a much deeper issue arises: how will a sentient artificial being be received by humankind and by society? Barry (2001) asks pertinent questions: *'Would it be forced to exist like its automaton predecessors who have effectively been our slaves, or would it enjoy the same rights as the humans who created it, simply because of its intellect?'* This is an enormous question that touches religion, politics and law, but to date little serious discussion has been given to the possibility of a new intelligent species and to the rights an autonomous sentient might claim.

DISCUSSION

The short-term concerns surrounding AI and robotics are mainly ethical in nature. This is in contrast to nanotechnology, the potential dangers of which cover a much larger spectrum and one that includes environmental risk. As shown earlier, weak AI tends to create concern with respect to its role as a tool for human interaction, throwing up issues of responsibility, privacy and trust. Applications in this area are emerging all the time, making 2003 the right time to begin public debate over these concerns. This is important for three main reasons. First, there might be a tendency for AI technology to creep into out lives largely unnoticed. This is because of the well-documented AI effect, due to which the major applications of AI research are mostly hidden from view because they are embedded in larger software systems. Second, many of these applications are morally ambiguous—a grey area of ethics that stands in stark contrast to Isaac Asimov's famously clear-cut three laws of robotics. Third, presuming that a public debate over AI can be initiated, there is little evidence to date that this discussion will affect military and commercial interests. Having said that, there is evidence of some attempt to flesh out a code of professionalism for AI. For example, in reference to AI and responsibility, Whitby (1984) writes:

> 'Where an AI system is introduced into any human system it shall be the responsibility of the AI professional to ensure that a human or group of humans within the system shall take moral and/or legal responsibility for the human consequences of any malfunction of the AI system.'

However, there is little sign in the literature that suggests these ideas have been followed up on.

Strong AI, on the other hand, asks much more fundamental questions as the field necessarily deals with human/machine relationships per se. As a consequence, the kinds of tools that might be necessary to begin debate over strong AI are not even here yet, so great are the implications. However, it is likely that this technology will not occur in our lifetimes; regardless of how often Professor Warwick is presented as an AI expert, the fact remains that his opinions are far removed from the majority view of the AI community (Colton, 2001). On the other hand, this report is by no means intended to downplay such potentially revolutionary developments as 'mere' science fiction. For, if the long-term potential of AI was to be realised, then it would surely have a demonstrable impact in a whole range of industrial and, in particular, service sectors.

CONCLUSION

This report began by stressing the need to provide background information on nanotechnology and AI. In doing so, it was hoped that the prospects of these emerging technologies to affect quality of life in the coming decades could be realistically assessed. One consequence of providing such an overview is that there can be no decisive conclusions as such; the industries characterised here are too dynamic and uncertain to generate any real sense of resolution. However, it is possible to highlight a number of important differences and similarities between nanotechnology and AI which go some way to shedding more light on their character.

Perhaps the greatest contrast between the two industries concerns public interest. Indeed, as this report has demonstrated, nanotechnology is widely regarded as a 'new' and exciting branch of science and technology. This belief has contributed to the massive period of growth that this high-profile and wide-ranging field is currently enjoying. AI, on the other hand, is viewed by many as an highly specialised and unproven discipline. One reason for this concerns the gross over-optimism that characterised the industry in the 1960s and 1980s. Another reason reflects the AI community's seemingly insurmountable difficulty in publicising its own achievements without whipping up general anxiety over machine superiority. The upshot of all this has been the field's struggle to attract funding in the past and it is likely that this trend will continue for sometime into the foreseeable future.

Revealing similarities also exist between nanotechnology and AI. There has been much talk recently regarding the convergence of traditionally separate scientific fields, in particular the blurring of the boundaries between the physical sciences and life sciences—perhaps even the first step towards the long sought after unification of physics, chemistry and biology (Howard, 2002). For example, the concourse of nanoscience, biotechnology, IT, and cognitive science ('NBIC') was discussed during a December 2001 NSF workshop. NBIC, it was agreed *could achieve a tremendous improvement in human abilities, societal outcomes, the nation's productivity and the quality of life'* (Roco and Bainbridge, 2003). In some ways, the above conclusion is hardly surprising given the ambitious and broad scope of the technologies discussed in this report. As pointed out above, 'convergence' largely arises from the wide availability of techniques and tools on offer today—the real innovation stems from the process of bringing individuals from traditionally separate disciplines together.

Most importantly for convergence here, it is possible that developments in nanotechnology could lead to advances in AI through improvements in computer miniaturisation, performance, or architecture, or through the sensor interface. In addition, it seems fair to assume that any futuristic nanobots would have to be imbued with a reasonable degree of AI. A second, more contentious similarity concerns reinvention. As demonstrated in this report, the 'rediscovery' of AI has been a virtual necessity for the survival of the industry; for nanotechnology the phenomena is less obvious but is arguably there all the same. That is, as a natural extension of the micromechanical and MEMS research that began in the 1960s, nanoscience is hardly 'new' as such; rather, 'nano' can be viewed as a useful tag with which to boost funding. Just what the consequences of this strategy will be, it is hard to tell. Ironically, AI provides an excellent example of a promising scientific discipline that has often resulted in disappointment. Whether the same happens to nanotechnology remains to be seen.

The second consequence of providing an overview is that certain elements of nanotechnology and AI development are bound to be overlooked. First, the difficulties of drawing out accurate statistics for corporate R&D have already been alluded to earlier. Second, there are wide ranging applications across the economy for sensors that can support industrial processes and be incorporated into new or existing products (Miles and Jarvis, 2001). The application of nanotechnology to this area should allow for improvements in functionality and much decreased size. Third, a more in-depth analysis of environmental concerns is warranted. This is because public acceptability of such risk is likely to vary considerably in relation to the application being considered. For example, the application of nanotechnology to computerisation is less likely to cause concern than those practices which might lead to the release of nanoparticles into the environment, such as the disposal of nano-based composites. Fourth, it is possible to conceive of a number of environmental goods that may arise. For example, the potential for gains in energy generation and efficiency have already been pointed out, and it is conceivable that dramatic improvements in environmental sensing and modelling could also be achieved. However, any pervasive diffusion of nano- and AI-based technologies in the coming decades is bound to have a significant effect on the demand for resources by industry, transport and the domestic sector. The way in which these more fundamental changes might impact on the environment would have to form the basis of a much larger technology assessment, in which long-term structural changes to global industry and commerce were considered.

Finally, it is easy to overlook the lessons that attitudes towards technological development teach us about human nature. This report has largely relied upon the technique of looking ahead, identifying technological possibilities, and assessing the likelihood of successfully moving towards their realisation. Significantly, this process mirrors that of technological innovators, a kind of thinking that often translates into the belief that technological development is autonomous—the ultimate self-fulfilling prophecy. To some extent we are already on this road. Most technologies covered in this report are within the bounds of current scientific possibility and it is just a matter of time, effort and expenditure before they are realised. However, the contrasting fortunes of the nanotechnology and AI industries remind us that much of this progress hinges on public approval. Ultimately, a 21st-Century acceptance model calls for technological innovations to be received on a voluntary basis where the perceptible usefulness of new technology products are balanced against associated risks that are shown to be manageable.

CHAPTER 23

■■■

Beyond Excellence: The Rich, Superrich and the Rest of Us

Allan Ornstein

The issues concerning *excellence* and *equality* go back to Greek civilization, when Plato wrote the *Republic* and the *Laws* and tried to define universal concepts such as truth, goodness, justice and the spiritual world of ideas. These twin issues continue to impact on society and involve a delicate and shifting scale with regard to the kinds of performance society chooses to reward, resulting in the conditions of social and economic mobility and the degree of stratification within society.

Most liberal and conservative pundits in the U.S. have their own ideas about excellence and equality of opportunity in education, jobs, and society in general. Many of us are unable to agree on what is equitable or fair, and how much we can stretch the embodiment of reform or the fiber of society. When large numbers of people perceive the system as unfair or rigged so that no matter how hard they work few rewards are achieved, the people who feel discriminated will stop working hard and thus fulfill preconceived expectations about their lazy or inadequate performance. The subordinate group may even adopt the terminology of the dominate group, especially if the latter group controls the institutions of society and the media.

Too much emphasis on egalitarianism can lead to mediocrity, indifference, and economic decline. Extreme egalitarianism leads to policies that handicap or penalize bright and talented people, whereby the goal of equal opportunity for individuals is replaced by the goal of equal results among groups. Such a society devaluates the use of tests and other forms of objective data. On the other hand, excellence carried too far can create social and economic differences, hostilities among groups, and a stratified society. Even worse, over emphasis on achievement and unbridled individual performance can lead to a discussion of the unequal capacities of individuals and groups, and an excuse for keeping people in a second-class status and for violating basic human rights. Finally, when excellence turns into winning at all costs or making loads of money without restraints, the process often leads to cheating or unethical behavior (sometimes criminal behavior).

Democratic societies tend to ignore differences in intelligence where possible; when it cannot be avoided, the blame is shifted to the institutions or agents of society. No group is supposed to be regarded as better or smarter than another group. Whenever differences in capacity are discussed in a democratic society, the politically correct view is that differences vary among individuals and not groups. In a heterogeneous society like ours, when we focus on differences in achievement or economic outcomes, the result can lead to a host of hotly contested issues. And when we compare group differences or outcomes, the debate can become highly emotional—focusing on differences in ability among different ethnic groups, accusations of racism, or using the race card as a means to stifle public discussion.

Given how American society has evolved, the ideal is to search for the golden mean which goes back to the ancient Greeks, and to achieve a balancing act which rewards merit and hard work and provides a floor or safety net for low-performing, slow running and weaker individuals. But despite this ideal standard for society, we are confronted with the harsh truth that this nation remains much more stratified than what its principles suggest. Moreover, there is very little movement from one class to another in American society. We would like to believe that through merit and hard work anyone can achieve the American dream. Our Founding Fathers rejected aristocracy and inherited privilege.

Yet we are heading toward the creation of a new aristocracy—much worse than the autocratic world that our Founding Fathers feared and tried to avoid. The new aristocracy is rooted in the rise of a new money class: Wall Street and the banking industry, the entertainment industry (including Hollywood stars, pop singers, and professional athletes) and the captains of industry. At the same time, we are witnessing the dismantling of the middle class which is the backbone of democracy. We are also beginning to question whether college is still the main avenue for achieving middle-class status, given the rising costs of tuition and debt incurred for attending college. For example, college tuition annually increased between 5 to 6 percent between 2000 and 2012, according to the College Board, running about 2–3 times the inflation rate for the same period.

THE VALUE OF A COLLEGE EDUCATION

Since the turn of the twenty-first century, college graduates have seen their wages stagnate while two-thirds of all undergraduates graduate with an average debt of $26,000 and masters' students compile an average debt of over $50,000 according to Helaine Olen in *Pound Foolish*. The total student debt in 2014 amounted to more than $1.2 trillion, a sum greater than the combined U.S. credit card debt and all auto loan debt. Increasingly, a number of pundits are questioning the economic value of a college education. Given $50,000 per year for four years (cost for college tuition and room and board for many private colleges), that is $200,000 placed in a money market or insurance account at age 18, compounded at 4% per year for 50 years (22 + 45 = 67 years, the age when Social Security starts), yields a better lifetime return ($1.4 million) than the difference earned between a college graduate and high school graduate (slightly more than $900,000). At 6% the yield is $3.7 million and at 8% the yield is a whopping $9.4 million or $8.5 million more than the lifetime income between a college and high school graduate. Properly structured with an insurance company or with a Roth account, no taxes have to be paid when the money is taken out of the account.

Another way for questioning the value of a college education is to compare the cost of state universities with private ones. Consider four major state universities, and their annual tuition cost for the year 2013/2014. (No other costs are considered such as room and board, registration fees, books, health insurance, etc.) University of North Carolina–Chapel Hill, $5,800; University of Wisconsin–Madison, $9,200; Ohio State University, $9,750; and University of Texas–Austin, $9,000–$11,200 depending on your field of study. Now compare these figures with the tuition of Ivy League schools: Harvard, $43,900; Dartmouth, $45,500; Yale, $45,800; Columbia, $46,800.

So the question arises: Is an Ivy League education worth 4.5 to 8 times the price of tuition of a major state university? Does the price differential mean an Ivy League graduate has 4.5 to 8 times better chance to succeed or achieve excellence in one's field? Given the issue of student debt, is the extra expense of about $35,000 per year or $140,000 total worth attending an Ivy League school? Is going to college in general worth the cost? Most "experts" say yes, because college graduates have a lower unemployment rate and earn more money than without a degree. But a growing number of college graduates who must pay the debt are questioning whether a college education justifies the debt burden. As *The Wall Street Journal* pointed out that from 2005 to 2012, the average loan debt increased 35 percent, adjusting for inflation, while the median salary of college graduates dropped 2.2 percent.

Not only does growing student debt have a detrimental effect on the ability of college graduates to afford a home mortgage, the *Journal* also reported that people under 40 with student loans have more other debt—credit cards, auto loans, etc.—and less net worth than their counterparts without student debt. As student debt gets heavier, it is safe to assume that other issues surface such as depression, low work morale, low job performance levels, less purchasing power and in turn a ceiling on economic growth.

And just to add salt to the discussion, consider the opinion of Laszlo Bock who heads up the hiring at Google. He admits he is willing to hire people without a college degree. He's not concerned about what you know or where you learned it, rather what value you can create with what you know. Of course, if we want an informed citizenry or a baseline for cultural literacy, college has value. If you go to college, you need to acquire more than broad knowledge. You need to acquire skills for the workplace and the ability to apply knowledge in a logical and systematic way. Going to Harvard or Yale does not necessarily guarantee this kind of outcome. One might even argue that people who have these traits get accepted to Ivy League schools and could develop the same analytical thought processes at Chapel Hill or Ohio State.

When it comes to comparing average starting salaries between graduates from the above four state universities and the four Ivy League schools, the difference is about $10,000 to $12,000. But the educational institution has much less direct effect on salaries once we introduce other factors: supply-demand for the particular job, market pay rates for people doing similar work, regional location of the job, candidates IQ, personality, and work (or internship) experience, parents' network of friends and colleagues, etc. When these factors or variables are introduced the direct effect of the college on starting salaries is miniscule—often not worth the differences in total tuition costs. Then there is always the notion of luck or the unaccounted for variance. This factor alone may account for as much as 50 percent of the monetary outcomes or the difference in starting salaries. The long and short of all the factors is simple: Predicting an individual's future capacity to perform on the job remains a hazardous undertaking, and considering only one factor (education) oversimplifies the process. When judging talent and ability, or someone's future performance on the job, we must not limit our thinking to a narrow or singular factor for hiring the best candidate.

In the meantime, tuition revenues for private colleges are beginning to peak and undergraduate enrollments are sliding downward because of price sensitivity—yielding a smaller pool of traditional students. Over the next several years, according to Michael Townsley, former president of Pennsylvania Institute of Technology, "small colleges with meager enrollments could be in deep trouble" and disappear. Part of the problem is the economy, but students increasingly are heading to state universities and community colleges (where costs are often $5,000 a year or less) to save on tuition.

RULING THE WORLD

So in a nutshell, who is the ruling class? Who runs the world? Certainly not those families earning $250,000 a year in 2013, a magical number the Obama Administration initially wanted to use for increasing taxes (Obama got the message; he wound up with a higher income level for raising taxes). In fact, on the East and West coasts, where living expenses are higher than the rest of the U.S., $250,000 suggests nothing more than the middle class or upper middle class. For some pundits, however, $250,000 suggests the top 2 percent. As for running the world, ordinary Americans (the bottom 99 percent) have no say. According to *CNN Money* report, the majority (76 percent of Americans in 2013) live paycheck to paycheck; in fact, most Americans live just above subsistence level but don't realize it—until they lose their job. Only 50 percent of working Americans have sufficient savings to cover three months of expenses in the event they lose their job, and 37 percent have no savings. But, then, that has been the human condition since the crack of civilization. And, we are supposed to be the fortunate ones. As Otto Bismarck, the Prussian chancellor, once muttered: "God has special providence for fools, drunks, and the United States of America."

The rise of the nation-state coupled with the global economy, has given rise to what David Rothkopt in *Superclass* calls a "national ruling class" and a "global power elite"—business and financial titans who run large public companies and banks, supra organizations such as the World Bank and International Monetary Fund, and who have huge influence on political leaders around the world.

These super elites have all the characteristics of the old Protestant elite, but with the essential difference that they operate from a global market and they have sway over more money and a larger share of the economic pie. They attend the same elitist universities such as Harvard, Yale, and University of Chicago, attend the same forums such as the Council on Foreign Relations and World Economic Forum, travel in private gulf stream jets, vacation in private ski havens like The Yellowstone Club, where they can mingle discreetly without bodyguards (since the place is protected by the Secret Service), invest in the same hedge funds such as the Carlyle Group and Blackstone Group and often illegally bury money offshore and thus avoid or delay for years the need to pay taxes and use tax loopholes to gift millions to their descendants without paying estate taxes. They get together at meetings and resorts with former presidents, prime ministers and CEOs; invite or nominate each other to corporate boards and foundations; trade inside information; and make each other richer. You would think that given the rise of a knowledge-based, high-tech society men and women with talent and ability would be in high *demand*. Given a world tilted in favor of the superrich, the demand may be superficial or overrated. Remember throughout history, people with high IQ and creative skills have been ignored or lay untapped in a society stratified by the monarchy and nobility class.

It matters little how smart or talented the superclass are; they belong to the right clubs and vacation spots, attend Ivy League universities, and through blood, intermarriage and mentor or father-son relationships continue to maintain power and influence. It is the same system of inherited privilege and political power that allows for the Bushes, Kennedys, Rockefellers, and DuPonts to live in splendor and influence, if not dominate, the world stage. It is similar to the power, influence, and money the nobility in Europe once had, and what the Old World monarchs passed from one generation to the next—and thus built and maintained a stratified society for thousands of years.

HARD TIMES FOR LABOR

As a nation, we face a choice. Either we build an economy in which the vast majority of workers can earn enough to adequately support their families or we build a government which is prepared to support or subsidize an increasing population that is the American labor force being left behind. Many workers in lower- and middle-skilled sectors can no longer count on full-time employment or employment at a decent pay scale. Moreover, their hours can be cut sharply from week to week based on the weather or business outlook. They have no union affiliation to protect their wages or working conditions. Moreover, the unions in the U.S. are struggling because of automation and global competition. Nearly half the workforce in the U.S. cannot survive on their own. They need various forms of welfare to make it on a daily basis, and thus create a new drain on taxpayers. For example, workers in restaurants, large chain-stores, and hotels earned $8.69 an hour in 2013, according to the Economic Policy Institute.

In the meantime, conservative politicians refuse to increase the minimum wage because of concerns for increased unemployment among unskilled workers and that extra labor cost will strain small businesses. The American workforce has been hollowed out for the last three decades—losing semi-skilled and skilled manufacturing jobs that can be performed more cheaply by machines or foreign workers. To some extent, it has splintered the working force into less educated workers (hotel, retail, food, etc.) and professional service workers (teachers, nurses, police etc.) that cannot be easily outsourced or mechanized. The workforce can also be categorized into full-time workers, with some health and pension benefits, and "independent contractors" without benefits who receive a "1099" tax form at the end of the year. These workers are locked into this new category because they cannot find regular jobs. The system has found an easy and cheap way to hire workers with minimal overhead as well as protection against employee rights, litigation, strikes etc.—and no minimum wage. The system can hire and fire these independent contractors at will, as the economy expands or contracts.

The U.S. labor force is also characterized by a growing skill gap. A recent study by the Organization for Economic Cooperation and Development (OECD) assessed 22 advanced, industrialized nations and 160,000 workers. Fewer than 12 percent of Americans passed in two or more of the six levels of literacy. While younger cohorts are generally better skilled and educated than older ones in other industrialized countries, in the U.S. the younger workers are less skilled than the rest. This suggests that the workforce skills in other industrialized nations will continue to overtake the U.S. It also means that "human capital" in the U.S. is waning. While the nation still rewards skilled workers, the supply is not keeping up—suggesting growing inequality of income among U.S. workers; skilled vs. unskilled. Those trends parallel the fact that 22 percent of U.S. high-school students drop out of school which is among the highest amounts compared to other OECD countries.

In another study, *Social Progress Index 2014*, involving more than 100 countries, Michael Porter of the Harvard Business School reported that U.S. citizens rank 39th in basic knowledge, and 70th in health and wellness; moreover, he concludes there is no direct relationship between economic growth and social/medical well-being. This is especially true when economic growth is not equal among the nation's population; or, if I may add, when business profits are earmarked to a tiny group or when we believe we live in a meritocracy in which great wealth is earned and deserved by only "job creators" or entrepreneurs who risk capital.

CONCLUSION

The economic calamity of the Great Recession should have shattered some of the cherished tenets of capitalism. But, John Cassidy, a financial journalist, sizes up the problem in *How Markets Fail*. He points out there are no hard-and-fast principles to eliminate or modify. Capitalism means different things to different people; liberals and conservatives have very different views on how to reform it. It so happens that the free market system has dominated American thinking since the election of President Reagan, whose goal was to downsize government and reduce taxes for the rich. Alan Greenspan, the chairperson of the Federal Reserve from 1987 to 2006, added fuel to the fire. He sold Americans on the ideas that financial markets are rational and self-correcting mechanism. The outcome was the worst financial crisis since the Great Depression, with no one held accountable or prosecuted for their role in the crisis (except in the case of overt fraud—such as with Madoff).

The conservative movement in the U.S. is anti-government, resents government regulation of corporate America, and views it as "Big Brother." So long as the American economy is marked by the closure or bankruptcy of plants making cars, clothes, and electronics—where the losers are working people—there is little concern for government regulation. When banks and Wall Street go under and stocks plummet, conservatives rally and come forth with government assistance. The argument is these institutions are "too big to fail" and must be saved in order to ward off financial disaster and save jobs.

Then there is the government-capitalist divide—or myth. More government regulations are considered a violation of individual liberty; they supposedly limit the vitality and innovativeness of society, and hinder workers and work productivity. The conservative pundits rely on a "Trojan horse"—a backdoor attack for limiting the size of government in order to enhance free markets—whereby the winner is the corporate or banking titan (or capitalist) and the loser is the worker. Why ordinary people are seduced by the notion of free markets probably has something to do with partisan politics and cultural issues that divide the nation. Of course, there is always Alexander Hamilton's viewpoint: The masses are stupid; they adopt herd behavior, and they will always be second class to the banking and manufacturing class.

Conservative economists and the moneyed class try to play down the misadventures of the financial sector, and then resurrect its reputation. But the losers of the socio-economic pyramid (the bottom 95 to 99 percent) should expect to feel the long slog of the economy: Unemployment, underemployment, foreclosures, and loss of pension funds. In the meantime, big business and big banking have quickly returned to the festive days of huge profits and bonuses. The public now assumes the game is rigged and that the government merely protects the rich and powerful in corporate America and on Wall Street at the expense of the people. To be sure, the people on Main Street are simmering with rage—a period in time similar to the French monarch and nobility class vis-a-vis the peasants that stormed the Bastille.

Let me sum it up in as few words as possible. The best way to nurture excellence is to build a society which discourages and limits inherited wealth and privilege and fosters a balanced playing field with real opportunities for ordinary people. The need is to recognize and reward different forms of excellence, and to provide special provisions for those who are slow, weak, or less than average since more than 50 percent of the population fall into these categories at any given period. Statistically speaking, your time will come! If we only reward the fast, strong and above average, inequality is bound to grow. We need floors and ceilings to reduce inequality, sort of a balancing act which must be worked out by political compromise.

More equality is possible if Americans choose it. What the people need to do is to use their voice and vote for political leaders who will put people before property, legislate a floor and ceiling in income and wealth, and pay people based on how their performance (or job) influences the common good—and not as a profit versus cost factor. There is some merit in periodically storming the Bastille, eliminating the old guards who have become entrenched (since power corrupts), and hanging a few rotten politicians in the village square—especially those who have betrayed the people and gotten fat and rich off the peoples' sweat and labor.

References

Beattie, Alan. *False Economy: A Surprising Economic History of the World* (New York: Riverhead, 2009).

Friedman, Thomas L. *The World Is Flat (*New York: Farrar, Straus and Giroux, 2005).

Huntington, James B. *Work's New Age: The End of Full Employment and What It Means to You* (Eldred, NY: Royal Flush, 2012).

Perkins, John. *Confessions of an Economic Hit Man* (San Francisco: Berrett-Koehler, 2004).

Prins, Nomi. *All the Presidents' Bankers: The Hidden Alliances That Drive American Power* (New York: Nation, 2013).

Rothkopf, David J. *Superclass* (New York: Farrar, Straus and Giroux, 2008).

Shlaes, Amity. *The Forgotten Man* (New York: Harper Collins, 2007).

Vogel, Kenneth P. *Big Money* (New York: Public Affairs, 2014).

APPENDIX A

∎∎∎

CHAPTER 1

This chapter focuses on the impact of neoliberalism as a system of scientific management illustrating a wide range of studies from other fields. It is argued that while there are important differences in how neoliberalism has been used across nations and disciplines, there are key principles and outcomes that can serve a specific function for scholars attempting a more careful examination of neoliberalism. Some of these outcomes are: the reduction of public funding for universities; the separation of research and teaching missions; higher numbers of temporary faculty; the suspension of the scientific author; the narrowing of research to focus on the needs of commercial actors; an increasing on market take-up to adjudicate intellectual disputes; and the intense enrichment of academic property in an attempt to commercialize knowledge, delaying the production and distribution of science. Together, these shifts suggest that the impact of neoliberal science policy and management extends far beyond the patent system into the methods, organization, and content of science. The argument is that scholars start to accept a detailed exploration of exactly how the external political–economic forces of neoliberalism are changing technoscience. Existing studies of neoliberalism and its effects argued that the impacts of neoliberal policies on the conduct, products, and organization of science have not been minor.

The character of universities is changing as new privatized rules of science management change the sources and quantities of funding. The strengthening of intellectual property protection and the linked insistence on the commercialization of knowledge are transforming the production and dissemination of knowledge. One example is when Evans points to a drop in publications by researchers engaged in public/private partnerships. Some other surveys have reported that research projects have been frustrated or even stopped entirely by disputes over MTAs. The focus upon patents only serves to divert attention from where the real obstacles have been raised. The cases also show that science is being produced for certain markets and their research. This narrowing is only compounded when the market becomes a tool for adjudicating scientific arguments. Contestations of what composes good evidence in power struggles over the creation of new markets call start to question the validity of the basic core of fields. It is possible that neoliberal science commands may leave us with ignorance. Neoliberalism continues to have profound impacts on the organization, practice, and social implications of science. The suggestion is that scholars agree to a detailed exploration of exactly how neoliberal theories of society are changing techno science. Such an exploration will require not just the more familiar elements of the toolkit, but also analysis of external political–economic forces: to understand the neoliberal regime of science organization and management. The key is to understand where it's coming from.

CHAPTER 2

Many people today assume automatically that technology is progress. There are still some criticisms of this view. This is partially because of wars and arms raises in the 20th century. Marx went to China in 1984, and it seemed as though the Chinese were incredibly hopeful about western technology. They had little sense that any problems might be created by technology. Many early Americans like Ben Franklin saw technology as a way to achieving social and political freedom for the masses. This was part of the revolt from totalitarianism. If some technology, especially in the factory system, would jeopardize these social and political goals, then that thing isn't worth its price in quality of life and should be rejected from the technology world. As America became more industrialized, the new industrialists who had both money and power came to see the technology which they helped produce as an end in itself. This is also a means to more purely economic ends.

The commonly used phrases like "manifest destiny" and "the conquest of nature" help justify the increasing forces of technology. This is also true even in the cost of the environment or Native Americans, all in the name of "civilization." Technological advancement is seen as advancement, period. Regardless of what social and political changes it might bring technological advancement is important. There is a great deal of optimism that if we continue to make scientific innovations of life, social and political ideals will take care of themselves automatically. The idea of technocratic seeing everything as parts of the machine, began to take control, and humanitarian goals like justice, freedom, and self-fulfillment became secondary. Technology was accepted unquestioningly, and efficiency and scientific progress were the main goals. "This is the stage that the Chinese seem to be at" says Marx. There was, however, some backlash from the technocratic view. Emerson, Thoreau, and others questioned whether we were remaking America for the better, and whether we were beginning to almost worship technology. They questioned whether new inventions were improved means to unimproved ends and whether we're becoming the tools of our tools. It was hard to take this too seriously when rapid improvements were being made in the material conditions of life. Today many people are starting to wonder if technology is always a good thing. The early notion of progress saw technology as a mere means to more important ends provided natural limits, and a way of assessing particular pieces of technology. If, however, we view technology as an end in itself, we're not led to ever question its value or place any limits on it. Marx says we need to consider what we want our technologies to accomplish. We can see that technology does not automatically mean progress toward our goals.

CHAPTER 3

When thinking about ethics, technology is often only mentioned as the source of our problems, not as a potential solution to our moral dilemmas. When thinking about technology, ethics is often only mentioned as a constraint on developments, not as a source and spring of innovation. In this paper, we argue that ethics can be the source of technological development rather than just a constraint, and technological progress can create moral progress rather than just moral problems. We show this by an analysis of how technology can contribute to the solution of so-called moral overload or moral dilemmas. Such dilemmas typically create a moral residue that is the basis of a second-order principle that tells us to reshape the world so that we can meet all our moral obligations. We can do so, among other things, through guided technological innovation. In discussions about technology, engineering and ethics, technology and engineering are usually treated as the source of ethical problems, and ethics is treated as a constraint on engineering and technological development.

CHAPTER 4

As the National Broadband Plan did not discuss the unique technology needs of the LGBT community, a Vision for Inclusion makes policy recommendations that could ensure the safe and universal access to broadband technologies for LGBT people. Similar to the National Broadband Plan, the Partnership opened the paper for public comment, giving LGBT individuals and allies the opportunity to share their views on the broadband needs of the community. A Vision for Inclusion lays out the different aspects of life in which LGBT people are impacted by broadband technologies.

CHAPTER 5

This chapter in this book is about women and girls in STEM. Science, technology, engineering, and mathematics (STEM) are widely regarded as critical to the national economy. Concern about America's ability to be competitive in the global economy has led to a number of calls to action to strengthen the pipeline into these fields (National Academy of Sciences, Committee on Science, Engineering & Public Policy, 2007; U.S. Government Accountability Office, 2006; U.S. Department of Education, 2006). Expanding and developing the STEM workforce is a critical issue for government, industry leaders, and educators. Despite the tremendous gains that girls and women have made in education and the workforce during the past 50 years, progress has been uneven, and certain scientific and engineering disciplines remain overwhelmingly male. This report addresses why there are still so few women in certain scientific and engineering fields and provides recommendations to increase the number of women in these fields. It provides a definition of STEM. This chapter also discusses preparation of girls for STEM fields, women in STEM in colleges and universities, women in the STEM workforce, why there are such few women and girls, and cognitive sex differences. Other topics this chapter discusses are how scientists and engineers are not necessarily the highest math achievers, and how women and girls might not be interested. The workplace environment, bias, and family responsibilities are also communicated. The last few topics they touch on are where do women and girls go from here, how girls' achievements and interest in math and science are shaped by the environment around them, how at colleges and universities little changes can make a big difference in attracting and retaining women in STEM, and how bias limits women's progress in scientific and engineering fields. This chapter also provides many graphs to show the statistics on the specific topic they are discussing.

CHAPTER 6

As research in game-based learning continues to expand, discussions examining the potential for gaming to increase student participation in STEM have also risen. Past research has found that there is a gender gap in science, technology, engineering, and math (STEM) careers. Accordingly, when considering the use of video games in the classroom there must be some attention paid to gender differences. This paper will provide a brief overview of the potential benefits of gaming in education, highlight some of the gender issues in gaming, and discuss the importance of game design for both enhancing learning and influencing students' future participation in STEM careers.

CHAPTER 7

The video game industry is a very large part of the economy today. This industry is continuously growing. One statistic shows that in 2011, 72% of American households play games on either a computer or through a game console. This industry has a value of over $25 billion and has employment of more than 120,000 citizens. More than half of the nation's parents believe that video games provide mental stimulation or education for its players. These statistics reflect the importance of video games in American society today. Games can help to encourage social development as well. As video games continue to become a greater part of the American culture it is important that we understand how important the impact of video games is on the population. Video games offer a form of entertainment to its players. It is possible to learn many skills through playing these games. Some skills are critical thinking, engaged learning, and positive social behavior. These could eventually be vital to students who would like to succeed in education. If students can learn to apply these skills and learning techniques to their schoolwork with the same passion, they can succeed. It is important to distinguish between "educational" games and "regular" video games. These types of games offer different ideas to students. One example in a game is that in Carmen San Diego, the player travels the world. This player uses information and clues from different geographical regions to hunt down an international criminal and her henchmen. In another game Number Munchers, the player controls a character that must navigate a web and "eat" numbers that fit certain conditions. These games are valuable to educators because they offer true substance to students in a manner that generates interest and activity. The value added from regular video games to education is harder to determine depending on your motivation. If gamers learn valid skills then they are more likely to be motivated to use these in games and apply them to education. The motivation in video games is essential. Many players want to win the game and have a good time in the process; this makes them apply themselves. If the players don't enjoy the game, then they stop playing and find something else to do. Most students are being forced to go through certain classes even if they are not enjoying the aspects of their education. The lack of motivation can be crucial and teachers need to find other ways to persuade students to apply themselves and shift their skills.

CHAPTER 8

While players of multi-player games are aware of their in-game economies, their growth and complexity would surprise many outside the world of gaming. With hundreds of millions of players around the world, MMOGs' in-game economies generate massive amounts of real dollars (i.e. MILLIONS), and real world economic theories can even be applied to these worlds. Many are now so big that game developers have hired real world economists to help them manage these complex systems. But with secondary economies, gold farming and other issues surfacing, are these systems in need of more attention, or even regulation? There is also the underlying theme that continues to grow as a by-product of video game economies.

CHAPTER 9

According to the National Center for Education Statistics, the percentage of undergraduate students taking at least one online class grew from 8%–20%. The Sloan Consortium states that approximately 5.6 million students enrolled in at least one online course during fall 2009, nearly 30% of all higher education students now take at least one course online. The percentage of students taking one or more courses online is increasing which reflects an increased confidence on the flexibility they afford. This shows that there is a boundary between the traditional and non-traditional ways of attending classes. Even classically traditional students at classically traditional institutions require nontraditional flexibility to meet their educational goals. Online learning has become the method for this change and it is forever altering the landscape of higher education. Classifying a student as "main campus" or "extended campus" or "distance" becomes meaningless in an environment where students take whatever courses they need in whatever location that best suits their requirements. These students are not concerned with unconditional labels; they are concerned with finishing the courses needed in any way that best fits their lifestyles. The type of students that commonly take distance learning courses are working adults or undergraduates who travel frequently. The Sloan Foundation has copied this concept called "localness." This means that student's access to education is always local to them, even if they do so through online learning. Students now have an option to take courses at an institution's main campus, regional or extended campus, completely online, or in a mixed mode format. Institutions can support "localness" by constructing programs that are flexible and that deliver courses in multiple ways.

At one specific institution, students moved back and forth between face-to-face and online modalities. It was estimated that approximately 20% of college student credit hours are generated online and that about double that number of students have taken one or more online courses. This type of behavior has become usual at both community colleges and universities. Demand for online and mixed mode courses continue to grow at a fast pace. Faculty and administrators who have not already changed to mixed mode or online need to recognize that students proffer their own campuses and respond accordingly with a supportive infrastructure. Institutions need to expand campus information systems to make it easier for students to select and register for online and mixed mode courses. On-campus classrooms will potentially need more multimedia and network capability to help bridge the online and on-ground environments for students. Campus technology communications might need to expand to accommodate greater numbers of students. Faculty will need to expand in order to prepare and support other faculty who will also be moving back and forth between modalities just as their students do. It is very common for a faculty member to teach face-to-face, online, and mixed mode courses. This is to monitor the behaviors of the students. Part of a strategic plan for these students, going forward, would be the need for the students to be supportive in the key components of the university.

CHAPTER 10

Can learning of mental imagery skills for visualizing shapes be accelerated with feature asking? Chemistry, physics, fine arts, military tactics, and laparoscopic surgery often depend on mentally visualizing shapes in their absence. Does working with 'spatial feature-masks' (skeletal shapes, missing key identifying portions) encourage people to use visualization strategies? This experimental study tested that hypothesis using an online computer game involving rotating and stamping a 3D cube on a 2D pattern. According to a chi-squared test, people who trained with 3D feature-masks reported using significantly more visual imagery strategies on a related visualization posttest. Spatial feature-masks provide a new building block for instructional designers to address educational outcomes involving visual imagery of shapes. The current study tested the hypothesis that "spatial feature masking" could encourage students to employ visual or visual imagery strategies in visuo-spatial problems. Spatial feature masking was defined as skeletal shapes, missing key identifying information, but with some remaining orienting shape information as support for visual imagery. The major results of the study were that participants who used the spatial feature-masks reported employing significantly more visual or visual imagery strategies on the posttest than did their non-feature-mask using counterparts. Moreover, across both groups, those who reported using visual or visual imagery strategies performed better on the posttest. These results strongly suggest that: 1) visual and visual imagery strategies were important for success on the posttest; and 2) spatial feature-masks are effective for encouraging people to use visual imagery strategies. Since the task in the current study was purely experimental, with no meaningful context for the participants, the authors suggest extending the use of spatial feature-masks into real-world, work, recreational, military and educational texts. Spatial feature-masks can be useful both as a research construct for investigating spatial abilities as well as a tool for instructional designers and educators in disciplines with visuo-spatial outcomes.

CHAPTER 11

In higher education institutions, students are given the choice between traditional classroom courses and virtual classroom courses. With the advent of technology in the classroom, this wave of instruction is becoming increasingly used. Nagel (2009) reports that the research firm Ambient Insight discloses that by 2014, there will be more than 22 million students taking online classes. Therefore, online courses need to implore strategies and activities that will be based on interactive and active learning. In addition, they need to continue to emphasize high critical thinking through writing, discussion, and inquiry. The activities as proscribed by Dixson (2010) call for the use of "collaborative activities, group discussion, and other forms of student-student interaction" (p. 2). These strategies are useful in online courses because they build a quality education and also teach the students the following characteristics—self-motivation skills, time management, assertiveness, initiative, and well-written communication. The students need to be self-directed, motivated, organized, independent, and take responsibility for their own learning (Mahoney, 2009). These students will be able to demonstrate creativity and innovation, communication and collaboration, conduct research and use information, think critically, solve problems, and make decisions, and use the technology effectively and productively (ISTE, 2011). These skills are extremely valuable for the students to possess and useful in future education and work related experience. In order for online courses to work well, El Mansour and Mupinga (2007) state both professors and students need to be trained in order to use the course management platform properly. With a more student centered approach, students are to take part in discussions and activities that teach specific domain knowledge and also other skills. These class activities are based in collaborative/cooperative group discussion, and other forms of student-student interactions (Dixson, 2010). Furthermore, students must be active rather than be passive by watching and listening to the professor. These online courses use audio, video, color, graphics, and animations in order to gain the interest of the student (El Mansour & Mupinga 2007).

CHAPTER 12

Gifted students are identified by individuals, such as teachers, administrators, and parents. These students are capable of high performance. Therefore, these students require differentiated educational programs and services that go beyond the regular school programs (Davis, Rimm, & Sieglem 2011). The differentiation of educational programs can be done through the use of technology. Periathiruvadi and Rinn (2012) believe that this differentiation through the use of technology "serves as an educational and creative outlet for some of the best and brightest minds in the world" (p. 153). It becomes essential that these students become engaged with what is considered to be 'complex technological advancements'. It is important to have the students engaged in the 'complex technological advancements' by relating it to the modes of technology that they are using. Addressing the social and emotional needs using technology becomes critical. The cognitive aspects are critical for the long-term functioning of the students in a professional setting. However, how the students use the technology necessitates a lot of critical analysis. The technology must be used in a productive, honest, and safe way. Therefore, there needs to be a structure at every aspect of the integration of technology in a gifted classroom, which is similar to how it should be integrated into a mainstream or special education classroom. There needs to be a logical reason for the technology's incorporation. The technology itself must allow the students to use it so that they are being the active users of the technology. It must build many cognitive and socio-emotional skills. The teachers must be able to use the technology in a productive manner. Finally, it must satisfy the goal of making students ready to be 21st century professionals.

CHAPTER 13

An electronic portfolio, also known as e-portfolio, is a collection of information that shows someone's work over a certain amount of time digitally. Teachers and students use e-portfolios to show what they have learned and the information they have gotten while in the course. These e-portfolios are a drastic upgrade from paper portfolios. This is because you can share more information with everyone in the course. This design has been around since the early 1990s. E-portfolios have influenced the way students around the world learn and present information. This way of studying is becoming more and more popular every year.

E-portfolios are used by students. One example of an e-portfolio would be a 12th grader that is collecting information throughout the year. After each assignment the students would upload the documents to their portfolio and at the end of the year the students would have assignments that show how much they have grown over the period of time. The students then have a year's worth of work in front of them. The student is able to reflect on the skills that they have learned throughout the year. This is important because the student can see where they have progressed or still have weaknesses in, instead of the teacher saying just telling them. The students are gaining critical thinking and communication skills because they are reflecting and writing about their experiences. Students are gaining technological skills due to the fact that they are spending more time on the computer. In addition to giving students important skills, e-portfolios can be used by students in high school to help them get into college. Students can show the colleges exactly what they have accomplished in high school rather than telling them. College students can benefit from having an e-portfolio as well because it can help them in landing a job. Job seekers make themselves noticeable to employers by having a collection of works that prove that they have the experience and skills necessary to accomplish jobs. Students greatly benefit from learning about and creating their own e-portfolio. E-portfolios seem to have a positive effect on students, employers, teachers, and institutions. They have all found a similar positive experience with this technology. This can help people express their personalities to others and help learn about their own strengths and weaknesses. This can teach important skills like technology, critical thinking, self-reflection, and communication. As technology in our lives increases, e-portfolios will become more and more important.

CHAPTER 14

As educators embrace learner-centered course delivery and curriculum design in which the student is an active participant in the instruction, the process of inquiry takes center stage. The learner-centered educator partners with the students encouraging them to continue their quest for discovery while building knowledge connections to the next levels of learning. The inquiry process is the foundation for high impact learning practices such as first-year experiences, learning communities, capstone projects, internships, and service learning that research has shown increases student engagement and retention. Reflection plays a critical role in moving the learning to the next level of inquiry. In order to move to that level, the reflection must include evidence of learning. The main outcome for learner-centered instruction is to engage students in the inquiry process and integrate their learning in all areas of their lives. The inquiry process and integrative learning need to become a habit of thought and connection that ignites learning and the construction of knowledge throughout a lifetime. The Lifelong ePortfolio Process is becoming a recognized method to facilitate inquiry, evidence-based reflection, and integrative learning. This process helps the student to connect learning with knowledge and develop the habit of lifelong learning.

CHAPTER 15

An approach to deriving such a large scale and multilingual resource by exploiting several facets of the on-line encyclopedia Wikipedia is discussed here. We show how we can build upon

Wikipedia's existing network of categories and articles to automatically discover new relations and their instances. Working on top of this network allows for added information to influence the network and be propagated throughout it using inference mechanisms that connect different pieces of existing knowledge. We then exploit this gained information to discover new relations that refine some of those found in the previous step. The result is a network containing approximately 3.7 million concepts with lexicalizations in numerous languages and 49+ million relation instances. Intrinsic and extrinsic evaluations show that this is a high quality resource and beneficial to various NLP tasks.

CHAPTER 16

For over three decades, Ray Kurzweil has been one of the most respected and provocative advocates of the role of technology. In his book *The Age of Spiritual Machines*, he argued that computers will soon challenge the full range of human intelligence at its best. He now studies the next step in this unavoidable evolutionary process. This process is the union of human and machine. The knowledge and skills embedded in our brains will be combined with greater capacity, speed, and knowledge-sharing ability of our designs. *The Singularity Is Near* portrays what life will be like after this event or a human-machine civilization. This is where our experiences shift from real reality to virtual reality and where our intelligence becomes non-biological. It can become trillions of times more powerful than singlehandedly human intelligence. This means that human aging and pollution will be reversed, world hunger will be solved, and our bodies and environment altered by nanotechnology to overcome the limitations of biology which include death. We will soon be able to create virtually any physical product just from information. These can result in drastic wealth creation. In addition to outlining these fantastic changes, Kurzweil also considers their social and philosophical outcomes. With its radical but optimistic view of the course of human development, *The Singularity Is Near* is certain to be one of the most widely discussed and provocative books.

CHAPTER 17

This is an article written by A. Hunter Dupree and he discusses the evolution of technology. He gives his view on the role of technology in society and the need for historical perspective. It is his own personal view on the history and evolution of technology. Mr. Dupree feels that if a modern approach is used in the history of technology, it might also be able to avoid the extremes of unlimited optimism and bitter pessimism by an analysis of the middle ground of cost and benefit. An understanding of many different rates of change and the relations between them and a quest for balance in the man-environment ecological system might provide a standard of value which would restore to proud and anxious modern man a measure of both courage and repose.

CHAPTER 18

This is an article written by Paul E. Ceruzzi. He discusses the evolution of technology. He provides the reader with his view on the Moore's Law and technological determinism reflections on the history of technology. He also expresses his own personal view on the history and evolution of technology. He feels that it is important to note at the outset that Moore's law was an empirical observation; it is not analogous to, say, Ohm's law, which relates resistance to current. Moore simply looked at the circuits being produced, plotted their density on a piece of semi-log graph paper, and found a straight line. Furthermore, he made this observation in 1965, when the integrated circuit was only six years old and had barely found its way out of the laboratory.

CHAPTER 19

Software systems today are an important part of each and every business model. Core product manufacturing, banking, healthcare, insurance, aviation, hospitality, social networking, shopping, e-commerce, education or any other areas are important. If any business has to be leveraged and simplified then software has to be integrated with the main stream business of any organization. Designing and development of any software system requires a lot of money, time, academics, domain knowledge, tools and communications. Though the software industry has developed quite a lot in the past, the percentage of software failure has also increased. This eventually led to the loss of money, time, and good-will, loss of information and in some cases severe failures of applications. Software could fail due to faults added in various stages of software or product development life cycle. This describes the case study of most common and severe types of software system failures in Software Industry. Every organization starts a project with the intent of deploying successfully to perform a function. There are reasons that this goal of the organization is not achieved due to faults which can eventually result in other failures. This could happen due to inappropriate project launch, planning, monitoring and control, execution or deployment of software systems. In bigger projects each phase of the product is considered to be a project. It is not a wrong statement to say that software failure could happen at any stage of software product development. Software failure is generally used when the software doesn't perform its planned function. The analysis of case studies pertaining to common and severe failures depicts that a software failure at any stage could lead to the loss of lives, financials, waste of time, effort, discomfort, stress, good will, reputation, confidence, peace etc. The application of software has pierced in every industry unlike traditional approached where software was altogether a separate entity. As software has become an integral part of every product and process, there is a need to make a full proof system so that the software failures could be avoided. There is a further requirement of root cause analysis of these software failures to understand the problematic area and suggest the areas of improvement in the current process as several corrective and preventive actions need to be taken while developing products and software systems.

CHAPTER 20

The essay is based on a Keynote Address to the OECD "High Level Meeting of the Committee for Scientific and Technology Policy." The topic is "Adjusting Policy to New Dimensions in Science, Technology and Innovation." The objective was to point out the difficulty in linking certain policies to certain measures of successful originality. The goal is also to nevertheless identify the broad policy characteristics that promote innovation. Innovation is a human activity. Precursors can be seen in an interest in the conditions for promoting invention. This appeared well before the industrial revolution and was an important theme in the rise of America's economic strength through the nineteenth century. Improvement has been associated with American economic culture for more than two centuries. It has been urged that increased attention to what is called the science of science policy, the efficient study of the detachment of our economy called science and technology. This includes the construction and validation of micro- and macro-economic models for science and technology motions. International organizations have been valuable players in this enterprise. They can do much to encourage deeper knowledge of the improvement ecology and provide better tools for policy makers. The deep effort is now starting to gather global information about improvement and its natural science is a valuable enterprise that must continue over a long period of time to be booming. Eventually we may learn enough to create reliable meters by which we can judge the health of our global ecosystem. There should be knowledge in the insights gained from centuries of experience with improvement. We know it requires a serious mass of largely educated individuals acting together in stable and open environments that can encourage open communication.

CHAPTER 21

The Internet was designed to be a decentralized system: every node should connect to many others. This design helped to make the system resistant to censorship or outside attack. Yet in practice, most individual users exist at the edges of the network, connected to others only through their Internet service provider (ISP). Block this link, and Internet access disappears. An alternative option is beginning to emerge in the form of wireless mesh networks, simple systems that connect end users to one another and automatically route around blocks and censors. Yet any mesh network needs to hit a critical mass of users before it functions well; developers must convince potential users to trade off ease of use for added freedom and privacy.

CHAPTER 22

New technologies feature prominently in our ongoing campaigns against genetically modified crops and nuclear power. They are also an important part of our solutions to environmental problems. Some include renewable energy technologies that are powered by solar, wind and wave power, and waste treatment technologies, such as mechanical-biological treatment. So while companies accept and rely upon the merits of many new technologies, we campaign against other technologies that have a potentially profound negative impact on the environment. This prompted companies to commission a comprehensive review of nanotechnology and artificial intelligence developments from an organization with a status for technological expertise. In the beginning of the report background information for nanotechnology is needed. In doing so, it was anticipated that the prospects of these emerging technologies had to affect the quality of life in the coming decades. One consequence of providing such an overview is that there can be no decisive conclusions. The industries described here are too active and uncertain to generate any real sense of a resolution. It is possible to highlight a number of important differences and similarities between nanotechnology and AI. The greatest contrast between the two industries worries public interest. As the report has demonstrated, nanotechnology is widely regarded as a 'new' and exciting branch of science and technology. This belief contributed to the massive period of growth that this high profile is currently enjoying. AI is viewed by many as a highly specialized and unproven discipline. One reason for this concerns the gross over-optimism that characterized the industry in the 1960s and 1980s. Another reason reflects the AI community's seemingly impossible difficulty in publicizing its own achievements. It is likely that this trend will continue for some time into the foreseeable future.

CHAPTER 23

The best way to nurture excellence is to build a society which discourages and limits inherited wealth and privilege and fosters a balanced playing field with real opportunities for ordinary people. The need is to recognize and reward different forms of excellence, and to provide special provisions for those who are slow, weak, or less than average since more than 50 percent of the population falls into these categories at any given period. If we only reward the fast, strong and above average, inequality is bound to grow. We need floors and ceilings to reduce inequality, sort of a balancing act which must be worked out by political compromise. More equality is possible if Americans choose it. What the people need to do is to use their voice and vote for political leaders who will put people before property, legislate a floor and ceiling in income and wealth, and pay people based on how their performance (or job) influences the common good—and not as a profit versus cost factor. There is some merit in periodically storming the Bastille, eliminating the old guards who have become entrenched (since power corrupts), and hanging a few rotten politicians in the village square—especially those who have betrayed the people and gotten fat and rich off the peoples' sweat and labor.

APPENDIX B

■■■

Significant Technological Innovations

Human thought and inspiration is the final frontier. The revolution/ evolution of technology is directed by society and its constructs. Here is a microcosm of technological development.

2400 BC The abacus, the first known calculator, invented in Babylonia

300 BC Pingala invents the binary number system

87 BC Antikythera Mechanism invented in Rhodes to track movement of the stars

724 Liang Ling-Can invents the first fully mechanical clock

1041 Movable type printing press invented by Bi Sheng

1280 Eyeglasses were invented

1350 Suspension bridges built in Peru

1450 Alphabetic, movable type printing press invented by Johann Gutenberg

1500 Ball bearing invented by Leonardo Da Vinci together with flying machines, including a helicopter, the first mechanical calculator and one of the first programmable robots

1510 Pocket watch invented by Peter Henlein

1576 Ironclad warship invented by Oda Nobunaga

1581 Pendulum invented by Galileo Galilei

1593 Thermometer invented by Galileo Galilei

1608 Telescope invented by Hans Lippershey

1609 Microscope invented by Galileo Galilei

1642 Adding machine invented by Blaise Pascal

1643 Barometer invented by Evangelista Torricelli

1645 Vacuum pump invented by Otto von Guericke

1657 Pendulum clock invented by Christiaan Huygens

1679 Pressure cooker invented by Denis Papin

1687 Newton, Principia: Newton's physics formed the foundation of modern science

1698 Steam engine invented by Thomas Savery

1671 Gottfried Leibniz is known as one of the founding fathers of calculus

1705 Steam piston engine invented by Thomas Newcomen

1708 Jethro Tull invents mechanical (seed) sower

1710 Thermometer invented by Rene Antoine Ferchault de Reaumur

1733 John Kay invents flying shuttle.

1742 Franklin stove invented by Benjamin Franklin

1752 Lightning rod invented by Benjamin Franklin

1767 Spinning jenny invented by James Hargreaves

1769 Steam engine invented by James Watt

1774 Priestly isolates oxygen

1779 First steam powered mills automate the weaving process

1781 William Herschel discovers the planet Uranus

1783 Hot air balloon invented by Montgolfier brothers

1791 Steamboat invented by John Fitch

1793 Eli Whitney develops the cotton gin

1798 Vaccination invented by Edward Jenner

1799 Humphrey Davy discovers nitrous oxide (laughing gas)

Oliver Evans invents the conveyer belt

1804 Locomotive invented by Richard Trevithick

1814 Steam Locomotive (Blucher) invented by George Stephenson

1816 Miner's safety lamp invented by Humphry Davy

Stethoscope invented by Rene Theophile Hyacinthe Laennec

1820 The Arithmometer was the first mass-produced calculator invented by Charles Xavier Thomas de Colmar

1821 Electric motor invented by Michael Faraday

1822 Charles Babbage designs his first mechanical computer

1826 Photography invented by Joseph Nicephore Niepce

1830 Lawn mower invented by Edwin Beard Budding

1831 Von Liebig discovers chloroform

Faraday discovers electro-magnetic current, making possible generators and electric engines

1834 Braille invented by Louis Braille

Refrigerator invented by Jacob Perkins

Combine harvester invented by Hiram Moore

1835 Morse code invented by Samuel Morse

Revolver invented by Samuel Colt

1838 Electric telegraph invented by Charles Wheatstone (also Samuel Morse)

Daguerre perfects the Daguerrotype.

1839 Vulcanization of rubber invented by Charles Goodyear

1842 Anaesthesia invented by Crawford Long

1843 Typewriter invented by Charles Thurber

1846 Sewing machine invented by Elias Howe

Rotary printing press invented by Richard M. Hoe

Pneumatic tire patented

1849 Safety pin invented by Walter Hunt

Monier develops reinforced concrete

1859 Charles Darwin publishes *The Origin of Species*

Etienne Lenoir demonstrates the first successful gasoline engine

1862 Revolving machine gun invented by Richard J. Gatling

Isaac Singer commercializes the sewing machine

Mechanical submarine invented by Narcís Monturiol i Estarriol

1866 Dynamite invented by Alfred Nobel

Lister demonstrates the use of carbolic antiseptic

1869 Mendeleev produces the Periodic Table

1870 Stock ticker invented by Thomas Alva Edison

1873 Christopher Sholes invents the Remington typewriter

James Clerk Maxwell states the laws of electro-magnetic radiation

1876 Gasoline carburettor invented by Daimler

1877 Phonograph invented by Thomas Alva Edison

Microphone invented by Emile Berliner

1878 Cathode ray tube invented by William Crookes

Edison invents the incandescent lamp

1880 Photophone invented by Alexander Graham Bell

1883 First skyscraper built in Chicago (ten stories)

Maxim invents the machine gun

1885 Motor cycle invented by Gottlieb Daimler and Wilhelm Maybach

Benz develops first automobile to run on internal-combustion engine

1888 Hertz produces radio waves.

Eiffel Tower is built

1891 Zipper invented by Whitcomb L. Judson

Rudolf Diesel invents diesel

1893 Wireless communication invented by Nikola Tesla

1895 Diesel engine invented by Rudolf Diesel

Radio signals were invented by Guglielmo Marconi

Auguste and Louis Lumiere develop Cinematograph

Roentgen discovers X-rays

1898 Remote control invented by Nikola Tesla

1900 Planck develops quantum theory

First Zeppelin is built

1901 Vacuum cleaner invented by Hubert Booth

1903 Powered airplane invented by Wilbur Wright and Orville Wright

1905 Einstein writes the Theory of Relativity

1907 Color photography invented by Auguste and Louis Lumiere

Helicopter invented by Paul Cornu

Radio amplifier invented by Lee DeForest

1908 Henry Ford mass-produces the Model T

1909 Bakelite invented by Leo Baekeland

1919 London to Paris air service begins

James Smathers develops the first electric typewriter

1923 Sound film invented by Lee DeForest

Television Electronic invented by Philo Farnsworth

1924 Electro Mechanical television system invented by John Logie Baird

1926 Robert Goddard experiments with liquid-fueled rockets

1928 Antibiotics, penicillin invented by Alexander Fleming

1931 Iconoscope invented by Vladimir Zworykin

1937 Jet engine invented by Frank Whittle and Hans von Ohain

Alan Turing develops the concept of a theoretical computing machine

1938 Ballpoint pen invented by Laszlo Biro

1943 Enigma: Adolf Hitler uses the Enigma encryption machine

Colossus: Alan Turing develops the code-breaking machine Colossus

Aqua-Lung invented by Jacques-Yves Cousteau and Emile Gagnan

1945 The atomic bomb

1946 Microwave oven invented by Percy Spencer

1951 Nuclear power reactor invented by Walter Zinn

1956 Optical fiber invented by Basil Hirschowitz, C. Wilbur Peters, and Lawrence E. Curtiss

Videocassette recorder invented by Ampex

1957 Sputnik I and Sputnik II: Sputnik I and Sputnik II are launched by the Russians

1958 Silicon chip: The first integrated circuit, or silicon chip, is produced by the US Jack Kilby & Robert Noyce

1960 Laser invented by Theodore Harold Maiman

1961 Uri Gagarin is the first man in space

Optical disc invented by David Paul Gregg

1963 Computer mouse invented by Douglas Engelbart

1967 Automatic Teller Machine (ATM) invented by John Shepherd-Barron

Hypertext invented by Andries van Dam and Ted Nelson

1968 Video game console invented by Ralph H. Baer

1969 The moon landing—Neil Armstrong sets foot on the moon

1971 E-mail invented by Ray Tomlinson

Liquid Crystal Display invented by James Fergason

Pocket calculator invented by Sharp Corporation

Floppy Disk invented by David Noble with IBM

1973 Ethernet invented by Bob Metcalfe and David Boggs

Personal computer invented by Xerox PARC

1983 Camcorder invented by Sony

1990 World Wide Web invented by Tim Berners-Lee

2001 Apple revolutionizes music listening by unveiling its iPod MP3 music player.

Richard Palmer develops energy-absorbing D3O plastic.

The Wikipedia online encyclopedia is founded by Larry Sanger and Jimmy Wales

Bram Cohen develops BitTorrent file-sharing

Scott White, Nancy Sottos, and colleagues develop self-healing materials.

2002 iRobot Corporation releases the first version of its Roomba® vacuum cleaning robot

Electronic voting plays a major part in a controversial U.S. Presidential Election

2004 Andre Geim and Konstantin Novoselov discover graphene

2005 A pioneering low-cost laptop for developing countries called OLPC is announced by MIT computing pioneer Nicholas Negroponte

2007 Amazon.com launches its Kindle electronic book (e-book) reader

Apple introduces a touchscreen cellphone called the iPhone

2010 Apple releases its touchscreen tablet computer, the iPad

3D TV starts to become more widely available.

References

Alchin, Linda. (2001) History Timeline. Retrieved from http://www.datesandevents.org. [Accessed October 2nd, 2014]

Woodford, Chris. (2008/2011) Technology timeline. Retrieved from http://www.explainthatstuff.com/timeline.html. [Accessed October 2nd, 2014]

APPENDIX C

End of Lecture Activity

Last Name: _____

First Name: _____

Id#: _____

Code: _____

Activity: _____

Summarize the Lecture:

_____

_____

_____

_____

_____

_____

What is STS?

_____

_____

_____

_____

_____

_____

_____

_____

_____

End of Lecture Activity

Last Name: _____

First Name: _____

Id#: _____

Code: _____

Activity: _____

Summarize the Lecture:

_____

_____

_____

_____

_____

_____

Is the current state of technology actually improving society compared to the last year? Why?

_____

_____

_____

_____

_____

_____

_____

_____

End of Lecture Activity

Last Name: _____

First Name: _____

Id#: _____

Code: _____

Activity: _____

Summarize the Lecture:

_____

_____

_____

_____

_____

_____

What is Moral Overload?

_____

_____

_____

_____

_____

_____

_____

_____

_____

End of Lecture Activity

Last Name: _____

First Name: _____

Id#: _____

Code: _____

Activity: _____

Summarize the Lecture:

_____

_____

_____

_____

_____

_____

What is the Vision of Inclusion?

_____

_____

_____

_____

_____

_____

_____

_____

End of Lecture Activity

Last Name: _____

First Name: _____

Id#: _____

Code: _____

Activity: _____

Summarize the Lecture:

_____

_____

_____

_____

_____

_____

Why is STEM needed?

_____

_____

_____

_____

_____

_____

_____

_____

End of Lecture Activity

Last Name: _____

First Name: _____

Id#: _____

Code: _____

Activity: _____

Summarize the Lecture:

_____

_____

_____

_____

_____

_____

Why is there no equality in gaming?

_____

_____

_____

_____

_____

_____

_____

End of Lecture Activity

Last Name: _____

First Name: _____

Id#: _____

Code: _____

Activity: _____

Summarize the Lecture:

_____

_____

_____

_____

_____

_____

What is your reflection on video games in society?

_____

_____

_____

_____

_____

_____

_____

_____

End of Lecture Activity

Last Name: _____

First Name: _____

Id#: _____

Code: _____

Activity: _____

Summarize the Lecture:

_____

_____

_____

_____

_____

_____

Would you spend your money on pixels?

_____

_____

_____

_____

_____

_____

_____

_____

End of Lecture Activity

Last Name: _____

First Name: _____

Id#: _____

Code: _____

Activity: _____

Summarize the Lecture:

_____

_____

_____

_____

_____

_____

Who were the participants in the spatial experiment?

_____

_____

_____

_____

_____

_____

_____

_____

End of Lecture Activity

Last Name: _____

First Name: _____

Id#: _____

Code: _____

Activity: _____

Summarize the Lecture:

_____

_____

_____

_____

_____

_____

What is the direction of online learning?

_____

_____

_____

_____

_____

_____

_____

_____

End of Lecture Activity

Last Name: _____

First Name: _____

Id#: _____

Code: _____

Activity: _____

Summarize the Lecture:

_____

_____

_____

_____

_____

_____

What is a gifted student?

_____

_____

_____

_____

_____

_____

_____

_____

End of Lecture Activity

Last Name: _____

First Name: _____

Id#: _____

Code: _____

Activity: _____

Summarize the Lecture:

_____

_____

_____

_____

_____

_____

How are e-portfolios used in this class?

_____

_____

_____

_____

_____

_____

_____

_____

_____

End of Lecture Activity

Last Name: _____

First Name: _____

Id#: _____

Code: _____

Activity: _____

Summarize the Lecture:

_____

_____

_____

_____

_____

_____

What is one way we could use e-portfolios that was NOT discussed in this book?

_____

_____

_____

_____

_____

_____

_____

_____

End of Lecture Activity

Last Name: _____

First Name: _____

Id#: _____

Code: _____

Activity: _____

Summarize the Lecture:

_____

_____

_____

_____

_____

_____

How can you transform Wikipedia?

_____

_____

_____

_____

_____

_____

_____

_____

_____

End of Lecture Activity

Last Name: _____

First Name: _____

Id#: _____

Code: _____

Activity: _____

Summarize the Lecture:

_____
_____
_____
_____
_____
_____

What is the Singularity?

_____
_____
_____
_____
_____
_____
_____
_____

End of Lecture Activity

Last Name: _____

First Name: _____

Id#: _____

Code: _____

Activity: _____

Summarize the Lecture:

_____

_____

_____

_____

_____

What is the role of technology in society?

_____

_____

_____

_____

_____

_____

_____

_____

End of Lecture Activity

Last Name: _____

First Name: _____

Id#: _____

Code: _____

Activity: _____

Summarize the Lecture:

_____

_____

_____

_____

_____

_____

What is Moore's Law?

_____

_____

_____

_____

_____

_____

_____

_____

End of Lecture Activity

Last Name: _____

First Name: _____

Id#: _____

Code: _____

Activity: _____

Summarize the Lecture:

_____

_____

_____

_____

_____

_____

What is the most common system failure?

_____

_____

_____

_____

_____

_____

_____

_____

End of Lecture Activity

Last Name: _____

First Name: _____

Id#: _____

Code: _____

Activity: _____

Summarize the Lecture:

_____

_____

_____

_____

_____

_____

How many dimensions in technology are there?

_____

_____

_____

_____

_____

_____

_____

_____

End of Lecture Activity

Last Name: _____

First Name: _____

Id#: _____

Code: _____

Activity: _____

Summarize the Lecture:

_____

_____

_____

_____

_____

_____

What is Shadow Web?

_____

_____

_____

_____

_____

_____

_____

_____

End of Lecture Activity

Last Name: _____

First Name: _____

Id#: _____

Code: _____

Activity: _____

Summarize the Lecture:

_____

_____

_____

_____

_____

_____

Chapter 21 was written several years ago. Has society changed? Why?

_____

_____

_____

_____

_____

_____

_____

End of Lecture Activity

Last Name: _____

First Name: _____

Id#: _____

Code: _____

Activity: _____

Summarize the Lecture:

_____

_____

_____

_____

_____

_____

What is the next step?

_____

_____

_____

_____

_____

_____

_____

_____

COPYRIGHT ACKNOWLEDGMENTS

■■■